BARBARA JACOBS is a novelist, freelance journalist, advice column ist and broadcaster who was born in St Helens, Lancashire. Her novel for young adults, *Stick*, won two major UK awards and her most recent book *Loving Mr Spock* (2003) was a personal account of her partner's battle with Asperger's Syndrome. She writes a weekly advice column for several London newspapers and lives in Leicester.

The Dick, Kerr's Ladies

The Dick, Kerr's Ladies

Barbara Jacobs

ROBINSON
London

Constable & Robinson Ltd
3 The Lanchesters
162 Fulham Palace Road
London W6 9ER
www.constablerobinson.com

First published in the UK by Robinson,
an imprint of Constable & Robinson Ltd 2004

A copy of the British Library Cataloguing in Publication Data
is available from the British Library

ISBN 1-84119-828-5

Printed and bound in the EU

2 4 6 8 10 9 7 5 3 1

For Jack Swift
1915–87

Contents

Illustrations

The Dick, Kerr Ladies Football Team
Lily Parr
Women working in a Munitions Factory 1918, *Mary Evans Picture Library*
Alice Woods in her running gear
Possibly Elaine Burton on the left, who would have been 13 or 14 at the time
Alice proudly displaying her winnings
Dick Kerr International Ladies AFC
The French Team in 1920
The actual poster for the football match played by Dick, Kerr's against France in Paris, November 1920

All pictures courtesy of William Parr except those mentioned separately

Preface

I didn't set out to write this particular book. I was researching women's football in general, but the passion I felt for the period and its social history was so overwhelming that when my publisher suggested that I follow my instinct and write a book about Dick, Kerr's Ladies, I was only too happy to comply. My enthusiasm was kindled by a personal attachment when I discovered that Lily Parr, the greatest woman footballer and the most prolific goal-scorer in English footballing history, was born in my own home town of St Helens. When I discovered that her team-mate, the inimitable athlete Alice Woods was also a St Helens lass, there was no stopping me.

In the course of very early research for the original book, I'd read David Williamson's *Belles of The Ball*, and Gail Newsham's *In a League of Their Own*, but both of these books which feature the Dick, Kerr's Ladies team and its extraordinary history, were about the game of football, rather than telling the women's own personal stories set in the turbulent post-War era, which was what interested me. I wanted to write human history, something real and raw about Lancashire women like myself, and about the cultural and idiosyncratic issues which make us what we are. I had to get back to basics, and I didn't want to rely on any previously published material.

I sought out an old University friend of mine, Ivan Waddington, Director of the Centre for Research into Sport and Society at the University of Leicester. It was at his instigation that I met Jane Ashworth, the author of *Kicking The Boys' Balls* and *Jane*, who had been doing post-graduate research, came along to meet me, bringing with her a crate full of books and the results of her own findings from newspaper libraries in the North East. Her contribution to this book, in terms of what she gave me access to, was invaluable.

Then I discovered the research papers and PhD written by Ali Melling of the University of Central Lancashire on this subject, and, on reading her PhD thesis, I had my first breakthrough. Through her footnotes I traced Dr Tony Dawson, of Liverpool John Moores University, and the nephew of Alice Woods. I met him, and his recollections of his aunt, and the part she'd played in the Dick, Kerr's Ladies were clear, precise and insightful. He then introduced me to Alice's surviving daughter, Lynn Fabian, and her husband, Joe. I travelled to Porthcawl, where they now live, and for a wonderful week she gave me access to all Alice's memorabilia, her diaries and the diaries of Herbert, and to photographs and mementoes of her mother. While Joe fed us on gourmet Italian meals, Lynn fed me her memories, without which this book could never have been written.

I still had to track down Lily Parr, just as Alice Woods had to do in 1917, and I knew, as Alice did, that it would be an almost impossible task. Just as I was beginning to despair, having sent out desperate messages to every web-site forum I could, I had an email from Roy Parr's daughter, on his behalf. He was Lily's nephew, and when I went up to St Helens to meet him, he took me to visit Bill, Lily's surviving brother. Both of them had a wealth of anecdotes and information about their childhood, and Lily's, and Bill had Lily's photograph collection, which he entrusted to my care. Some of these photographs are reprinted in this book.

Meanwhile, because the research had to be so wide-ranging, I'd tracked down someone who knew about the French connection, and about Alice Milliat, the extraordinary French athlete who set up the first French women's football team, Charlet Silvain of Fechain Athletique Club, and we set up an exchange of information and images. I'd also contacted Jean Williams of De Montfort University, author of *A Game For Rough Girls*, who tried to put me in touch with the American descendents of another Dick, Kerr's star, Alice Mills. I discovered Adrian Sill, the webmaster of the Doncaster Belles website, who had some valuable archive images. The book was coming together.

First I had to go back to St Helens, to trawl the superb archive of the Gamble Institute, which is unparalleled in its collection of St Helens' industrial and historical material, but which guards it with some severity. Vivienne Hainsworth was helpful, however. Finally, I had to abandon my forages, leaving them to my historian cousin, Peter Harris, who battled manfully against his own disability and against the forces of conservatism (or do I mean conservation?) at the Institute, to complete the searches of St Helens newspaper archives. Only the National Newspaper Library in Colindale protected its possessions more jealously, but at least it had all the cuttings I required from the UK and from the USA. The British Library, where I read an entire collection of 1920s fourpenny novelettes, was far more approachable, and Leicester University Library with its extensive Local History collection was wonderful, as was Kay Relf at De Montfort University Library.

All in all, I spent eight months in research, travelling through England and Wales, surfing the Internet constantly, signed on to every genealogical database until I'd researched the birth history of every girl in the Dick, Kerr's team, devouring information. I haunted the Family Records Centre, ordering birth certificates, I researched military history, industrial history, the history of tram cars, early twentieth century feminist history, economic treatises, books about glass-making, mining history, cotton spinning and weaving on both sides of the Atlantic, ships' menus and Atlantic crossings, Music hall, St Helens (including St Helens Chat), Preston, oral histories, pictorial histories, video-tape of television programmes, Pathé News downloads, radio shows and websites in Britain, the USA, Canada and France. I enlisted the help of the librarian, Matt Bennett, at Pawtucket Public Library, USA, who could teach some British librarians how to be a public servant. And I had help from the football statistician Tony Brown in trying to identify the mysterious David Brooks.

And just when I thought I might finally start to write up the room full of research material I'd gathered, by lucky chance I found Tony Frankland, grandson of the extraordinary man of vision, Alfred Frankland, who was the driving force behind the Dick, Kerr's Ladies. Tony was inspired to set out on some family research of his own, and what he discovered, and passed on to me, threw fresh and intriguing light on the whole story.

Then, after all this academic digging, I had to forget

everything I'd read, and just write the story of these wo-men's lives, and remember my own history, and mark the points at which our stories touched. The brain-numbing research has to be the invisible partner in the narrative. But I have to admit to it, and I have to thank, from the bottom of my heart, every person whose name I've mentioned, those I may have forgotten, and thank Luke, my son, for listening to me obsessing about this project, day after day, for ten solid months, until the typescript was finished and emailed to Nick and Gary and Andrew and the team at Constable & Robinson

Finally, I have to clear up something which runs counter to official wisdom. The National Statistics research unit has recently given its opinion on relative values of the pound, over the last two hundred years or more, and has issued its own guidelines as to the comparative value of the pound in your pocket, now, and in years gone by. Its decision is that values have increased by less than x100 compared with 1918. You'll discover, on reading this book, that my instruction is to multiply Great War figures by 200 to arrive at a figure comparable to today's values. The figures arrived at by the National Statistics research unit come from various government supply agencies. Mine are based on the figures given in Maud Pember Reeves' detailed collection of figures of domestic budgets in Lambeth taken by the Fabian Society in 1913 and published in a book, the title of which refers to the average pay of an unskilled male labourer in that year, *Round About A Pound A Week*. This is essential reading for any social historian. In 1913, the average wage of a working class man was little over £1. It is now a little over £200. The weekly costs of bus transport to and from work in London were then 5p. They are now £10. The weekly shopping budget for poorer families was 5p per head. It is now £10 per head. The weekly rental of a cheap two-bed-roomed property in Lambeth was 40/45 pence. Today it is around £90 minimum. Weekly fuel costs, canteen lunches, clothing of all kinds, work out to a x200 comparison. Although some foodstuffs were comparatively more expensive in 1913 – sugar, milk and butter/ margarine – others are relatively cheaper, like fish and other proteins. Overall, the budget evens out at x200 for working class wages and out-goings. So this is what I've based my figures on, because my book is about the working classes, the factory workers, not those whose income, purchasing power and purchasing choices can distort the figures. My figure is in the context of the people whose stories I'm writing. I hope that in sharing those stories, I can share the passion, the unrelenting graft, and the uniqueness of being a Lancashire woman.

One

Ex Terra Lucem

The streets in Gerrard's Bridge, St Helens, were lit by gas, as were most of the houses. In November 1917, when Alice Woods went searching for a girl called Lily Parr, the light cast by the gaslamps was flickering and fitful. Few people from the relatively well-to-do areas would think to wander there after dark, when pickpockets, rough sleepers, falling drunks and gin-sodden fishwives would be likely to lurch from doorways, groping the nearest passer-by.

Looking for an unknown child here, on the dank and sooty nights of winter, was a task no woman in her right mind would have taken on. But Alice had promised to find Lily, and with Jane, her tiny sister, who would have been easily overpowered by a passing breath of whiskey, let alone a full-grown Irish labourer, she walked night after night through the dark and fog and cold with sudden blarings of drunken song from the street-side pubs breaking the sound of their hurrying footsteps.

And then, one night, they heard something through the fog and dark. It was a beat as regular as a metronome with three separate but perfectly even notes – bam, ping thud; bam,

1

ping, thud. It was only when they drew close that they could see what was making the sound, but Alice had already guessed. The thud was the sound of a leather football. The ping was the sound of a football striking metal. And the bam was the boot of someone who could aim, relentlessly, and with total precision, to drive a sodden leather ball against the ornately corrugated stem of a gas-lamp, and to retrieve it, and drive it again and again and again. Only a born footballer could have done this, forcing the ball to bounce accurately rather than deflect at any arbitrary angle from the corrugations. The lamp juddered, the light flickered, and in its shadows was Lily Parr, a lit cigarette dangling from her lips, practising.

Jane was frightened by the vision of this angry superchild who stood at least five feet ten, much taller than any man in the Woods family. Alice was breathless with excitement. Lily was unconcerned. She stood staring at them, the football she had stolen expertly back-heeled into her hands, the burning end of the cigarette too close to her lips.

'What dost tha bloody want, Woods?' she asked and flicked her cigarette butt, still burning towards them.

Alice was unperturbed. Football girls called each other by their surnames to avoid the confusion between so many Lilys and Alices and Florries.

'Dick, Kerr's wants us to play for them, on Boxing Day,' she said.

'Tha'd best ask me mam, then. Coom on! Watch out fer't pigs, and mind you don't step in t' shite.'

She led the sisters out of the light, and into the back entry next to an end-terrace house which abutted on to a small factory. Pigs. Their stench and the sickeningly overpowering smell of the swill they were nuzzling and grunting over, must have turned the stomach of the more delicate Jane. This was a sight and a smell she would never forget, but would recount with shudders every time Lily Parr's name was mentioned. She had never seen anything like this to which the word home could be applied. The back yard was 'home' to a family of pigs. And amongst the pigs, like little yellow messenger boys, some hopeful chicks ran, flapping their small wings. There was a stable of sorts behind the house with two carts looming out of the foggy dark. And a horse. Or two. This was a small terraced house, in the middle of a town, with barely enough room for the three women to squeeze in through the gate in amongst the pigs and the chickens, and it had the look, and the stink, of a ramshackle barnyard.

Alice saw past all this. She was slightly in awe of the towering teenager who walked like a man and talked in the deep husky tones of a man, and yet who had the nervous round-shouldered head-down stance and apologetic shrugging gesture of the terminally and childishly shy, or the prodigiously tall. Lily's bluster and roughness was no more than a cover for the frightening awareness that she was, and always had been different. Special.

Inside, the house was chaotic. There were unidentifiable children racing through the cluttered spaces, wearing less than the requisite amount of clothes, their noses, and eyes, running yellow and green. There were two huge halves of butchered pig, hung up in the back kitchen doorway, slimed with salt. On the hearth of the living-room cooking range was a cardboard box of day-old chicks, trying to breathe, and being helped by a man in a flat cap, blowing the smoke of his cigarette into their unformed lungs.

3

'Me dad,' Lily announced in her broken voice.

Me dad, George Parr, didn't remove his cap, he was too busy with the chicks.

'And me mam.' Lily added.

Lily's mam approached, weary, hair in her eyes, hiding under her full-length grubby pinafore the next pregnancy, and holding in her arms, another baby, obviously too sick to nuzzle. And she, mam, was obviously special, too.

In fact, she was a grand lass, Sarah Pennington, now Sal Parr. She had always been a grand lass, when she was twelve and in service. There was something solid and indefatigable in her, even in those days, something of heft, maybe. But she had the same bearing as her errant child – tall and stately if given the chance – although her head didn't droop like Lily's. She looked exhausted and worried, which went without saying with so many children round her feet, and only one elder daughter, around Alice's age, to help out. There was a youth, slouched somewhere, too.

'Dick, Kerr's come in fer me, mam. Boxing Day. Can I play?'

Sarah looked at the two women who had entered with Lily, and nodded.

'Will she mind yer?' she asked, pointing to Alice.

Lily grimaced.

'Yes, Mrs Parr. I'll look after her,' Alice smiled.

And she was true to her word, looking after the wayward child as they travelled away from St Helens to take on the world.

When people ask me where I come from I say Liverpool. Sometimes I extend that and say Merseyside. But either way I'm lying. Liverpool is certainly where I misspent my youth

4

– drinking cappuccino at the El Cabala before Starbucks was invented, heckling the Sunday soap-box speakers at the Pier Head, dancing at the Cavern, going to concerts at the Philharmonic Hall – but Liverpool was a bus or train journey away from my home in Prescot, just outside St Helens. I was born in St Helens.

St Helens, in my memory, is a smell. Or rather it's a series of overlapping smells, varying in pungency, sometimes several of them working at once, and all of them announcing St Helens' industrial past and its claim on me and on history.

It was with this most visceral of the senses that I marked my visits to grandmother Ellen's house in the 1940s, and that I now take both of us back on that journey to find out about these two extraordinary women, the footballers Lily Parr and Alice Woods. They could only have been born in this raw scar on the edge of the Lancashire coalfield, a town whose motto is the almost unbearably apposite *Ex Terra Lucem*: 'From the earth, light'. The light is coal. And light is also the glass mirror through which we look at ourselves, and the glass window through which we look at the world, and which the coal gave birth to. Coal and glass were the town's two industries, and Alice and Lily came one from each of these separate yet intertwined communities.

My grandmother Polly's family were all colliers, hulks of men with names like Rafe, and Smack, and Cute, but grandmother Ellen, my father's mother, married a glass-blower, and their home stood next to the one of the glass factories – UGB, which we called Used Glass Bottles, but which I think was United Glass Bottles.

Nothing changed much, externally, in the Depression

5

which nearly killed St Helens between the wars, so the smells I remember must have been those which suffused the town after the Great War when Lily and Alice were kicking balls around.

My parents and I used to come down into town from Prescot on a number eight trolley bus, past Portico and Toll Bar and the Bird in th'Hand and down Croppers Hill, and it was only at this point, right on the edge of the town centre, that the smells kicked in. The first of these was the powerful odour of malt and hops from the brewery, Greenall's, immediately to the right of us. That brewery was the second big industry to establish itself in St Helens. At the time, at the start of the eighteenth century, the town was little more than a verdant valley with a small church, St Ellyn's, lying between the four settlements of Windle, Parr, Sutton and Eccleston. Each of those villages had its own identity, and there's still a degree of separation between the inhabitants of each of the four – Alice would announce herself, for instance, as being from Sutton rather than St Helens. Most of the coalfields were on the Sutton edge by 1916, but originally the coal was found, and mined, in Parr, and its benefits were appreciated when Liverpool became a transatlantic port. St Helens produced the nearest coal to light its fires. With coal came miners. And with miners came thirst. The supply of ale was written into their wages. Ale didn't deteriorate in the heat of the dank tunnels, so Peter Greenall, a local land-owner, set himself the task of producing it.

Then, overlying this, and almost immediately as the bus trolleyed down Westfield Street, came the faintly hospital smell of pharmaceuticals: Beecham's Pills. Thomas Beecham set up here long after the valley had turned into a treeless Victorian hotchpotch of jerry-built housing for industrial workers, infested by things with any number of legs which scampered up the walls and through the yards, and appeared in kitchens overnight. Thomas Beecham, who had been an agricultural labourer in Oxford, mixed up and ground down dried hedgerow remedies into pills, and went on the road selling them at fairs, but finally settled in St Helens, where he announced they were worth a guinea a box, and built the first pharmaceutical factory in the world.

After we'd passed the Beecham's factory, we'd get out of the bus on Bridge Street, into a fug of smoke which hurt my eyes and closed up my throat. But the smoke itself had different identities, each with its separate industrial note of ferocity. Men, in my childhood, used to breathe it in and spit it out (why didn't the women?) so there was grey spittle in the gutters and on the pavements, and on every bar of the coal ranges in the living-rooms on which the cooking was done, and in every sawdusted pub we passed, where spittoons sat on bars. There was the smoke from the domestic coal fires, smoke from the kilns, which was grittier and dully red, and there was bitter smoke from the coking coal of the factories, which was the grittiest of all. It left an acidic taste in my mouth that crunched when I ground my teeth together and tried to hold my breath as we crossed the road into Canal Street, holding tightly on to my mother's hand, as this was the smelliest place of all. The St Helens Canal. Stinky Brook.

The St Helens Canal was responsible for the filth and was the fraud upon which St Helens was founded. Liverpool, and the Cheshire salt fields needed coal for their industries, especially the new detergent industries which relied heavily on alkaline salt to create soda ash, an essential ingredient of soap. St Helens had coal in abundance, but no easy way to carry it in the eighteenth century, except by cart along a winding turnpike road. Waterways of any kind which had the potential to link with the River Mersey, Liverpool, and Cheshire, were examined as a means of transporting bulk supplies, but the only stream which ran through St Helens was the rather lifeless, sullen Sankey Brook. The answer was to build a canal, of course, and engineers had blue-printed canals as the answer to transport problems. They were expensive, technological, but they could work.

Unfortunately nearby Salford had already applied to build a canal, and the request had been turned down by Parliament. So the investors in the St Helens transport scheme and Henry Berry, the engineer who had been given the job of creating a natural waterway, fooled Parliament (and cheated themselves out of the history books) by applying instead to make the Sankey Brook navigable, knowing that this was totally impossible. The application was nevertheless passed by a Parliament suspicious of new-fangled ways but willing to try them out in small corners. Berry went ahead and built his canal, using the water of the Sankey Brook, alongside, to fill it. Legislation permitted 'cuts', in certain parts of rivers which were un-navigable, but not an entire cut, as Berry's was. It was fraudulent.

The Sankey 'Navigation'/St Helens canal was the first ever complete canal in Britain, built by Berry in 1757, preceding the Bridgwater canal by four years, and inspiring that construction, but no one could ever claim it as such because the Government had been conned by Berry's back-ers. It's a typical St Helens' tale. The town was built on cuts through landscape – and red tape. Within fifty years, the creation of the canal had drawn further industries to St Helens, which then started to pour their effluent into it, and its feeder brooks. Copper smelting brought in a contingent of Welsh workers from the Pary's (Parry's) mines in Anglesey, and more mineral residues to pollute the brooks. Then detergent manufacture – led by Josias Gamble, of Procter and Gamble, a canny Irishman trained as a theologian but with a consumer's interest in chemicals – joined the pollution battle, and trees died and grass turned to ashes in the idyllic valley. The conversion of salt into soda ash by the Leblanc process pumped hydrochloric acid gas into the air and chemicals into the canal. To make one ton of soda, two tons of waste was produced, which had to be dumped somewhere. And it was. St Helens was a dump. It was also a furnace in which things and money got made. Stinky Brook remained as the legacy.

Canal Street, which was the next stage on our regular navigation to grandmother Ellen's house, had a further olfactory joy in store for the three-or four-year-old kid I was then. As we joined it, Pilkington's Glass, by then the town's biggest employer, and the company originally developed as an investment by Greenall's clever brothers-in-law, had a treat in store: the Hotties. This was a point where steam from the glass manufacture poured into the canal, sending a mist of heat into the filthy waters and the thick smoky air. The stench of the Hotties was unbearable. It was a mix of every chemical and metal known to humankind. Think bad eggs, stink bombs, brass cleaner, industrial bleach and Izal toilet paper. That's as close as I can come to describing this horror which haunted my childhood. No one ever explained its purpose to me, and it was, to my small self, the kind of stinking mist which might descend from outer space – a common feature of the science fiction I'd listen to on the radio – and turn into slimy green creatures with one eye in the middle of their foreheads, which would roam the earth looking for children to eat.

We'd cross the railway lines on Canal Street next. Railway lines were a feature of every part of the St Helens landscape, as far back as when James Stephenson had run the Rocket just three miles down the road. There were half a dozen or more railway stations in this small town, servicing townships, factories and mines. The first lines we passed were internal, carrying wagons from the part of the Pilkington factory on the left to the other side on the right. Here, the smell was of dust and engine oil, and that strange cokey odour which used to hang in the clothes of my grandfather William when he returned home from night turn after eight hours of shovelling glass-dust – cullett, into the furnace at Pilkington's. And then we had to walk into Ravenhead Road under the bridge of the real railway, built from the local sandstone, blackened with soot and heat, a fearsome, dark place to penetrate, and sited over a dip in the road so that urine and dog faeces and grit and the inevitable lumps of coke and coal and swirls of dirty sand washed by rain would congregate under it. I never could listen to the story of the Three Little Billy Goats without shuddering because I knew where the Troll lived.

Sometimes we could avoid the Troll Hole by taking a left turn through a desolate area of dumped sand, pink with glass-maker's rouge, and scrubland decorated by oil patches and by two stagnant ponds, which grinned fluorescently at us as we walked by. There was a scum of neon green on the surface and frostings of something coloured candy pink, and gleaming pools of prismatic oil. And here, too, the air was full of strange white fibres that I could easily imagine might have been fairy dust. No. They were the lethal outpourings from Fibreglass. That any of us survived this deserves respect. Many didn't, including my uncle Peter, a gifted journalist, dead at 24 from tuberculosis. My father, Jack, survived TB, but had been born with lung problems which carried him off in the end.

My own St Helens 1940s' childhood was untouched, it seemed, by any but industrial processes, and my life has been disrupted by its lethal legacy. But it was the cauldron in which any number of today's global companies were first smelted, and in which Britain's first revolutionary transport systems were built. It deserves, surely, to take its place in the historical records of how Britain was manufactured.

The manufacturers themselves moved on, leaving their huge homes and grounds as parklands for the workers who lived with the pollution, and took their recreation in the former gardens of their departed masters, who had promised to look after them well. Their sport of choice, typical of mining communities, wasn't football as in north Lancashire, but rugby, which was played with a vengeance on Saturday half-days. Two of my grandmother Polly's brothers, Smack and Cute Bate, played for the local team, Saints, and no doubt their nicknames, given to them by fans and team-mates, derived from their style of play. Sport is an antidote to the inevitability of death by industrial causes, and has its own graveside humour.

Alice Woods was born into that cauldron and that rugby-playing tradition in 1899, to elderly parents. Her mother Margaret was 48, and her father James (Jem) was 49. The family had been miners in Sutton for generations. St Helens' women had the highest fertility rates in Lancashire, but this very late birth must have come as something of a surprise to

11

Margaret, who must have thought herself well into the menopause when she found herself, yet again, pregnant. She had been producing babies since she was 23, starting with John, who didn't outlive childhood, but then went on to produce Thomas, James, Elizabeth Ann, Jane, and, after a seven year gap, young John named after his elder brother who had died. And Alice.

More surprising than this late conception, must have been the news that Margaret was expecting twins. But Alice's twin was stillborn, and she began to grow, as a baby, at an alarming rate in a family in which all but the two youngest children were barely over five feet tall, and the girls very much shorter than that.

By the time Alice was three, her father had died. She was brought up in a home managed by her older brothers, whose word was law, and by her mother and two older sisters – Elizabeth Ann, a seamstress, and Jane, who found work at Pilkington's glass factory. The men appeared to dominate the home, as miners tended to do, but the industry and gentle manners of her older sisters made a deep impression on Alice, as did the quiet dignity of the real head of the household, Margaret. Lancashire women have legendary toughness and control. Their home on Sutton Road was spotless, or as spotless as it could possibly be in a town which belched smoke incessantly.

The three-bedroomed terraced house with its scrubbed and pumiced front doorstep had not only a back yard but a small forecourt, with just enough room for a wooden bench. Here the collier sons, still with blackened faces, would sit and smoke and wait for the water to boil for their tin bath or a sluice over the slop-stone in the back kitchen with coal tar soap, and watch the carts go by, and the trains, and wave to other miners who sat hunched on their haunches in their metal-trimmed clogs outside the pub opposite, 'The Pickled Egg'. It was actually called The Royal Oak, but mining communities call things by names whose origins are hidden in some folkloreish or idiosyncratic past. Nicknaming, or 'kenning', is a way of life.

As important as the pub opposite, and the neighbouring pub, and all the other pubs in the street, was the Wesleyan chapel directly facing Alice's home. St Helens has a dissident history, as do other mining towns, but even by mining standards the non-conformity in this town was both its strength and the source of its frequent unrest.

I'm not using the term non-conformity in its religious sense, here, as one of the non-conformist elements in St Helens was its Roman Catholic past. All its greatest aristocratic landowners, like the Parr family (after whom that township was named, and whose daughter married Henry VIII), and many of the town's wealthy benefactors, contributed to the support of the Jesuit community in St Helens. Their number was once swelled by the sublimely gifted if effete and appalled Gerard Manley Hopkins, who said that St Helens was probably the filthiest place he had ever seen. The Roman Catholicism in the town was augmented by the influx of Irish labour during the Irish Famine in the mid-nineteenth century, but the religious balance leaned towards anything other than Anglicanism: the Church of England congregation was always in the minority in St Helens. The second church to establish itself, after St Ellyn's was a Quaker Meeting House in the seventeenth century.

At the conventionally dissident Protestant end of the scale, many industrialists were strictly Methodist, and Wesley himself preached and lodged at the home of one of the copper factory managers, in 1782, and from there made an impression on the town's religiosity. Faith, rather than good works, was a message that always went down well in industrial communities, which had no time to spare for extravagant expressions of phony benevolence. Isaac Watts, the great hymn writer, said more aptly what was in their hearts, stealing beautifully from Shakespeare's 'Golden lads and girls all must. / As chimney-sweepers, come to dust', and this was sung lustily:

> Why do the proud insult the poor, –
> And boast the large estates they have?
> How vain are riches to secure
> Their haughty owners from the grave!
>
> They can't redeem one hour from death,
> With all the wealth in which they trust;
> Nor give a dying brother breath,
> When God commands him down to dust.
>
> There the dark earth and dismal shade
> Shall clasp their naked bodies round;
> That flesh, so delicately fed,
> Lies cold and moulders in the ground.
>
> His honours perish in the dust,
> And pomp and beauty, birth and blood:
> That glorious day exalts the just
> To full dominion o'er the proud.

The Wesleyan church opposite Alice's home was newly built and very impressive. It had a graceful arc of stone steps leading to its door, where a choir would gather on Christmas Eve to sing carols. Behind the church itself was a huge schoolroom, in which most of the area's children would be tutored on Sundays, in secular as well as religious studies. Alice's family wasn't Methodist, but was grateful for the facilities and the convenience, so this was the church they would conventionally attend on Sundays, the entire family in suits, flat caps and white scarves for the men, and beautifully tailored dresses and hats for the women, made by the seamstress of the family, Elizabeth Ann.

On weekdays, Alice attended Sutton National School with her brother John. It was round the corner from their house, and opposite an Anglican church all schoolchildren attended for twice-weekly services. Sometimes, one of her friends from school would also take her to the Welsh chapel on Sundays, where all the services were held in Welsh. Religion, to the mining community, was just another means to an end. If St Helens was dissident, it was also pragmatic in its religious leanings. Because of the keen competition between churches to provide education for the miners' children, the town was incomparably well served by educational establishments. Zealots of every religious persuasion would be appointed as pastors to this dirt-poor working-class community, and were furiously driven to save souls and children, entering upon almost impertinent fund-raising among the local dignitaries, so that these poor mites, they argued, could have the rudiments of a decent education. The result was that when Education Acts were passed, and School Boards put in place across Britain, St Helens didn't need one. The Wesleyans and the Church of England and the Church of Rome with its busy disciplinarian nuns had already made more than ample provision to furnish all

15

local children with the three Rs on weekdays, and ample doses of religious education on Sundays.

Moreover, the very powerful trade unions which had developed in conjunction with Friendly Societies had their own educational resources, which provided for a lifetime of political and philosophical adult learning, making these mineworkers the most articulate and politically active in Lancashire with almost a century's history of strike action. Dissidence goes hand in hand with education. Alice's education was superb, and by the time she had left the parochial school in Sutton at fourteen, not only could she number, but she also wrote with a fine copperplate hand, and her reading had included the plays of Shakespeare, for which she developed a strong liking and a keen memory, 'Golden lads and girls' included.

There was another passion which fired the miners and their children. Sport. Everyone played something. Alice and John, after school and in the holidays, would climb the bank behind the house, a piece of wasteland between two sets of railway lines where everyone gathered to play games. It had been created originally by railway engineers carving into a natural plateau and dumping the topsoil as they excavated for the Sutton junction of the L&NWR's St Helens line, and for the sidings and engine sheds near Dutch Barn Bridge and the lines which ran into Sutton Glass Works. From up there on the bank you could sometimes see, through the smoke, the foothills of the distant Pennines beyond Parr Stocks and Parr. The 'Old Bonk', as this area was called, was quickly transformed into an informal sports arena.

A football pitch was carefully measured and marked out, although it also doubled as a rugby pitch. Around its perimeter a running track was made, of exactly 200 yards, then covered in cinders rescued from domestic and industrial fires. The sports enthusiasts, John and Alice included, carted it all up there in barrows and buckets and whatever other containers they could find. All the Woods family played some sport, but the youngest two, best friends in a home dominated by much older siblings, were allowed a little leniency in indulging their natural sporting abilities. John was turning into an accomplished footballer, even before he left school, and as for Alice, trained on the cinder track she had helped create, she could run like a miner's whippet.

She grew to be a tall young woman, close to five feet six inches in height, loose-limbed in that casual manner of all natural athletes, slim but muscular, with an extraordinarily strong round face – not moon-shaped, nor even sun-shaped, but shaped like the planet Jupiter, the bringer of jollity. This was a face you noticed and would be drawn to, even through a crowd of faces in the street or on a photograph, with a broad, softly smiling mouth, and laughing, conspiratorial eyes. The first time I saw a photograph of her, I recognized her as a woman who loved life and was in control of hers. She was self-composed, confident, competitive – even with her brother – and she knew how much she could win with her unique talent.

Alice's sprinting won her accolades and prizes. They were anomalous, perhaps, in the home of a miner, the kind of frippery knick-knack which has no useful value and which sits comfortably in the homes of those who give dinner parties or have a nice chrysanthemum display in the hall. They were the tokens and totems of aspiration – an ornate glass fruit bowl decorated with filigree silver, silver cruet

17

sets and gravy boats, silver sugar bowls with tongs, finely wrought mustard dishes, manicure sets and bonbon dishes. Alice won all these, chosen as prizes by the burghers of the towns she competed in. All very nice, and very much valued by the family. They were something to be placed in the glass-fronted cupboard, and cleaned regularly to divest them of the coal dust which seeped through the windows. They were objects displayed in the parlour, a room unused by most of the St Helens' families except as backdrop to a coffin. I can almost hear them saying, swollen with familial pride:

'Our Alice won summat at races today.'

'Oh, that's nice, Alice, that's very nice.' And then a pause. 'What's it for, Margaret?'

'For the hundred yards.'

'Yes, I know, but what's this wassisname for? Would's't use it thissen? Like what do it do?'

'It's for t'put mustard in.'

'Ah, reet.' Another pause. 'It'll look reet nice in t' cabi-net.'

Far more importantly for the community than her mustard-pot winnings, it could bet on Alice. Betting was always a way of life down the mines, and every sporting event was the scene of odds being whispered and coins changing hands. In straight athletics races there was little opportunity to do this, especially when Alice was taking part, as she was the best in the north, and word got around so the odds were rarely any good, but if it was a handicap race, where starters were staggered, the odds could be the subject of speculation, Alice always made the day for the St Helens miners who had backed her.

In 1914, Alice's world changed, as did her brother John's.

18

War was declared, and he was drafted into the army. For a year or so, he'd been engaged as a footballer for Stalybridge Celtic, not a team of much importance, but he'd already shown great promise and hoped to make his career at one of the top clubs in time. The family waved goodbye to him, their youngest and most gifted, tearfully. Alice was heartbroken. John was her best friend, her big brother, her protector, and she clung to him and didn't want to let go. He reassured her that this war would be over by Christmas. But what happened that Christmas wasn't the end, although the soldiers thought it might be.

On Christmas Day 1914, on the Western Front, German and British troops called an informal truce, and instead of war played football in No Man's Land. It's one of the defining moments of the Great War, meaningful not only because of what it says about those called upon to fight unnecessary battles, but, as significantly, for what it says about football as a common language spoken even by those supposedly on opposite sides, a language that John understood. The matches played at Christmas 1914 brought a day's false hope that the end of old enmities was in sight. But perhaps it was just an end to the naivety about why and how the war had started, as this soldier's ballad at the time suggests.

> Twas Christmas in the trenches
> Where the frost so bitter hung.
> The frozen fields of France were warmed
> As songs of peace were sung.
> For the walls they built between us,
> To exact the wrath of war,
> Had been crumbled and forgot,
> For evermore.

19

Oh ma name is Francis Tolliver.
In Liverpool I dwell.
Each Christmas come since WWI
I learnt its lesson well.
That the ones who call the shots won't be
Among the dead and maimed.
And on each end of the rifle, we're the same.

In 1914, concerned that Britain didn't have much of a land army except for the small British Expeditionary Force, as the country had always been protected by its navy, Kitchener started a desperate drive for volunteers to fight the land war in France and Belgium. For a time, it seemed that the first volunteer army would be enough. It wasn't, so the brainchild of Lord Derby was conceived – wouldn't it be so much more inviting if men were encouraged to volunteer in bands of happy comrades? It could be fun. This was the Pals scheme. The men who enlisted as a group, from the same town, workplace, family, club, or pub were guaranteed that they would be in the same regiment, sent to the same front lines, and would train, live and fight as bands of mates, as they had always done in their games of dominoes, darts, and football.

It seemed a wonderful idea. Recruiting offices in towns and cities all over Britain were overwhelmed by swathes of laughing friends, wanting to face the Hun together, undivided – first in Liverpool, Lord Derby's fiefdom, with men like Francis Tolliver, then in the depressed industrial North West, and finally in the whole country. In Scotland the entire Heart of Midlothian football team, then leading the Scottish League, enlisted together, not realising what was to come: six of that championship eleven died on the Somme in 1916.

The Somme. The very first of its battles was at Serre, and it was the Great War's equivalent of Balaclava. Thousands of British soldiers were commanded by some sodden military planning officer to march towards the enemy, in a disciplined formation, to take this piece of territory to relieve the pressure on the fighting at Verdun. The generals thought the Germans had been decimated by two days of bombardments. They hadn't been. They had excavated deep into the chalk, where the mortars couldn't reach them, and as the British advanced they emerged and shot them down. They didn't have a hope. Tangled in barbed wire, still in formation, they were slaughtered like fish in a net.

My grandfather William, a 16-year-old recruit to the Pals scheme in one of the East Lancashire regiments, was a messenger-boy to that theatre of mass destruction, carrying the orders from Headquarters to his friends that would send them to their deaths. And the North West, which had been so solidly behind the recruiting scheme of its famous grouse-shooting local aristocrat, Lord Derby, finally discovered the fatal flaw in the Pals scheme. Of those killed, wounded or missing in action at Serre, 584 were from the cotton town of Accrington, just up the road from St Helens. Seven hundred and twenty Accrington Pals had enlisted together. Now the overwhelming majority were together in death and that loss of life devastated an entire Lancashire community – fathers, brothers, sons, husbands, and lovers, all gone.

The Lancashire lads, the Scots kid soldiers, the cheerful Cockney chums, the canny lads from the North East had all believed the hype and their wives and mothers and children and sweethearts had believed it, too. But John McCrae put them right:

21

In Flanders fields the poppies blow
Between the crosses, row on row
That mark our place. And in the sky
The larks, still bravely singing, fly
Scarce heard amid the guns below.

We are the Dead. Short days ago
We lived, felt dawn, saw sunset glow,
Loved and were loved, and now we lie
In Flanders fields.

The Somme was a dreadful turning point in a war which was running out of control. In order to keep it going, conscription was brought in. This time, no one was swamping the recruiting offices, but there was no choice. You had to be there, go through the selection process, drink bleach if nothing else worked. But, queried the commentators – of whom there were few – when the men had gone, how would industry, especially that created by the incessant appetite for the accoutrements of war, be manned? And that was when the Home Front was invented. Just as our boys were fighting the Hun in some foreign country, so our plucky women could fight their own war, by rolling up their sleeves and getting down to some really hard work, in the name of patriotism. They could call themselves the Home Front. They should be made to feel that their contribution was just as nationally vital as that of Tommy Atkins. It was a spin worthy of an industrial-strength washing machine.

Suffering bereavements and rationing, working in government-controlled industry, this Home Front business was just another way, it was said, in which women could show their loyalty to their country. The audacity of this call to arms is almost laughable in its shifting of goalposts. Women, pre-war, had had to be kept in their place.

Now, when government took over the manufacture and supply of arms in 1917, requisitioning factories for the purpose of fabricating war goods, women were called upon to make munitions, filling shell cases with TNT which turned their skin yellow and made their teeth drop out, operating welding equipment, and all for half the pay that a man might command.

In Lancashire, working for a living had never been a novel proposition for young women: it had been economic necessity. The cotton spinning and weaving industries in north and east Lancashire depended on the dexterity, cleanliness and neatness of small pairs of hands, as did the clothing industry which set up at its side. These women mill-hands were poorly paid. On the other end of the scale, in St Helens, women had been working underground in collieries until late in the nineteenth century, and at the outbreak of war were still employed as 'pit-brow' girls, working on the surface, grading and sorting coal. Those who couldn't find such a job, like my grandmother Polly, were sent off into service, scrubbing out and living in the attic rooms of the homes of solicitors, bankers and doctors in the industrial heartlands of the country, where hard times and hard work had led to a Darwinian survival of the toughest and strongest girls, who, unsurprisingly, were also the most fertile. Polly was one of thirteen surviving children, my grandmother Ellen one of eleven. But in the large families that these tough women produced, their own daughters went through the mill too, or on to the pit brow, or into the clerk class, until they married – and occasionally even afterwards. So the cycle continued. Lancashire had a reputation of producing 'hefty lasses' who could survive anything. Now they could keep the home fires burning.

In 1917 Alice was drafted into the converted Sutton Glass Works, only a short walk from home, as a munitions worker. Margaret didn't know how they would manage without her for the cleaning and the cooking, and the laundry on Mondays.

It was the laundry which was the real problem. Laundry always was. Monday was allotted for laundry, which is why joints were roasted on Sundays, to give the women cold cuts to heat up after the battle to get clothes washed and dried on washing days. Washing for the entire family was done in a boiler, often in an out-building in the back yard, but usually in the back kitchen itself. Water would be poured into the copper – a huge tub conventionally made out of copper – and a fire lit underneath with sticks, and then coal. When it boiled, the family bedding, the cotton sheets and pillow-cases, could be boiled in the water, and the men's Sunday shirts, and the white singlets and pants. There was a dolly, a probe with four feet, which could be swirled around and pushed into the boiling water, but you had to add soap, soda, and if you were affluent that week, a bag of dolly blue to disguise the yellow or greying of the worn fabrics. Some items were pre-washed against a corrugated-glass washing board on the slop stone in the back kitchen. Coloureds could be dunked into the copper after the whites had been removed, hand-rinsed, and mangled. Mangles were huge metal monsters with aggressive rollers, and provided there were at least two of you to hold and fold the rinsed sheet, standing at each end of the yard, pulling taut and folding first across the width, and then in a sequenced dance along the length 'To me', 'To you', and back to width again, sheets could be arranged to fit into the temperamental mangle, and have their excess moisture squeezed out. Then there was the hanging out on lines stretched over the yard, and sometimes over the street, and by sunset, most of the clothes and bedding had been hung out to dry in the smoke and grimy rain. By Monday night most of the sheets had been ironed with a flat iron warmed in the coals of the fire, and hung up in front of the fire on 'maidens', clothes airers, or hauled to the ceiling on a system of weights and pulleys to hang like accusations over the cold cuts and dripping. Men hated Mondays with a vehemence more than matched by that of their toiling and exhausted partners. Washday was always a battle, and a muscular activity. Alice had been wonderful as a muscular partner, and she would be missed on laundry days. She always smiled as she worked, and that was as good as sunshine on a wet November Monday.

The job at the munitions factory, though, worked out well. Prior to the Home Front, women in domestic service like my grandmother Polly earned around 12 pence per week. To put this into context, as a very rough and ready guide which you can use throughout this story, converting that rate into current values would involve doubling it then multiplying by 100. This method of ready reckoning has been worked out by examining the details of wages and budgets in working-class homes in Lambeth in 1913, as detailed in the Fabian report by Maud Pember Reeves and published as *Round About A Pound A Week* in 1913. So, in this case, women domestic staff were earning around £25 for a seven-day week, although lodging and food was free. Women factory workers, mill-hands in the Lancashire cotton industry for instance, earned between 50 and 60 pence for a five-and-a-half-day week – between £100 and

£120. A working-class man would earn twice that sum. The rental of a house was a little less than 50 pence, a large Sunday joint cost five pence. And women munitions workers could earn as much as 50 pence a day, the equivalent of over £500 per week, £25,000 per annum. For an eighteen-year-old girl, as Alice was, this represented a huge and hardly believable fortune, and an invaluable contribution to the family income. I have to add, here, that men too young or too old to be called up for war service, and working alongside the women earned twice that rate, despite constant promises of equal pay by the Ministry of Munitions.

Alice's intelligence was noted by the overseers drafted in from the Army to assess the women's skills, and instead of selecting her to work on the heavy lifting and welding in the forging shop, for which her strength would have made her eminently capable, or filling the shells, she was assigned to a more responsible role, numbering the completed shells, and transferring that number on to the shell case. It was hard work and demanded total concentration, but she, like all the other munitions girls, had to grind out a twelve-hour day, for six days a week, to earn the better money that munitions work paid.

The press wallowed in a frenzy of disapproval. Sensational stories were written of the excesses of these young women – a munitionette entering a pub and pulling out a wad of notes from her knicker leg, demanding drinks all round, in front of two of our noble heroes, wounded soldiers who were down to their last shilling. And another entering a department store and buying a fur coat off the peg (how dare she!). Women were said to be indulging in orgies of drinking, with champagne most commonly cited as the drink in question for London munition-factory workers, and spirits for the Northern workers. The price of whisky had been set at £1 (£200 in current terms) to discourage this practice. It was all very silly reporting. In fact, drunkenness as a way of life dropped dramatically in the war years, partly due to the fact that pub opening times were strictly reduced from their traditional 18 hours per day to a more sober six, with two hours at lunchtime and last orders at nine thirty.

That these girls might fraternize with soldiers was also a moral concern to a society which had forgotten that soldiers were young working-class men and the girls young working-class girls, who had been able to fraternize happily before the lights went out all over Europe. So, to limit potential hanky-panky, women's patrols were set up in 1917. These presumably more worthy women, suited and booted into uniform, issued with torches, walked their beat in twos, shining their torches into dark places – park benches and shop doorways – lest anything untoward should be happening involving two young people of the opposite sex.

Uniforms were well-liked by the moral majority, and by those anxious to create the illusion that the girls at home were toy soldiers, replicas of their brothers at the Front. So Alice was kitted out in a long, waisted and buttoned overall with lapels, and a matching little cap to restrain her long hair. Women's hair, traditionally, was never cut in Lancashire. She was then issued with a variety of badges to inform her superiors who she was, that she worked in 'Shells', and what her status was. These stood in for the regimental badges and medals worn by soldiers. Inevitably, her supervisor was male, and suited. But only the girls wore the black armbands, and by late 1917 they were the rule rather than the exception.

But the factories did have problems. Unused to such a high proportion of women and girls, even in Lancashire, they had inadequate facilities for women. Toilets were often dirty, and men didn't often require a cubicle, or even a urinal. Government-appointed female factory inspectors had to tour the factories to ensure that the environment was suitable for girls, many of them barely out of childhood. Swearing by the men was frowned upon, as if the girls hadn't heard this language in their own families, or used it themselves if the need arose. And some of the girls were, quite frankly, wayward. They giggled and raced round and chattered incessantly, and were rightly forgiven their natural inclination to let off steam. But they had to be managed, and something useful found for them to do in their break and meal times.

On the Western Front, the YMCA had built 'huts' suitable for soldiers' rest and recreation, where they could play board games or cards, read and relax. This same system was thought suitable for the munitions factories too, so many of them had a YMCA or YWCA 'hut' on the premises, where the girls could sew and knit and read and sing – and as this was a Christian organization, there was an element of soul-uplifting in the huts, too. Some factories employed women as welfare workers. These women might have been those in the voluntary sector in peacetime, or were recruited from the tiny band of educated women, many with university degrees, who needed to do something towards the war effort

But neither the welfare workers, nor the perfectly well-intentioned ladies of the YWCA, could do much with the noisiest teenage girls. These had been used to burning off their energies by play-fighting with their brothers, running along the street playing hopscotch, whooping over games of hollies and jacks, and generally behaving like free spirits, as hefty lasses tend to. It was vital, therefore, that some form of sport was provided so that these girls could tire their bodies out sufficiently to allow their minds to concentrate on the jaundice-inducing job of filling shells with TNT. Although the school curriculum at the time didn't provide sports facilities for working-class girls, just an occasional bout of drill, these girls weren't particularly good at sitting still. At Alice's school, Sutton National, drill consisted of marching on the spot, clapping hands above the head while doing star jumps, jumping on and off school benches, all in rigid precision, in lines and formations. Occasionally there were skipping ropes. They weren't lucky enough to be provided with tennis rackets and hockey sticks or a horse to ride – not even a bicycle.

Whether it was the welfare workers' idea or that of the girls themselves is unknown, but it became a ritual within munitions factories for these girls to gather outside in the yard, rather than in the warm hut provided, and play football with the factory youths. Someone had always brought a football into work, and besides playing the fifteen minute-a-half game at their meal times, the girls and boys set challenges for each other – breaking third-floor windows, for example.

The role of the welfare ladies was now clear: to harness this energy and enthusiasm for football by forming the girls into a rough-and-ready team, perhaps even allowing them to set challenges to other munitions factories, or another group of workers within the factory itself, to play a game on some piece of waste ground. Teamwork, they thought, was an essential requisite of the efforts to be made on the Home Front.

And so munitions-factory teams, amateur and ill organized at first, sprang up all over Lancashire, as far north as Whitehaven, as far south as the North Wales border. And as if by the magic of word-of-mouth, teams started in the North East, in Wales, in Scotland, in London, and some in the South West around the naval munitions factories. Sometimes the girls played the boys, a practice which had been banned by the Football Association in 1902, but wasn't applicable to matches played on the most convenient piece of flattened land.

Women's factory football was filling a need, both for the participants and for the spectators, should there be any. In 1916–7 the men's League games had been largely suspended when footballers were drafted. An order at the start of the war had also deprived the factory workers and colliers of Sutton of the pleasures of their racing pigeons: for the duration of the war, these pesky creatures that could carry messages to the enemy across the Channel had been outlawed. So there was little to do, or to bet on, on those Saturday afternoons off work. Britain was missing football badly.

There was another factor behind these games: charity. When the entire war effort was planned, no one had any idea of the consequences in terms of human suffering. Yes, allowance was made for there to be men killed, although mobilisation was never envisaged as numbering millions of young men travelling to another country and never returning. That was a problem in itself. More worrying to the economy was the overwhelming number of those wounded and mutilated in body or mind. There was no room in the military hospitals for these disabled soldiers, nor funds to pay any kind of living allowance to those who would never be able to work again as long as they clung on to life. By late 1917 every town and city had its Disabled Soldiers' hospital and charity fund, emergency centres for returning soldiers. Some limbless, some with severe head wounds, some suffering from extreme shell shock or trench foot, they arrived in their droves, and there was no money for the necessary staff or equipment. The women's matches provided that money, and were a more enjoyable form of fund-raising than the traditional concerts. They got the girls out in the fresh air – and fresh air was a valuable commodity for those who worked underground, so the miners encouraged their families to play whatever sport they chose.

And, as I've said, women in the north of the country had always played football. There's no gender tag on balls reading 'Men only please', and kicking them or anything roughly ball-shaped has always been the most accessible game to play in the streets, down the 'backs' – the ash-strewn land behind rows of terraced houses – on any piece of waste ground, or the pub forecourt, for any poor kid, male or female. Across Scotland, there was a tradition of married women of a town or village playing regular matches against single women as a way for the male onlookers to select a lusty bride. And in 1895 a deliciously-named woman, Nettie Honeyball, an educated, middle-class feminist and leading sportswoman of her day, arranged a fixture between the North and South of England Ladies at Crouch End. In the same year, Lady Florence Dixie was touring Scotland with a women's football team she managed. But nevertheless, sports provision for girls and women was largely organized according to social status.

31

For middle-class and aristocratic women, where money was no object, and nor was risk, tennis, golf, swimming, lacrosse, hockey, rowing, shooting, and riding were included in the curricula of the top girls' public schools. But all these sports needed equipment, which had to be bought by devoted and affluent parents. Nettie was privileged – and Lady Florence Dixie was a titled legend. Her father was the Marquis of Queensbury, who had educated her at home alongside her brother. She shared her brother's books and his sports, was tutored to feel no disadvantage in being a woman, became a writer and explorer who travelled widely on horseback in Patagonia and was the special correspondent of the *London Morning Post* during the Anglo-Zulu war in South Africa. No one thought to object that she was somehow overstepping the boundaries of what could and should be done by women, because she was a Lady.

But working-class women, and football – no, not as a public display, please. Not until Nettie's match, reported quite disparagingly in the *Manchester Guardian*: 'When the novelty has worn off, I do not think that women's football will attract the crowds'. That was written by a 'Lady Correspondent', so it shows how little hope there was of a modicum of sisterly appreciation between the classes who wrote for newspapers and the classes with dirty boots. Nettie died soon afterwards, and her socially reconstructive form of feminism, bringing a women's street game to the middle-class masses of Crouch End, died with her.

When at the end of 1917 it was decided that each section of her factory should form a women's football team. Alice was amongst the first to volunteer her services. Home on leave, John put the final touches to her footballing skills and techniques.

Naturally, she was chosen as one of the Shells team. She was famous in this small community, and more than fulfilled her promise as a footballer. And naturally, in the eagerly awaited football final played on 13 April 1918 at the recreation ground at St Helens Junction between Shells and Forgings, Shells won. They were a rough and tough-looking team, dressed in a restrained dark strip laced at the neck, under which some, Alice included, wore a blouse, with long knickerbocker shorts, and stood, or knelt down, gracefully clutching one knee, for their photograph to be taken. Surprisingly, the team included one mixed-race girl. I had never realized that by 1917 St Helens already had African-Caribbean immigrants who had married into their community until I saw the photograph, and I still can't explain or identify this girl. None of the women had bobbed their hair, but they had pinned it back, or wore a munitions cap over it. Alice was bareheaded, and one of only two on the photograph who managed a smile for the camera, already a natural star. But then, she'd been photographed many times before, after her athletics triumphs.

And there was to be one further and crowning victory for her there, too. In the summer of 1918, an athletics meet was held at Blackpool, the Northern Counties championships, under the auspices of Mr Hardwick of Salford Harriers. It was the first women's race meet to be held under AAA laws. In the 100 yards, Alice fell when approaching the tape, and the fifteen-year-old prodigy Elaine Burton – trained by her father, who had been a hurdler – sailed past. But Alice won the 80-yard championship against the same opposition. Few other Ladies' championship races had been held, and none under stringent AAA regulations, so she could, and some-times did, call herself the British 80-yard champion. Elaine

Burton's father went further in 1919, claiming his daughter to be world champion in the pages of *All Sports Weekly*, in a slot reserved for fathers to brag about the sporting success of their prodigious daughters. Alice was furious. She wrote to the periodical, stating that she had beaten Miss Burton on many occasions, and had never herself been beaten, except when she fell, and that she would bet £25 that Miss Burton couldn't beat her in a straight race.

It was an uncharacteristic outburst of competitiveness for Alice, usually so self-composed, and the sum was outrageously high, the equivalent of £5,000. It was, if she but knew it, a working-class gesture – offering a bet and a sum of money. But this was athletics, and she approached her sport with a dedication that was always ferocious. It was what made her, ultimately, such an exceptional footballer. Mr Burton wrote a letter in reply, very pompous, very patronising, very defensive, saying that his daughter was now back at (boarding?) school, and that there was no way he would disturb her studies. This time he backed down from the claim that Elaine was world champion, and merely said that she would be, one day soon. In fact, Elaine became a sports teacher, entered Parliament in 1950 and was later elevated to the peerage. She and Alice remained on good terms, but I wonder if what sparked Alice's fury at the time was a quiet frustration about the way women's athletics was a sport in which an affluent family background and a home or education in a big city helped in the drive for success. In international meets, most of the women athletes were chosen from the newly-formed London clubs, catering to undergraduates, or had a middle-class background. Miners' children weren't readily accepted into athletics, and it certainly wasn't going to associate itself with the betting fraternity. So much for Alice, and her record-making time for the 100 yards, 12 seconds. It was a British championship time, and never recognized. So much for level playing fields.

Still, there was always football. When munitions factories were closing down in 1919, the success of and interest aroused by the brief flurry of charity women's football competitions was encouraged by the announcement that there was to be a St Helens Ladies football team. Alice, now back in a domestic role at home, and still in training, went for a trial. She had no football boots – they had been supplied by the Shells' team she'd played for. So she went into the trial wearing her side-button boots, her everyday shoes, and her mother was furious when she got home, her clothes and boots caked in mud.

'I got into the football team, though, Mam,' she said as she set about trying to remove the mud from the little eyelets in her boots.

'Ee, it's enough for me, our Alice, to have one footballer in t'family. Why don't you stick with the running?'

John had returned home from the war, intact and unhurt, and about to sign for Halifax Town, who were scouring the country for footballing talent, and had been forced to look as far afield as the 'wrong' side of the Pennines. But Margaret was adamant. He was not to leave home. He'd been away in the war and she'd been worried sick over her youngest boy, and there was no way she'd let him go again. This was a family so close-knit that only Government orders or marriage, Margaret decided, would prise them apart ever again. It was a rule she would never break. But Halifax was desperate, and John Woods was a brilliantly gifted young footballer, so after months of trans-Pennine wrangling he signed for Halifax Town, and they supplied a taxicab to transport him every Saturday to the games, and then back home again to St Helens and Margaret – now approaching her 70th year, and becoming quite dependent on her children.

Alice played football, despite the pressures on her at home. In her second match with St Helens Ladies, played at Wigan in late 1919, she came up against a team from Preston, the famous and formidable Dick, Kerr's Ladies. Alice scored the single goal for St Helens' Ladies. Dick, Kerr's scored six.

As she came off the pitch at the end of the game, a dapper man in a bowler hat and an expensive overcoat stopped her.

'That was a fine performance. Excellent. I'm putting together a team for New Brighton, Boxing Day, and I wondered of you'd like to play for Dick, Kerr's, on loan. Could you write to confirm? We shall, of course, pay your expenses, and the charabanc could make a small detour to pick you up in St Helens if you wish.'

He asked for her address, which he wrote in a flowing hand in his notebook, and gave her his card:

Alfred Frankland, Hon Secretary, Dick, Kerr's Ladies.

'Oh, and by the way, Miss Woods, I'd very much appreciate it if you could make the same offer to that outside left I saw here too. Parr, I think her name was. Miss Parr. She's an exceptional young player. You could perhaps offer to act as her chaperone?'

Alice stood there for a while, as the teams and the crowds disappeared into the gloom. She knew that this was what she'd dreamed of. Even one game with Dick, Kerr's would mean more to her than . . . Well, perhaps as much as winning the Northern Counties sprint race. But what would her mother say? Would she let her go all the way to New Brighton, a place she'd never been, and on Boxing Day, too, a family occasion, when her older brothers and Elizabeth Ann all came round with their children? And what about this Parr girl? Alice had no idea where the child lived, as she'd never attended the trials. She'd just turned up at the first match and offered to play, and announced at the end of it that she'd turn up for the next one, too. She was a mystery; a girl of very few words. And most of those were words that Alice had never allowed to slip through her lips – indeed, had never even thought.

But when she finally arrived at the hut which served as the dressing room, Lily had disappeared.

'Anyone seen the game ball?' someone was yelling, searching through a mass of bags and discarded kit. 'It's the only one we got!'

'I reckon that Parr kid pinched it. She was in and out of here like a shot, still in her kit. Said she had to catch an earlier bus. Anyone know where she lives?'

'Gerrard's Bridge, I think,' someone said.

'Gerrard's Bridge?' sighed the lady trainer, the wife of the secretary. 'I suppose we might have guessed! Is she going to be more trouble than she's worth?'

'Noooo!' everyone screamed together.

Lily Parr, fourteen, hauntingly beautiful in a sullen, dark way, just out of school – if she'd ever bothered to go – foul-mouthed, never without a Woodbine in her mouth except when she was playing, a kid who took her chances to pocket anything left lying around, was the best woman footballer they had ever seen.

Two

Booted Up

I ought to put you in the picture about Dick, Kerr's Ladies, and about the dapper man, Alfred Frankland, who had requested the pleasure of Miss Woods and Miss Parr as guests in his team for Boxing Day, and whose determination helped the women find their place in history.

Alfred came from the Fulwood area of Preston. If you don't know Preston in the north of Lancashire, you may have read about it as 'Coketown' in Dickens' novel *Hard Times*. Sent there as a reporter to cover the problems in the cotton industry in the mid-nineteenth century, Dickens saw the city's industrialists as hard pragmatists, and the mill-hands as exploited workers denied the opportunity to let their spirits run free. He should have come to St Helens, because although the cotton-spinning and -weaving indus-tries that settled in Lancashire and produced the industry's technology had their hard times, St Helens with its mining disputes and chemical pollution was a better example of exploitation. To St Helens people, 'Stelliners', Preston had it good. It had broad Georgian squares and countryside with-in easy reach, and employment for women in jobs which paid adequately. Even though Preston was in decline because of the decline of the cotton industry in the face of cheaper foreign competition, it diversified into other industries, which brought some prosperity and hope. It was beautifully sited on the Ribble estuary; it had quaysides, and had become a railway and road transport centre.

It was also the home of Dick, Kerr's.

All tramway enthusiasts know Dick, Kerr's. Its name was on the tramcars of almost every city in the UK, including the famous Blackpool and Isle of Man trams. Replicas of its luxury bogie open-tops are sought after by collectors worldwide, but if you didn't nod sagely when the name was first mentioned, it's unlikely that you're a bogie open-top connoisseur. The firm still bore the name of Mr W. B. Dick, although his connection with the industry had ceased in 1889, before the company moved to Preston from its original base in Kilmarnock. The public face of Dick, Kerr's was the younger partner and relative, John Kerr, an enterprising, inventive Scot with a determination to succeed, who first brought the works to Preston, following a complex agreement he'd entered into to build and operate a tramway system in Carlisle. It was important to relocate south of the border, and to drum up money from some Manchester investors, so in 1899 an empty factory was found in Preston, with access to waterways on the Ribble estuary and to railway lines. The factory was faced, on the opposite side of the road, by a thirteen-acre piece of reclaimed wasteland, at the time used as a sports ground, but this land, too, was bought by John Kerr and his syndicate, and another factory erected. So, a factory built on a sports ground? Reparation for that would be made, one day.

John Kerr threw himself into Preston society as one of the important figures in the redevelopment of the town. Preston itself was never an eyesore, although to those of us from South Lancashire it was merely a staging post on our annual Blackpool excursions. It was a place we passed through, the last city before the sea and the Pleasure Beach. John Kerr retained his family home in Scotland, and then bought a home in London, so perhaps he had the same feelings about the city as I did, that he was just passing through. He kept a yacht on the river Ribble, built a pied-à-terre for himself adjoining the factory, and soon entered politics – the sort of canny move we might expect from this entrepreneur with a Northern work ethic and a paternalistic factory-owner mentality. He was Unionist MP for Preston for two years, but in 1912 he too retired, and in 1919 the company became incorporated into English Electric.

By 1915 the factories were engaged almost exclusively on war work, the conversion having been superintended by another Scot, the works manager James Connor. War supplies covered rather more than the manufacture of shells. Dick, Kerr's war efforts included supplying locomotives, cable drums, pontoon bridges, wagon chassis, various wagons, cartridge boxes, 30,000 horseshoes and 75 pontoon boats, and, briefly, some seaplanes constructed in another factory along the coast, in Lytham St Anne's. But munitions was its biggest job, and by 1917 it was producing 30,000 shells per week.

To manage the paperwork involved in the distribution of these war goods, clerks were drafted into the factory from the army personnel at Fulwood Barracks, and one of these was a local man who had volunteered for Army duty at the beginning of the war – Alfred Frankland, the former manager of a tailoring establishment. He was in his mid-thirties, married with a young son, and was, so everyone said, 'a natural gentleman'.

Frankland was astute and a natural organizer. His father was a mechanic in the cotton industry, his elder brother had started work as a storekeeper at Dick, Kerr's and worked his way up into a highly placed clerical job, his younger brother worked in a solicitor's office and his sister, who had been a cotton weaver, later trained as a nurse at Whittingham hospital, a mental health institution. Alfred, however, on leaving school rose from retail assistant to manager at a gentlemen's outfitters and had learned the importance of appearance over reality. He was scrupulously dressed, wore a bowler hat and a fine alpaca overcoat, always had a fob watch in his waistcoat pocket, and inspired respect with his fine manners, his command of English, and the connections he'd built up over the years with the gentlemen who had bought their bespoke suits in fine Yorkshire woollen worsted from the shop. He was a keen amateur sportsman.

He had looked from his office window and seen the munitions girls at Dick, Kerr's kicking a ball around in their breaks. Under the leadership of one of the workers, Grace Sibbert, whose husband was a prisoner of war, these women had already played one match against the youths of Dick, Kerr's when Alfred started taking an interest, and he became involved when a plan was hatched to play a bigger match on Christmas Day 1917, in aid of the local hospital for wounded soldiers at Moor Park. Actually, the women were originally invited by the Matron to perform a variety concert with recitations and singalongs, but decided, perhaps rashly, to put on a football match instead. Grace, in poor health, was worrying herself sick over the possible fate of her husband. No one quite knew what prisoner-of-war status actually meant, although grisly stories emerged from those who had escaped and found their way, with the help of underground movements in France and Belgium, back to the Allied lines. British soldiers who escaped by this means reported being attacked by German women with buckets of quicklime, of being forced to work as manual labourers or miners, of having little food, and of being constantly moved around from one camp to another. Most of those who escaped were seriously undernourished and close to death. Grace heard these stories, and of course little snippets of gossip and sensational media reports, and so was frantic with daily exhausted hope and frequent tears. Alfred Frankland offered his proven organizational help. And just look at the very shrewd move he made, immediately she accepted this help – he booked Deepdale, the ground of Preston's championship-winning football club, for the match. Now that took some chutzpah.

The significance of this choice can't be underestimated. Preston North End was one of the leading football clubs in the country, with a host of celebrated former players still haunting its hallowed turf and some employed, then, at Dick, Kerr's. There was Bob Holmes, he was still around, former captain of England, an ex-member of the squad which had carried all before it in the old championship days. There was Jack Warner, another former player who had achieved iconic status, and when Frankland had booked the ground, he'd been able to nod to some of these men whose footballing deeds would never die and tell them, 'I've got a couple of likely girls in this team. Maybe you wouldn't mind taking a look at them, sometime? When you're not too busy. I know it's an imposition but . . .'

Frankland placed his adopted team of ladies centre stage. He gave them credibility. He put them on a real football pitch, in front of a crowd which would bring their memories of great games with them when they lined up at the turnstiles. He was drawing a parallel between the Dick, Kerr's Ladies and a top men's team. He was saying, 'This is serious.' And 10,000 people heard him, because 10,000 poured through the turnstiles on that Christmas Day, to the accompaniment of the works' brass band booming out Christmas carols.

Ten thousand was not quite a capacity crowd, but it was more than just a great show of support. It was huge. Some had poured in to support a good cause. Some came to gawp at women in shorts. Some came to laugh, at first. But all came because this was football at Deepdale, again. Not just hefty girls kicking each other, although on a bitterly cold Christmas day with acrid smoke hanging over the hoar-frosted pitch, there had to be a degree of heftiness on show. And imagine how the hefty girls in shorts and boots themselves felt, that lump-in-the-throat moment when they raced into the ground and emulated their heroes by kicking in, and then stood on that magic centre circle to toss for ends, just as they'd seen those great players do, Saturday after Saturday.

There were three in particular who, playing for a crowd that had come to watch a novelty game, a distraction from the Christmas stuffing, quietened the giggles and the heckling of the men in the crowd, their cheeks glowing with the Christmas spirit in a bottle in their back pockets.

'Watch yer hats!' they shouted, as fondly knitted striped caps were blown away.

43

'Aye, keep yer hair on!'

'Oooh, look, she's got her stays too tight! No wonder she's winded!'

That heckler was obviously the worse for wear: his pals had already made a guffawing point of noticing that the women weren't wearing corsets.

'She's got a nice little right foot on her when she tries . . .'

'That blonde 'un can't half crack on, too . . .'

'But it's like watching a slow-motion Kinema film, you got to admit!'

'Ah, shurrup and watch the bloody game. It's not North End, but t'aint bad.'

'Not bad at all . . .'

'Hey, Ref, that lass knows more than you about football. She wor never offside, like she says! Just lissen to her, wilt tha?'

The blonde, as the men said, couldn't half crack on. She was Florrie Redford, the centre forward for the Dick, Kerr's Ladies. She had pace and vision, could pick out a pass, and if her kicking lacked the power of male footballers, her skills and determination, her relentless running, more than made up for any lack of muscle. The statuesque one with the 'nice little right foot' and the face of a school games captain was totally in control of that game, bossing the defence like a pro. She was Florrie's best friend, right back from when they were at school together – Alice Kell, the captain, an all-round sportswoman who played golf as well as football with her father and brothers. And there was dark-haired Lily Jones in defence, who knew the offside rule, never shied away from a tackle, made the blocks, refusing to let the opposition players get by her on the wing. These three women were to form the backbone of the team Alfred

Frankland had now decided to manage, and to make the best in the country.

Alfred Frankland legitimized women's football. And his vision and belief had already taken him further than any number of male 'football secretaries' who had entrenched themselves in the seats of power in factory-girl football throughout Britain. He had booked Deepdale for a further three matches, in February and March. The cost was high. The Christmas Day match alone was £20–£4,000 in today's terms. Then he went further and booked Deepdale as the training ground for the girls, for daytime mid-week training. He was telling them, and the world, that they were a valuable commodity.

Just how valuable was evident as soon as the books had been balanced. Despite the heavy cost incurred by the infamous Entertainment Tax levied on football, against which everyone in the game was up in arms, and the ground costs and expenses, almost £200 clear profit had been raised for the hospital. That's the equivalent of £40,000 today. It was an astronomical sum – rather more, one would imagine, than would have been raised by a couple of pierrot acts, a dog in a hat and ruffles jumping through a hoop (if such a dog could have been found), and some noisy renditions of 'It's a Long Way To Tipperary'.

The match at Deepdale on Christmas Day 1917 was one of those moments when everything works out just fine. To crown the occasion, Dick, Kerr's won the match by four goals to nil. And why shouldn't they, when they had already acquired a coach, Mr Birkenshaw, and two expert assistants, Bob Holmes and Jack Warner, to teach the finer points of football to the girls who had learnt the basics from their brothers and fathers? And a lady trainer with a towel and first-aid kit. And a helpful welfare worker. And the nod from the works manager, James Connor, who was delighted by the Ladies' performance on such a daunting occasion, and said so.

But unless events develop from potentialities, there will never be a story. Alfred Frankland made sure that the story would continue, and that he would write it. A team from Lancaster had challenged Dick, Kerr's to a football match, and this was next on the agenda. Following that, another game was booked against the munitions workers from the Barrow-in-Furness shipyards, and on Good Friday 1918, one against Bolton Ladies. And at the Lancaster game, Frankland saw the means by which the team he'd taken under his wing would continue to grow in stature. He did something that had only ever been heard of in professional football circles – he poached a player from an opposing side.

Molly Walker was the outstanding Lancaster player in that match, and it was her nippiness, her eye for a pass, her pace and her all-round expertise which held Dick, Kerr's to a 1–1 draw. And there was Frankland, frowning in the dugout in his finely tailored overcoat, flanked by the veterans Holmes and Warner, resting their heads on the heels of their hands, and muttering about a team only being as good as its best player, and Molly Walker being the best player on the pitch. And she couldn't half run.

Alfred Frankland must have worked hard to persuade Molly Walker to move from Lancaster, only a few miles north of Preston, and come to join his team. How he did it is uncertain, but he had that dignified air of the natural gent, and a way with mothers, and look what he was offering – first class training, a backroom staff of devoted workers who washed the kit and provided refreshments, a chance to play on a field of dreams, perhaps a job at the factory, and payment in lieu of any time lost from work.

This last was probably the clincher for Molly. By the start of the 1918–19 season, Alfred Frankland was able to announce that Dick, Kerr's would be strengthened by the addition of two new players from Lancaster, Molly Walker, and Mrs Lord. Mrs Lord failed to materialise. Perhaps Mr Lord was opposed to the idea. But Molly, with her sharp features and sharper feet, and her tall, slim frame, did make her appearances for Dick, Kerr's, and continued to do so, scoring the goal which won them the match in their first game of the new season, again against Barrow, at Deepdale.

Is player-poaching illegal? No. It's clever. Call it a transfer if you like, and it happens all the time in football. If you're trying to build a great team you have to take your chances when you see them, and this idea of bringing in new players from outside may have been an entirely new concept to the amateur master-builders of women's football, but it worked. It also marked out yet another way in which Alfred Frankland was unafraid of the big idea, even if others around him merely saw the game of women's football as a passing fad which would be over after the war had finished, or as a novelty way of earning some money for local charities, or as a way of keeping recalcitrant teenage girls happy and focused on their jobs. Alfred, even at this early stage, was the consummate professional, and he was determined that his team would be run along professional lines. Hence the expenses and payment in lieu with which he tempted Molly Walker.

Each girl in the Dick, Kerr's team earned payment in lieu – ten shillings each time they played – in recompense for missing a day's work. Converting that sum, yet again, that's £100 per game. Munitions-factory girls, as I've said, were well paid, and this was their day rate. Yet Saturday was usually a half day, and the girls were playing at a ground in Preston to which they could easily travel after completing their morning's work. To put this 'expense payment' into an even clearer perspective, professional footballers, earned £2 per week during the war years. The scale of the payment to the girls is a tangible mark of respect, and shows a scrupulously fair level of accounting and accountability. At football, just as in the factory, the girls earned a fair day's pay for a fair day's work. And those who had to travel were paid their travelling expenses too. Dick, Kerr's Ladies were treated like ladies, by the perfect gentleman, Alfred Frankland.

When the accounts of that first tremulous season were finalised, a gross sum, before tax, of over £800 had been raised by the team, £554 net. Expenses for the matches worked out to a little over £23 per match – a very reasonable sum, given that this covered expenses for both teams that had played, and that the costs of reimbursing the Ladies and the team backroom boys must have amounted to at least £9 for each match. The remaining sum would have paid for laundry, which was done by Alfred's neighbour Mrs Sarah Stanley, and travelling expenses. Moor Park Hospital benefited from the majority of this money, but almost £200 was divided amongst other worthy causes – poor children, war pensioners, other hospitals, and, mysteriously, Preston Station buffet. Perhaps it was in desperate need of a facelift, considering the amount of human traffic passing through there on its way to and from the Western Front.

But the 1918–19 season was now in full swing, and being

played out against rumours that the war might finally be coming to an end. American troops, having joined the Allies in 1917, had brought much-needed reinforcements to swell the ranks, the Germans seemed to be retreating, and although Dick, Kerr's Ladies were beaten 2–0 by Whitehaven, despite Molly Walker's pace and skills, on 9 October, the big game was finally won on 11 November 1918. The war was over, and the streets of every town in the country were thronged with people and flags for week-long celebrations, even delayed fireworks parties.

The Armistice, though, failed to produce the results people had hoped for. While there was a temporary euphoria over the end of hostilities, the old grievances which had existed in Britain before the war had been exacerbated, rather than dulled, despite the granting of some form of women's suffrage. Women over thirty who either owned or rented property, or were married to someone who did, had been given voting rights in February 1918. The next election, it was promised, would happen imminently, and the next government would produce a land fit for heroes.

More importantly, for the Ladies already established in this particular corner of the war story, what would happen to them? Alice Kell, Lily Jones and Florrie Redford were ready for anything. They had accepted that the end of the war would herald a period when life might change drastically for them – not that they cared. They were hefty lasses. Survivors. All were prepared to accept a drop in income, or even unemployment. The boys who had fought the war were coming home, and if the girls could find work in the post-war economy, it would be a bonus.

Not everyone was as stoical as these mill girls. For years before the war erupted, there had been problems in the relations between those who had and those who made do. Even during the war, socialist tendencies were strengthening, helped by the example of the Russian Revolution and other European revolutionary movements, and with the trade unions now flexing their muscle, soldiers and the navy threatening to mutiny if there was any further mobilisation of troops abroad, the police force becoming angry about their treatment, seething unrest turned into strike action. Here's a letter to a newspaper written by a London clippie which encapsulates the distrust which replaced the gung-ho attitudes of the Home Front.

The 'bus girls have stopped work, are striking,
And to seek for the cause you'll not wait,
But in fairness to me and my comrades
The whole cause and reason I'll state.

A boy with a badge on his lapel
Boarded my 'bus in the town
And his voice was both bitter and hard as he said;
'It's the likes of you girls let us down.'

There was truth in the tale that he told me;
He'd been to apply for a job,
He was married and asked a man's wages –
They offered him 'thirty-five bob.'

And the firm who refused to employ him
Told him straight what their reasons were;
'We can get the same labour from a woman to-day
At less wages and so we choose her.'

Is it fair to work for less money,
To steal the jobs from these men
Who have been through hell's gates just to save us,
Who have risked their all time and again?

Our firm is not out just for show, girls;
It's a business, a paying concern,
And wherever the labour is cheapest,
To that labour employers will turn.

But they don't kid the girls on the 'buses.
We want the same pay as the men,
So that when the great fighting is over
They can take up their jobs once again.

Just back up and stick to each other,
Don't notice what people may say;
We've stood by the boys once before, girls,
And we're going to stand out to-day.

What the government didn't expect was collusion and
fellow-feeling between the men, who pre-war had always
held the jobs, and the women, who now did the jobs, but
who knew that they were being paid under the odds, and
that their underpayment could allow unscrupulous employers to try to drive a wedge between returning soldiers
and the sisters, wives and sweethearts who had waited for
them, and filled in for them. Women backing men was an
unexpected collaboration in the last few months of the
war and the years afterwards, but working-class women
were never the enemies of their mates. The class war, in
the days when class mattered, was stronger than the

gender war. Men and women, in many parts of the country, weren't battling it out. They were shoulder to shoulder, showed proper respect to each other, and worked on an old tradition of us against them. 'Us' was real people, even if some of us had decent suits and overcoats and bowler hats. 'Them' were just names or ciphers like Kitchener and Lord Derby, the government, and the generals who had sent the Accrington boys and the Pals brigades to certain death. Yes, women over thirty with property had managed to get the vote, but did it matter? Not a lot to this woman on the London omnibus. But she would have to face the fact that thousands of women would be made redundant to make room for the boys who were back in town.

And did that mean that women's football would have to yield to the men's game? Alfred Frankland didn't think so. He had, still, the highest hopes for his women, and was prepared to back them to win. He just couldn't be convinced that because women were being forced out of their jobs to make way for the returning men, this could be a problem for his band of sisters. He believed in them, and would make special provision for them. Dick, Kerr's Ladies, a brand he had designed, would not disappear. He had set his mind on that.

As the man with the big idea, he could see advantages in the unfolding unrest of December 1918. Munitions factories would be closing, and the factory teams would be disbanded. This would mean that the best women footballers from the teams that Dick, Kerr's had played might be lost to the game for ever. And he had a winning hand. Dick, Kerr's, now English Electric, was a huge organization which could easily restructure itself and its workforce after the war. It wasn't specifically set up as a munitions factory, as some of the others had been, but had merely adapted its output. Given that many of the Dick, Kerr's munitions workers would retire to start families now that their men had come home, there might still be work available for women who wanted it. And, since he had the ear of management, and the support of people like James Connor, and the gratitude of the aldermen and councillors of Preston for the vital charity work his team was doing, perhaps he could actually offer work to some of these footballers? It was a thought. And, when he expressed it to the influential committee which had now been set up to run the Ladies' team, they liked it, too. So Alfred Frankland once more dipped into the transfer market.

He needed to. On 21 December Dick, Kerr's had been beaten by Lancaster Ladies, and there was a big match to be played at Deepdale on Christmas Day against Bolton, a strong side. If Dick, Kerr's lost the match – the poignant celebration of its anniversary, with all the expectation that celebration entailed – the supporters might see the entire exercise as a damp squib, and voices could be added to the one or two cynics who were predicting the end of women's football in Preston. He acted very quickly. Between the defeat on the 21st and the match on the 25th, he had persuaded three of the Lancaster Ladies to play for Dick, Kerr's. And he had chosen wisely, selecting the three stars of the team, and promising them that their footballing careers and their earning capacity would not be over, if they took this chance and made the move. There would be a job for them, if they wished, at Dick, Kerr's. And ten shillings when they played football. And they'd be joining their friend, Molly Walker, whom he'd already co-opted into his squad.

The arguments were persuasive, and the team had two new stars for its Christmas Day match.

Goalkeepers are born, not made. They have to be as big as a midden door, with arms muscled by years of laundry work, and have the kick of a mule. Annie Hastie, from a Scottish family, was such a woman. And as for Jennie Harris, she was incomparable. She wasn't the conventional footballer. Barely four feet ten inches, she was tiny, but she was bursting with energy and enthusiasm, could dribble a ball as if it was attached to her foot, and was an astounding sprinter. And she had an eye and a foot for goal. Her centre of gravity was so low, her feet so fast and neat, that she could run rings round any plod-footed defenders, wrong-foot them and be away before they'd realized they had a job to do. Jennie was not only a star in the making, but she was bright and funny and always cheerful. The team loved her from the start, treating her like a gifted cheeky little sister.

Jennie didn't score in that game, and it has to be said that some of the accolades went grudgingly to a member of the Bolton side, Florrie Haslam, who scored twice. But Molly Walker, the first transfer, got one reply, and Nellie Mitchell, another Dick, Kerr's striker, evened up the score. A draw was not a bad result for a Christmas Day match against tough opposition. It would do. Well, more than do, really. A very respectable sum was raised for the Preston charities again, and everyone went home to their mince pies secure in the knowledge that the team would survive the threats to women's football.

The third star who had been persuaded to join Dick, Kerr's couldn't make the Christmas Day match, but she was there to shore up the defence for their next match on 10 January – Jessie Walmsley. She was the very heart and soul of heft, not the fastest off the blocks with that five-foot eight, size 14 figure, but if she'd been in some ancient army, she'd have been on the drawbridge, with a pikestaff, repelling all invaders. She was a country girl with a mass of straw-coloured frizzy hair which burst from either side of her large cap, a broad sunny face, and legs like girders. Jessie was pure gold and steel.

Plans such as Alfred Frankland's for his team can often go awry, because there's a downside which the eternal optimist and planner ignores. The downside here – or it may have been all part of the plan – is that as Dick, Kerr's swooped on the best footballers from Lancashire, inevitably he was weakening the opposition teams which might have survived the closure of the munitions factories. His scheme was one of short-term expediency, but if other teams were denuded of decent players, and lost hope because of this, who would Dick, Kerr's play? The answer to that appeared to be that Dick, Kerr's would play the best teams in the country, not merely in Lancashire, and by beating the best teams in the country, would itself become the best team. A match was arranged with Newcastle Ladies.

Newcastle was one of the strongest women's football centres in the country, with many different factory teams. The enthusiasm of miners' and furnace-men's daughters in the North East for football was intense, just as it was in St Helens, and their combative ability came out of the same forge. The team was mostly made up of the Bolkow, Vaughan Ladies, an impressive brawny band of large-bosomed and fearsome women, captained by Bolkow's legendary Winnie McKenna, the most prolific goal-scorer of any of the women's teams. Winnie was a twin, a strange and perhaps unimportant feature of several of the women footballers of her day, but the fact that her twin was a brother could explain her prowess. In most of the women players' histories there's a strong connection with a brother, close in age, who taught them the rules so that they could help in the daily street football games. She was a cheerfully defiant player, not over-large like some of her team-mates but strikingly good-looking, and her years of playing in boys' teams gave her grit and determination. It was Winnie McKenna who drew the crowds to St James's Park, the rightful home of Newcastle United.

There's a parallel here. The most successful side in the North East had adopted the policy which was making Dick, Kerr's the most successful side in Lancashire, and had inspired other Lancashire teams to do the same – it had used the men's ground, which had lain dormant for several seasons to lend credibility to the women's game, and to provide a venue big enough to raise the charitable funds which the North East so desperately needed in the last year of the war and the first years of the peace. Moving the game to that ground produced a response which even Alfred Frankland had never been able to drum up, because though there was close to a capacity crowd at Deepdale in March for a match for which Dick, Kerr's 'borrowed' three Bolton Ladies and gained a 1–0 victory, the crowd that greeted the return match at St James's Park in September 1919 was 35,000 strong.

Everyone had known that this was going to be a popular fixture. Dick, Kerr's had its newest star on show, Florrie Haslam who had wowed the critics with her exceptional play for Bolton. By the first half of the 1919–20 season these two teams of football's best were the strongest in the country, and they had realized that there would be a good public response to the fixture. But 35,000? That's a bigger crowd than most present-day Premiership matches can draw, although we have to make allowance for the smaller numbers who can crowd into today's all-seater stadia.

What did that tell the world? It said that women's football was no longer a minority spectator sport. Within only two years of its cautious and chaotic beginnings, it wasn't only fun for those who played, but it was a magnet for those who actually enjoyed watching football. The credibility exercise had worked – although in Newcastle, the United board was only united in its indifference to the women's game. The board had rented out the ground very reluctantly because they welcomed the money. There wasn't the same sympathetic and co-operative relationship between the organizers of the men's game and the women's team which operated in Preston, just a macho Tyneside disdain, evidently not shared by the male supporters who turned out in their tens of thousands to watch the wee lasses play. Nor was it shared by the thousands of unemployed discharged ex-soldiers who wandered the street of Newcastle looking for that land fit for heroes, and who had even had a song written about their plight:

> When the fighting was at its fiercest
> And everything looked black
> This was the promise that cheered us on:
> 'You'll get your old job back!'
>
> We were not professional soldiers,
> Fighting was not our game
> We were only peaceful citizens
> Who fought hard just the same

We sacrificed our wives and kids
And homes to do our bit
But now the door is closed to us
It seems hard, we admit

For I can't get the old job
And can't get a new
Can't carry on as I used to do
I look around me, and what do I see?
Thousands and thousands of fellows
A lot worse off than me

In Piccadilly, friends pass me by
I'm absolutely stranded in the Strand
And I confess I was contented, more or less
When I was stony broke in No Man's Land

Think, too, what a crowd of this size must have raised for Newcastle ex-soldier charities. In a world before telethons and satellite-beamed fundraising concerts, all those women, newly redundant from their munitions jobs, all those strikers and the distressed of the depressed North East, had found a shilling for the entrance fee. On the basis of what we know about the Dick, Kerr's gate receipts and accounts, the money paid to charity by Newcastle United Ladies, after tax, must have well exceeded £1,200, the equivalent of a quarter of a million pounds. Unbelievable. And how much pressure would that have taken off the Exchequer, struggling through election year trying to show that it could manage to support its war-wounded and unemployed?

So whatever had happened to the predictions that once the men's games started again there would be no support for women's football? And to the forecast that the munitions workers' teams would be wiped out by the closure of the factories and the nature of women, which was to return to the domestic hearth and start making babies to replace the missing million, now lying in France and Belgium and places that couldn't be accurately pin-pointed on a map before the Great War began?

In part, they were correct predictions. Some of the factory teams folded for those reasons. But instead of a plethora of enthusiasts who just wanted a kick-around, and who didn't understand zonal marking, stepping-up, and indirect and direct free kicks, there were super-teams of women developing who actually knew how to play and wanted to play, and whom the crowds wanted to watch for their ball-skills. In Lancashire, Bolton was still going strong, despite the loss of their best player, Florrie Haslam; Vickers Ordance had managed to keep a team together, and there was a newly formed team culled from the former munitions girls which the Dick, Kerr's Ladies had just beaten 6–1. St Helens.

So all that backtracking and midfield play has brought us back to St Helens, to Alice Woods, making her way back home after the match, with Alfred Frankland's precious card held tightly in her hand, and in her mind the unanswerable question – how to find Lily Parr?

Alice found it easier, on her return home, to confide in her sister Jane than in her mother. She knew that her mother would fret and worry about the match at New Brighton, and would surely not allow Alice out into the infamous hellhole of Gerrard's Bridge, reputedly the home of Lily Parr. Jane was always there as a substitute mother to her younger brother and sister if there was a problem. Margaret was best left out of it, as she no longer had the energy to deal with whatever these two got up to. It had been Jane who had engineered the compromize solution for John which allowed him to play for Halifax, and Alice impressed on her older sister that it was vital for her to find Lily, and to be allowed to play on Boxing Day. Jane couldn't refuse Alice, the baby of the family, anything. Not that usually she needed to, because Alice was the least demanding girl in the world, normally. This time, though, she was desperate, and Jane promised to help.

'I'll come round wi' you to find her. No need for mam to know,' she said. And, despite all odds, she and Alice went on those nightly missions until they'd located the child playing solitary football against a lamp-post in the back-streets of Gerrard's Bridge, and braved a yard full of pigs to bring her the invitation from Alfred Frankland, as promised.

The notorious Gerrard's Bridge was in the Windle township of St Helens. Only one area in the town had a worse reputation, and that was Greenbank, off Canal Street, but the houses there were gradually demolished and replaced – which in most cases was easy to do as they'd been hastily erected, and had neither sewers nor foundations. In South Windle, the houses were of a slightly better quality, but the area had its poor reputation for much the same reasons as Greenbank: that it was in these two areas that the Irish immigrants settled, during the Potato Famine in 1847. The Irish had a bad reputation for drinking, and for thieving, but the real reason for the notoriety of the area was that in a town where everyone was struggling against poverty, those in Gerrard's Bridge and Greenbank were the most deprived. They were the poor who were despised by those a little less poor who would find any reason to discover someone they could themselves look down on. Where Sutton was a mining community, Gerrard's Bridge was home to the unskilled labourers who would take anything going at the glass works, the chemical works or even the Alkali works, the factories where the discredited Leblanc process churned out poisonous fumes across neighbouring terraces. These were unpleasant conditions in which to work, but were the only options for the totally unskilled.

At the centre of this community was St Mary's Lowe House the huge Roman Catholic Jesuit settlement, and many of the children went to the convents there to be taught by nuns, whether or not they subscribed to the faith. But the wealth of the foundation of St Mary's, evident in its gilded artefacts, stood in judgement on the poverty it surveyed, and to which it ministered. Shoeless children were taught in the convent, and families who hadn't eaten for a while could be provisioned by the worthy sisters. Even within the community there were many, newly arrived from Ireland and forced to lodge with local families, who were said to be dirty, ragged and up to no good.

Lily had been discovered on Union Street, where she lived in the kind of squalor often talked about in the neat homes of the miners. Except that it wasn't actually squalor. It was just Gerrard's Bridge, and getting by, with a little help from the livestock and Sal.

Lily was born here in 1905, the fourth child of Sarah and George, who had been childhood sweethearts in the old days and had got together even while Sarah was in service and George worked as a labourer in the glass factory. They were meant for each other. George had the kind of face I've seen often in St Helens, with a craggy strength and inde-finably handsome, in an almost Celtic and romantic way.

He must have been a stunner. His looks passed to the wide-mouthed and sad-eyed child Lily, who may have forcibly reminded him of his own young self – anxious to look after weaker things and animals, but too inarticulate to be able to express complexity, which left him lost for words and inclined to grunt, so most people never saw the love which Sal saw in him. Sal was strong, a big lass in every way. When George was struggling she took on a coal round, delivering bags of slack from her own cart. But that was later. At the beginning, they rented a house on Union Street where Lily was born, the fourth of their brood of children, and then moved into the end house, which used to be a shop, and had a stable in the yard, which Sal let out to carters and their horses, and the loft over it she let to a down-and-out Irishman, Smelly Kelly.

Lily's oldest brother John defied the tradition of Gerrard's Bridge, which was decidedly rugby-based, and as he grew older became more interested in football, playing as goalie for the pub team next door. It was a raucous neighbourhood, where games and matches went on every night, all night, on the gravel patch at the pub, Chessie's. His sister Lizzie wasn't interested in all that, although Bob, the next brother, joined in. But Lillian, Lily, eight years younger than John and the middle child of the family, was always a tomboy. From her earliest years she wasn't listening to what Lizzie and her mother shouted at her. She just wanted to be out playing with the boys, and her brothers John, Bob and the younger George, who accepted her as one of them, since she could cuss and spit and smoke from the age of ten, and they taught her how to play, everything. She was as adept at rugby as she was at football, spending hours on her own perfecting the technique of the power kick. She'd sorted that out by the time she was thirteen and in football could score from any place on the pitch, or in rugby kick the finest penalty or drop goal. A left-footer, her ability was natural, magic, but honed by her refusal to conform to the art of being a woman. She wasn't having any of it.

Bill, her youngest brother, was born at the start of the war, in 1914, when she was nine. John by that time was 17, and was called up to serve as a stretcher-bearer at the Somme. Like my grandfather William, his youth and strength conspired to make him cannon-fodder, but he returned unscathed, and by 1919 had told the stories of his miraculous escapes so often at Chessie's that they could all join in with his recitations. But he was still a great goalie. And his sister, Lily, who played for the 'single men' in their weekly match against the married men, was a great striker. The best. Everyone said so.

Then Elsie was born in 1918. She was never going to live. George, who bought day-old chicks in the market and tried to hand-rear them, knew what the odds were, and knew they had a losing fight on their hands with Elsie, who was as much of a weakling as Lillian had been a wunderkind. But the baby, thanks to Sal's devoted care, lasted until her eighth year. At the time when Sal was visited by Alice and Jane, she was pregnant with Doris, her youngest, born when Sal was 43, in 1920, and still fighting for Elsie's life. Doris just had to get on with it.

Sal was tired and fraught, but didn't want to give up. She battled to save the doomed Elsie, tried to discipline George and Bill, but finally gave them to the nuns to educate. And Lily? No one had ever been able to understand her. She was a law unto herself, pleased herself, ran amok, and as the middle child in the brood, got a little lost amongst her brothers, although, as everyone said when trying to excuse or explain her latest escapade, she had a good heart and could always find you what you needed if you were short, even if she had to pinch it. She meant well. She were 'guduz gawd', were Lily.

Yes, Lily had a heart as big as a football pitch, and on that Boxing Day, when she and Woods lined up to have their photo taken in the smart striped shirts and the little striped caps with the Dick, Kerr's Ladies, it almost burst with pride, though she wouldn't let on. For both Alice and Lily that match represented – and they knew it – a way to escape into a different kind of life. They didn't let themselves down. They were doing something they loved, and they did it supremely well, so why shouldn't it be their lifeline?

Alfred Frankland also knew that they were *his* lifeline. These two, that exceptional athlete who could burst from centre half into attack and score goals, and that outside left whose passing and striking power he'd never seen in a man, let alone a fourteen-year-old girl, were the two to complete his extraordinary side, already packed with football stars, and lead Dick, Kerr's to the championship of Britain, and perhaps beyond. They were the key players. He had plans, yet again. So he made them an offer they couldn't refuse – join Dick, Kerr's, move up to Preston, be given a job at the factory, and earn ten bob every time they played a match. He couldn't say fairer than that, and no one had ever turned down that offer.

Standing between Alfred Frankland and his winning ways, however, were two formidable St Helens mothers. There was no way, no way on God's earth, as Margaret repeatedly said, that Alice was going to leave home and go up to Preston to play football. She was needed at home to look after herself and Jem and Jane and John. Alice was the perfect little mother who could turn her hand to anything, and was invaluable to the family, and the extended family and the brood of nephews and nieces. And Sal, exhausted Sal in the final stages of another pregnancy, told Lily that if Alice didn't move to Preston, she couldn't. She was only fourteen and Alice was minding her. She trusted Alice because Alice was a level-headed St Helens lass who wouldn't let the big town, Preston, go to her head.

Sal and Margaret were having none of it. Family pride and St Helens pride rose up against the challenge to the coalminers and glassworkers. Mill-work had always been seen to be so much more ladylike, and the mill towns always thought they were a cut above. Not this time. So, as 1920 began, and Dick, Kerr's started out on yet another annus mirabilis, neither Lily nor Alice was in the side. To make matters worse, they were happily playing for St Helens Ladies, the best they could do. But St Helens Ladies was proving formidable, as a side. These women were tough as old football boots, and skilled, too, with an enthusiasm and energy for the game that was rarely seen. And their menfolk supported their ambitions.

To understand why this was, you have to look, as a comparison, at the development of women's soccer in the United States. In that country, where football was dominated by the rules of a different-shaped-ball game, soccer had developed as a minority sport, played mostly by immigrants from Britain. It was seen as effete, and slow. And when it was taught at collegiate level, it slowly developed into a game accessible to women, and gained approval as a woman's game. In the same way, in St Helens, as I've said, rugby football, the League rather than the Union game, predominated. St Helens actually had several separate rugby teams, St Helens (Saints), and St Helens Recs being the leading two. Rugby was a man's game. Soccer was a minority game – a woman's game. It seemed only right and proper to the men of St Helens (of whom it is said, 'St Helens born, St Helens bred, Strong in th' arm and thick in th' ead') that soccer were for t' lasses. They never thought to question this presumption, which was just as well for the women's game in general, and for their daughters and sisters in particular, who threw themselves with typical St Helens' abandon and strong-arm tactics into their newly discovered activity.

But in the haphazard organization which characterised women's football, Liverpool Ladies had agreed to play Dick, Kerr's in February. This new team was a team in name only, created before there were eleven ladies to play, and had only agreed to a match because they'd been challenged by Dick, Kerr's and needed the charity money, and the publicity. So, with the match looming, and few players available except the outstanding full back Daisy Clayton, Liverpool Ladies was caught short and had to draft in the St Helens Ladies to provide six of their best players to fill the gaps. Lily and Alice, the stalwarts and stars of St Helens Ladies, were two of those six and played on the Liverpool side, which won 2–0, Alice scoring one of the goals.

A defeat for Dick, Kerr's at this stage in their development wasn't healthy, but the girls Dick, Kerr's were so anxious to attract weren't allowed to leave St Helens, and Alfred Frankland had to find a way round that, especially when Liverpool Ladies beat them again a few weeks later. It was an unprecedented series of results. No team had ever beaten Dick, Kerr's twice, let alone consecutively. Liverpool Ladies was riding high.

Ungracious in defeat, Frankland went over to see the parents of Alice and Lily, separately, to talk straight to them.

St Helens likes straight talking. In fact, St Helens never listens to anything else. It's a laconic but blunt mind-set which appreciates honesty even if it disagrees with the proposition, and even though it prefers to keep its own hard feelings to itself until the time is right. It has a vocabulary which reduces language to one word where seventy-odd would do. Its all-purpose response to any series of sentences is the enigmatic 'Aar', which is very different in inflection and intention from the open acceptance of 'Aye'. Sal listened patiently as Alfred confessed how crucial her daughter was to his team and outlined his plans for Lily, whom he admitted was the best player he had ever seen. She could lodge, in Preston, in the family of another of his young players, a very decent family too. She was now fifteen, and a job could be found for her at Dick, Kerr's factory where she would be paid and have money to send home or take home if she wanted to travel back to St Helens on Sundays. Sal said, 'Aar.' Alfred told her that this was his final offer, although he was bluffing. He desperately needed these two girls and would do anything to get them into his team, otherwise Dick, Kerr's would lose its claim to be the best in the country.

Sal decided that Lily was now old enough to make the decision for herself. It would be a painful wrench to lose her oddball middle child, but if the girl had set her heart on a career in football, why not? It was the only thing she'd ever been interested in. And anyway, she, Sal, had gone away into service at twelve. Fifteen was almost grown up.

'If I get me own room,' was Lily's proviso. Cheeky. She'd never had space to herself in her life, in amongst all those children and animals, but she knew that was what she wanted more than anything else. She wanted privacy and the right to live her own life without unnecessary questions about her unconventional behaviour. And she wanted to play football.

But if Lily's co-operation was immediately secured on Alfred's assurance that she would indeed have her own room – he was unsure of this but he would try to arrange it – Margaret refused to budge. Alice was not leaving St Helens.

This brought Alfred up against an obduracy he had never before encountered, and he could think of no way in which he could yield further ground. But why not, instead, give way completely? So that's what he did. He agreed that Alice Woods should play under the auspices of the Dick, Kerr's factory but she would never have to have any affiliation to the firm. She would continue to live in St Helens.

Under Alfred Frankland, Dick, Kerr's had now taken the final step in becoming, in all but name, a semi-professional squad. First he'd agreed payments 'in lieu', even to those who, like Alice, didn't have a paid job as such. Then he'd poached opposing teams to get women to transfer their allegiance to his team, and secured jobs for them. He'd even argued successfully for Florrie Redford to continue to play for Dick, Kerr's when she left the munitions factory and got a job at Whittingham hospital to train as a nurse. He'd finally given grudging acceptance to Florrie Haslam when she wanted to return to live in nearby Bolton after the munitions work finished. And now, he'd followed his pragmatism and decided that as professional footballers often didn't live or work even just a short bus-ride from the town whose strip they wore, he could have Alice Woods in his squad, although she had no connection with Preston, and would never live there as long as she played. He was sure that the committee would agree that this was in the club's best interests.

The Dick, Kerr's amateur factory football team, of Preston, was by now neither a factory football team, nor Dick, Kerr's, as this name had been officially merged with that of English Electric, nor was it totally a Preston-based team, and as for it being amateur – well, more or less. Perhaps, by now, more less than more.

But the information that Alfred Frankland didn't give to the mothers of St Helens, or to their daughters, was that he wanted Dick, Kerr's to represent England at football.

Three

Entente Cordiale

The last thing on Lily Parr's mind was being offered the remote chance to play some foreigners. What concerned her immediately was trying to settle herself down in the foreign country of Preston with little Alice Norris. Alice at fourteen and a reserve-team member for whom Alfred Frankland had high hopes, was a year younger, and an entire life-time less street-wise than Lily. She'd lived for all of her life in a neat home in Preston, with her parents and sister, and had recently started both at the factory and in training with the team.

Theirs was a well-ordered house where meals were on time, men were seen but not heard, and no one smoked or cursed or spat on the pavement. That this cuckoo lodger, taken in as a favour to Mr Frankland, should be shyly sulky and noisily assertive by turn was a little upsetting for Mrs Norris. Lily too was upset. She had left the affectionate squalor of her own familiar home with its pigswill boiling in the yard and its chickens defecating on the kitchen floor for this prim and proper set-up, where the meals were half the size she'd been used to. The pigs and chickens at home meant there was never any skimping on bacon and eggs. And there were always big fat black puddings, made in one of the wash-boilers after the back-yard slaughter, using the pig's blood which was collected by the bucketful and tipped in with generous scatterings of snowy white pig fat and bucket-loads of groats. Lily herself had helped make the puddings, stirring the claret-coloured mixture. Here, in Preston, there was no black pudding to be had, or chunky slices of home-salted and cured bacon or eggs with fat yellow double yolks spilling over the plate that you could dunk your bread in. There was bread and butter cut into triangles instead of doorsteps, and nobody was supposed to speak with their mouth full.

Lily's appetite was legendary at home in St Helens, and was given its due respect. As in the home of my great grandmother Sarah Bate, families were fed helpings according to their height. The tallest were served first and the most, with the explanation that in their case the food had further to drop, which is why Smack and Cute and the other seven boys had plates piled with the meat and vegetables of the stew, and little Polly had to make do with the gravy and barley in the bottom of the pot.

And as for the room in Preston, Lily was incandescent with brooding rage. Mr Frankland had promised her a room. What she found, on her arrival was a room with two beds, prettied up with matching eiderdowns, and a little conversation corner where she and this little kid were supposed to spend long hours being chums and brushing each others' hair. Alice Norris was all right, and she was fair to middling at football, but she wasn't a brother, and she was in Lily's space. There was only one thing for it. Lily man-handled, kicked and bumped out of the room everything she could find which might suggest that Alice intended sleeping in the same room as her. Alice's possessions were bundled up and left on the landing, and Mrs Norris, who hadn't quite taken Alfred Frankland's instructions on board (she had assumed the two girls would make such lovely little friends) had to admit defeat. Alice was turned out of her own room and for the first time in her life had to share a room with her sister. Alice Norris and Lily never did strike up that friendship. Mr Frankland was informed about the behaviour of his star and the copious numbers of cigarette ends which Lily stubbed out on any handy surface, and had the grace to appear a little embarrassed. But he had other things on his mind: he was trying to set up an international fixture.

So what gave Alfred Frankland the confidence and position to issue an invitation to the Ladies of France? This showed him to have, as we say in Lancashire, more front than Blackpool. Well, for a start, he'd been kept on at the factory, after his war draft had finished, the only one of the Army chaps to be given that distinction. It was because he'd worked so selflessly in the promotion of the company's charitable effort, helping raise hundreds of pounds towards the post-war reconstruction of Preston, and other Lancashire towns. So he had the ear and the support of the Scottish management structure of Dick, Kerr's which prided itself on Presbyterian benevolence, or paternalism, if you like. In addition, mayors and aldermen, the great and the good of Preston were grateful to him. And he had the respect of the Army by whom he had originally been employed and which, garrisoned at Fulwood Barracks, played an important part in Preston society.

What's more, he now had a stage on which he could

work. Dick, Kerr's factory had been built on a piece of waste ground which had been used as a sports field. In 1920, English Electric and the management team of the Dick, Kerr's factory resolved that as a post-war priority they would put that disservice right and bought Ashton Park as a recreation ground for the company. This was to stand as their war memorial and in a mansion house in the centre of the park a plaque was erected in honour of those Dick, Kerr's men who had been killed in the war. This park had a small golf course, tennis courts, cricket pitch, and a specially constructed football ground, too, which was to provide facilities for both the men's and women's football teams of the factory. A Mr Aldington was appointed to be in charge of all these wonderful facilities, and Alfred Frankland immediately co-opted him on to the committee of the Ladies' team, then let it be known that it might be wise to vote him in as Chairman, just as he'd very cannily invited James Connor, then Works Manager but now retiring with an MBE, to be President. He realized the importance of getting the men with power to take an interest in developing the women's game.

Alfred had been told of the proposed visit to France of a men's team of amateur footballers representing England. This information could well have come from his Army contacts as Army engineers were still engaged in some post-war reparatory work in France and Belgium. France had been an old enemy, but now, despite some lingering prejudices about the French it was a new and needy friend. Establishing a rapport with France, and showing ourselves grateful and generous to a nation which had been devastated by a war on their own territory, was an extension of the charitable works already undertaken in Britain.

Municipal offices, everywhere, were deluged with paper-work and good works as cities 'adopted' towns in France, sending food aid and workers across the Channel.

And we have to take account of the fact that France, once considered to be part of a distant European continent was now a country that many of our young men had visited, and they'd realized that it was not quite so distant or different as they'd been led to believe. Some French words and expressions had even reached Lancashire, imported by returning troops, and San Fairy Ann ['*Ça ne fait rien*: it doesn't matter'] passed seamlessly into dialect. It was the first French I ever heard, from my grandfather William for whom it was a favourite expression and I didn't even realize it was a foreign language. To me it was like those kennings and nick-naming, just another local expression whose origins were lost in oral history.

Alfred's military intelligence, or whatever had given him the idea of writing to French Ladies' football teams in Paris and passed on some addresses or contact names was deficient just in one respect. There were actually no women's football teams, in France. There were certainly no women factory-workers teams developed from the need for working class women to let off steam while doing wartime munitions drudgery. In Paris, and in some other large cities, there were athletics and sports clubs, and football had occasionally been played by the women who attended these clubs.

The two nations divided by the Channel had, perhaps unsurprisingly, completely different sporting cultures. In France, sport was dominated by the aristocracy, as it was universally in athletics. Over sixty percent of the participants in the first Olympic Games were from the highest echelons of society. Sport was for those with leisure and money, while those who worked for a living had to be content with street games in their occasional hours of freedom.

The founder of the Olympic Games, Baron de Coubertin was himself from this highly conservative and monied background, and was totally opposed to women being involved in sport at all. His view, when he converted the world to his notion of some effete classical nobility which could be reinvented through international sport, was that the role of women in this representation should be 'to place laurels on the head of the victors'. He thought sporting activity made women's bodies look disgustingly and nauseatingly ugly, and that women should strive to appear beautiful. That was their job. Lancashire women would have called him a bit of a posh pansy mardy arse. Lily might have had a more brutal version of that expression. But his mission was to produce a Graeco-French ideal of the ungirt runner, very Charles Hamilton Sorley – very, very poetic . . .

> We swing ungirded hips,
> And lightened are our eyes.
> The rain is on our lips,
> We do not run for prize.
> We know not whom we trust
> Nor witherward we fare,
> But we run because we must
>   Through the great, wide air.

What was acceptable for those with breeding and money, especially women, like Lady Florence Dixie, was totally out of the question for ordinary mortals. France had its very own equivalent of Lady Flo in the Duchesse d'Uzes, a formidable huntress and racing-car driver who had founded a sports club for young women. And it had held the world's biggest ever spectator sport for working class women when the whole of Paris was brought to a standstill by a twelve kilometre race in 1903 from Paris to Nanterre by the Midinettes, the women workers in the garment district. But the spectators there came to gawp at sweaty women, just as they gawped at women acrobats or dancers in the Folies Bergeres. *Liberté*, *egalitié*, *fraternité*, one of the greatest of all revolutionary mottos, didn't extend its coverage to equality of the sisterhood until 1944, when French women were allowed to vote.

French women weren't content to be entirely decorative. They played sports, but they embraced their menfolks' cheesy idealisation of ancient history. Isadora Duncan was their heroine. She was an American rebel, who dressed in her floating version of ancient Greek robes while performing 'Greek dance' to sun gods and Grecian deities: an aesthetic athleticism which prioritised women's beauty, and cared not a fig about women's rights. Women's sports' clubs had arisen out of this devotion. Besides 'Greek dance', they sprinted, rowed, shot arrows, threw javelins, and leapt obstacles in much the same way as they imagined the ancient Greeks had done. Their clubs had often been founded by men, supported by one or two feminists, who suggested that the women add to their skills a gentle finesse in football, and in *barette*, a French version of Rugby, but only in order to demonstrate the skill and pace of the natural all-round athlete. And how do you think the aesthetes and athletes of these recently-formed Parisian clubs reacted to a request from a football team in Lancashire, albeit couched in grandiose language from the pen of the redoubtable Alfred Frankland, which said, basically, 'Come and play our factory at footie?'

Astonishingly, the French clubs, Femina Sport and En Avant, accepted the invitation. French women had never before taken part in any international sporting event, but they held a serious day-long trial at the Elisabeth stadium to select those women who were most skilful. The French athletes were couturiers, milliners, teachers, secretaries, and the lower echelons of the educated middle class, who had enough time on their hands to dress in Greek robes and dance enchantingly.

The team was chosen by a woman who had already established herself as the pioneer of women's sport in France, and who, by 1920 when Frankland's invitation arrived, was the secretary general of the Federation Française Sportive Feminine. Her name was Alice Milliat. The story told of her is that she was born in Nantes in 1884, worked as a translator, was very well educated, and a champion rower who set several records. She was also a feminist, one of the few in France, and was the only woman on the original organising committee of Femina Sport. This much is beyond dispute. But the reason she had a unique voice in French sport was because she was a childless widow. In France single women had little status, and married women were severely restricted to their domestic duties. In addition, her husband had been an Englishman, who had died young, and because of her awareness of the greater emancipation of women in England she had the confidence to challenge orthodoxy in France. Imposing, stocky and muscular, outspoken, a natural leader and campaigner, she was in both shape and style unlike the

chic French girls who attended her sports' clubs. She, like
Alfred Frankland was on a mission. Hers was to have
women's track and field events admitted to national and
international athletics by the French chauvinists who ran
the Olympic movement, and was a mission which would
employ her throughout her life and bring her into contin-
uous conflict with the IOC. Sending a team of footballers
to play against some tram-factory women in Preston,
Lancashire, was hardly commensurate with her lofty feminist aspirations, but it was a start. Within the month, Alice
Milliat had selected her team, informed Dick, Kerr's that the
team would arrive in a week's time, and kept the Press
informed of her every move.

One of the leading British newspapers of the day, the *Daily
News*, had a stringer based in Paris. Alice Milliat's contact
with this man, John Bell, set up the publicity machine which
Dick, Kerr's needed. It was from Bell that the nation heard
about this French team due to play in Preston, in the most
intriguing detail. 'From our Own Correspondent' the *Daily
News* announced – on its front page. What a coup! And the
description of the preparations for this tour was in the
language its readers would understand. Bell included a full
description of the natty outfits which would be worn by the
specially selected French Ladies – horizon blue (whatever
happened to horizon blue?) shirts with a red, white and blue
cockade on the breast, navy breeches (shorts), and black
stockings and black berets – 'capped like the Blue Devils of
Alpine fame' said Mr Bell, very cleverly adding a note of
Allied solidarity to the proceedings. The story immediately
alerted other news sources of the proposed tour, and they
lined up their photographers and reporters to be present at
the Dover dockside on April 27th when these chic appari-

tions appeared, and to obtain some suitably feminine quotations from these 'slight' French girls, reputed to be 'full of nervous energy'. Perhaps nervous energy was a good thing to have in 1920.

The importance of this press involvement may have passed you by, so put yourself back in time. Let's just go back to Gerrard's Bridge, and the gas-lights. All of the working-class homes in Britain, and many of the homes of the more affluent neighbours were gaslit. There was no electrical circuit to carry radio into homes, nor, in April 1920, any radio service. The BBC started in 1922. The only mass media in existence were the newspapers and the cinema. The press was the only source of current information and news which could be accessed in homes and the country lived in relatively localised communities served by local newspapers. If there was a new trend, a drum to beat or an axe to grind, it had to be done through the press.

Preston, was sent into a panicky flurry of activity. This was a unique event. They had only a week in which to arrange a tournament which would impress two nations. Just a night before the arrival of the French team football grounds had not yet been secured, and battalions of telegrams were sent to all the football clubs in Britain to try to find suitable venues. Liverpool, the Anfield ground, was mentioned as a possibility, but discounted. Deepdale was, of course, the natural choice, and was made available for the first match. Stockport County offered the use of their ground, as did Manchester City. But the locations were all very Lancashire, and what was needed, if this was to be a tour worthy of the name, was a venue for the final match which would take women's football out of flat caps and ferret country and into the belle-monde. The whole point of this tournament was to raise the profile of women's football and introduce its glories to the metropolis. Chelsea finally came up with the offer of the necessary London football ground with only hours to spare. Then, all that remained was for Alfred Frankland, along with the Reverend Sinclair of the Lancashire and Cheshire division of the Discharged Servicemen's organization, to make his way to Dover to greet the French women, led by the indomitable publicist Alice Milliat, and a score or more of reporters from all the leading national dailies. His time had come. And his team would be stars.

This team included a by now dizzied Alice Woods. She was to play football against a team from France, and if Lily Parr had no idea what that might entail in terms of manners and sartorial elegance, Alice certainly did. Wardrobes of clothes would have to be made, and since Lily didn't have any sense of high fashion, or fashion of any height, clothes would have to be made for Lily too. She had taken Lily's measurements, and was hard at work in St Helens, buying up fents (fabric remnants) at St Helens Market Hall to turn them into the costumes which might be suitable for both of them on the charabanc trips arranged for the foreign girls or at one of the dos.

Dos were an important feature of this proposed tour. Lancashire likes a nice function of an evening, with a glass of sherry for the ladies, speeches of welcome and thanks, doilies and serviettes, plate pies – fruit, particularly rhubarb, and savoury including the speciality meat and potato – a hunk of breaded ham for carving, bread and butter cut across, perhaps some sardine sandwiches, or meat-paste, wedges of crumbly Lancashire cheese, and a Victoria sponge or two with raspberry preserve oozing from their fat centres and a sprinkling of icing sugar on top. Sometimes, someone would do a turn, perform a party piece:

> Last night I lay a-sleeping,
> There came a dream so fair;
> I stood in old Jerusalem
> Beside the temple there.
> I heard the children singing,
> And ever as they sang,
> Me thought the voice of angels
> From heav'n in answer rang;
> Me thought the voice of angels
>   (*this was a trilled note, a-a-a-angels*)
> From heav'n in answer rang.
>
> Jerusalem! Jerusalem!
> Lift up your gates and sing,
> Hosanna in the highest!
> Hosanna to your King!

That was Lancashire's favourite performance song. William Blake's 'other' 'Jerusalem' was a gradely song, but not in the same class as this one. Everyone joined in the chorus and, if there was enough brown ale, sometimes the verse too. It had the suitably rotund open vowel sounds and robust semi-religious fervour that inspired its best brass bands, but could just as easily be undertaken by gentlemen in the pub and was tearfully poignant if sung by a tremulous mezzo-soprano holding a white lacy handkerchief who really went to town on the trilled angels. You could almost hear the wings.

So Alice had to make two entire wardrobes of clothes –

evening wear for these functions, and street clothes – and they had to compete with the very best the *midinettes* from the *haute couture* capital of the world could produce. It may be worth reminding you that in 1920 most of the clothes worn by women and children were made by them and their families in their own homes. In fact, even in my own day it was very rare for any girl to have a 'shop dress' and needlecraft was a skill which was highly prized, but which my mother never quite mastered despite her frantic cobblings on a Singer sewing machine. For the Whit Walking Days of my childhood, the highlight of the St Helens year, when the whole town turned out in its various religious and Trades Union squads headed by banners, and flower girls, and high-stepping sequinned girls carrying pom poms, and silver bands, someone always had to be drafted in to make my annual posh frock from white nylon seersucker with frills down the bodice and over the shoulders, and a satin sash.

Alice, Jane and Elizabeth Ann, however, were supreme in the art, and, with their pincushions, thimbles and assorted silk threads at the ready, set out to make Alice, and the ugly duckling Lily, some nice blouses and skirts, something serviceable in brown satin for the evenings, a few hats, and a spring coat each. Coats weren't de rigueur in St Helens, and were very much an unknown quantity because the conventional outerwear for women was a shawl. This was an all-purpose garment, knitted or more usually crocheted in the evenings, which could be hotched up to provide a hood in case of rain. Even Sunday church was a shawl occasion, best shawls of course, with a brooch at the neck. So for Alice this was an experiment in fashion, just to show she was in the know about top-coats, and was to be a large belted coat in a bold check Irish tweed, which she had specially selected, and to match this she made herself a large floppy velvet beret which picked out the green in the check. She was particularly pleased with this.

Margaret had given reluctant permission for Alice to stay in Preston, at the home of Alice Kell, for a few days, 'Because there's dos', she told everyone, and added, trying not to sound too swanky, 'and she'll be stopping in London. In an hotel.' The gravity with which this was uttered reflected the gravity of the situation. London was a world as far away as France to the factory girls and their families. Two generations down the line, I didn't visit London until a school trip when I was 13 and in the third year of grammar school, and I distinctly remember the apprehension of visiting this huge and famous place, where coronations happened and picture postcards were actually of real things that could be seen and visited and touched, and where everything was so fast and crammed, and, somehow, so much superior in every way from the places and people I knew. If, at 13, a grammar school girl whose parents owned their own home could have this intense reaction to London in 1958, how much more terrifying, educational and self-indulgent must the prospect have seemed to Lily, Alice and the others, whose experience of travel had been limited to Blackpool, Preston and the famous sophisticated resort of New Brighton with its acres of rock and its pools of vomit from the sickly trip on a ferry from Liverpool?

Their view of London life, too, wasn't informed by the radio or television, as mine was. London for them was what happened in newspapers, where in huge landmark buildings, men were tried for poisoning their wives, women wept while giving evidence for Breach Of Promise cases and brutal murder was an everyday occurrence. As for hotels, they were always a totally unknown quantity to those from the parsimonious North. No one I knew from Lancashire had ever stayed in one. Boarding houses, with ketchup bottles on the tables and sticky bri-nylon sheets on the beds, or Yorkshire Dales' guest houses with rain on the windows and damp up the walls, and pink Camay soap and hand-towels, were the best I had ever luxuriated in until I was over thirty, and that only very occasionally.

It's hard to underestimate the impact that this introduction to a world outside the industrial north, with its small horizons, smoke-darkened skies and die-hard earth-bound community traditions was going to have on the lives of the girls from St Helens. But it's equally hard to underestimate the natural joy, energy and luminosity which these two amazing women and their team-mates would bring to a war-weary if superficially sophisticated post-war entente.

As Lily was gawkily trying on her new clothes, and the silly plant-pot hat with a flower in which Alice assured her she looked 'reet nice', Alfred Frankland was in Dover trying to meet and greet the French ladies, but got no further than Alice Milliat, who, he was relieved to hear, spoke perfect English. The Mademoiselles themselves, however, were hidden behind a human wall of press photographers and reporters with notebooks, trying to answer questions in a language they'd recently tried to learn. The press got exactly the quotes they were looking for from this elegant group of *femmes du monde*. The French captain, Madelaine Braquemonde, bemoaned the fact that her hat had blown overboard on the wet and windy crossing and announced that the first thing she would do in London was to shop for a new one. 'But,' she added, much to the delight of the journalists, 'tell me about the Lancashire girls. They are big, strong and powerful, n'est-ce pas?'

Yes, they were, many of them. And the French girls, struggling to hold on to their hats in windy Dover were sleek and elegant, petite and photogenic. The contrast in style had been immediately noted and captured the imagination of the reading and spectating masses. These French women included shorthand typists, a student of philosophy, a nurse, two dressmakers, an accountant, an interpreter, a dentistry student, and only two factory girls, the sisters Laloz. They were typical products of the French women's sports academies and clubs, and were hurdling the barrier between warring factions, just as that emblematic football game in the trenches had done. In this case the barrier was class distinction, alive and well in Britain. It's ironic that it took a team from another country to break the rules of English society and give a lie to the assumption that football was a rough game played by rough women from rough areas, and that nice girls didn't play.

Two days later, Mr Birkenshaw, the factory brass band and the Dick, Kerr's Ladies were waiting at Preston station to meet their opponents from Paris. Alice and Lily and the girls were resplendent in their new outfits – nice belted woolly tweed coats, big hats, pussy-cat bows at the necks of their blouses, sensible buttoned walking boots on their down-to-earth feet, the height of Preston fashion as worn by those who didn't have to dress up for work and only have Sunday best, as evidenced here, in which to posh up for visitors.

The demoiselles who emerged from this train were sleek Flappers. They wore pared-down, close-fitting dark coats which skimmed their bodies, and underneath the coats, waistless dresses which hung from the clothes-peg-slim shoulders. On their heads were neat cloche hats, and their hair was fashionably bobbed and shining. To the strains of *La Marseillaise*, boomed out by the prize band, gasps and gawps from the waiting crowd and the popping of flash bulbs, they sashayed from the train in their high-heeled shoes. The tiniest one, Mlle Ourry, the goalkeeper, was dwarfed by the giant fluffy toy rabbit she waved, the team mascot.

If Preston was taken by surprise it was certainly not going to show it. The band missed a beat or two and recovered between '*enfants de la patrie*' and '*le jour de gloire est arrivé*'. There was a job to do and a do to get to, and Dick, Kerr's had supplied exactly the right transport for the job – a wagonette from its own factory, draped with the French flag, and with four beautiful bay horses, tricked out with red, white and blue head-pieces, to draw it. The French Ladies squealed with happiness, unable to quite understand Northern English hospitality, but loving every minute of their rapturous reception. Alice Milliat tremblingly held a huge bouquet, presented to her by the small daughter of one of the worthies and dignitaries who, all gowned up in full regalia with chains of office, formed the welcoming party. Some of the ex-service personnel wore their uniforms and medals as a mark of respect to their Allies. Thousands lined the street as the procession was formed. Whit Walking Days, the arrival of the Circus, band competitions through the streets: Preston knew how to lay on a big procession and how to stand and cheer as it went by. The brass band led, of course. Then the wagonette with the beautiful athletes and the giant rabbit, and the large lady with the bouquet. Then motor cars from which the major and aldermen could wave.

And some Army vehicles carrying the soldiers from the Fulwood barracks. Finally, in an open charabanc decorated with black and white stripes and a Union flag, the Dick, Kerr's Ladies in big hats.

By the time the procession reached the Bull and Royal Hotel the pale ladies of France had red roses in their cheeks and tears in their eyes. Outpouring of public affection, like this, was something they had never encountered before. The band struck up 'God Save The King' as the French girls alighted, and although they were pursued by photographers, they broke off their skilled posing to rush over to the band, stand to attention, and sing the only English words they had learnt, the words to the National Anthem. This show of solidarity brought a huge cheer from the crowd as soon as the last tiddley pom had been blasted out. Then, energised rather than drained by their journey and totally flummoxed by the no-nonsense and no-holds-barred warmth of this small northern city, they were ushered into the cabbage-and-beer-smelling dark-panelled dining room of a typical market hotel. Goodness knows what they thought of their overdone beef, the fluffy Yorkshires, the roast potatoes, long-boiled cabbage and soft carrots of the dinner that had been specially prepared for them and the Dick, Kerr's team, or of the eating habits of Lily Parr, who reached across them with not so much as a 'pardon' as she helped herself to seconds and more gravy from the dripping jug and polished off everyone's leavings. She'd declared loudly before the meal that she could eat a buttered frog, a Lancashire expression, but perhaps one a little less than tactful in the circumstances. But by the end of the meal, with its speeches of welcome and thanks and its glasses of warm sherry for the ladies, everyone more or less knew everyone else despite the miming and pointing to overcome the language barrier. A local policeman who had been posted in France during the war and could manage to get by quite well in the language despite his strong Lancashire accent was called inside from his position as doorkeeper to provide additional interpreting.

Immediately, Carmen Pomies felt at home, which was strange because her home was petit bourgeois, and she herself was at University, taking a degree in dentistry. But she was a big girl with the broad shoulders and muscular legs of a javelin thrower whose elegance was less pronounced than some of the others. The tiny Ourry was given much attention.

'Is that their goalie? She'll get bloody lost 'tween posts!'

Lily couldn't take her eyes off the small girl with the large rabbit, even as she was shovelling huge rounds of beef and gravy from her knife to her mouth.

'She's bloody smaller than bloody Harris!' she splurted, and the Dick, Kerr's Ladies choked on their beef dinner, in goggling, giggling agreement.

And if Carmen felt herself close immediately to those other big lasses, as did Genevieve Laloz, the factory girl and reserve goalie, and her sister Suzanne, the sleek tiny Ourry and others from gay Paree felt an immediate sisterhood with this bloody (Jennie) Harris, who had taken time to try to learn some French and was desperate to try it out. Her facial expressions, as ever with Jennie, were more expressive than her mispronunciations and as hysterically funny. Alice Woods couldn't stop laughing, and soon all the French were joining in with the laughter and discarding their cloche hats. Even the dignitaries at the top table, hot under their aldermanic robes had slipped them off to eat a very nice jelly and tinned-peaches trifle in their shirtsleeves and belts and braces.

It was a laugh. A feast. A fête.

And even after everyone insisted, even Lily, that they were replete, or 'full to bleedin' bustin' ' there was another do to be attended that night. The French Ladies were rounded up, with much hilarity about their mouse size, and jokes about looking for them under chairs, and attracting them with wedges of Cheshire cheese, to be taken in yet another charabanc to the glories of the Dick, Kerr's factory canteen, where a dance with tea and triangular paste sandwiches and sponge cake, had been arranged in their honour.

It was a proper dance. A section of the work's band played, as everyone took their partners for the Valeta, the Military Two-Step, the St Bernard's Waltz (which they all loved because they could stamp their feet), the Barn Dance, a Ladies' Excuse Me, and a Waltz, in which the little French women were whisked off their light feet by Works' Managers and floated like tiny dark butterflies around the room. Lily wouldn't and couldn't join in, even though Alice tried to drag her into the stamping dance. But she made her presence and her husky bellowing voice felt at the end of the evening when pretensions to grandeur were finally abandoned and the dance ended up with Lily with cigarette in place leading the Hokey Cokey, and a Conga, before everyone burst into a lusty rendition of 'She's a Lassie From Lancashire' with the French girls desperately trying to learn the words and sing the chorus

She's a lassie from Lancashire
She's a lassie that I hold dear
  (*NB the correct pronunciation of Lancasheer*)
None could be fairer
Or rarer
Than Sarah
My lassie from Lancashire

The day following that gut-busting reception, there was a morning's tour of Horrockses, a cotton factory. Then after another dinner where the visitors toyed with a hotpot then passed their still-heaped plates to Lily, the girls were all taken by charabanc up the Ribble valley, out of the smoke of Preston, and into the green hilly countryside round Whalley and Clitheroe and the Trough of Bowland, where brooks ran, and hedges burst into blossom, and tiny lambs jumped as if on wires, and it was all so achingly lovely and so unlike the soot and chemical wastes of St Helens that Alice wanted to cry. There was such a difference between mill-towns and St Helens. Cotton weaving and spinning may be done in mills with huge chimneys, but it has to be carried out where the water is clean, and the air is fresh with damp. Industrialists did try, in the nineteenth century, to bring elements of the cotton industry to St Helens, the roughest end of the journey of the white American product. St Helens was thought to be good enough for the bleaching process. It wasn't. Even cotton bleaching couldn't contend with the polluted air. St Helens did have something called the 'country' to go to for a Saturday afternoon out, but it was only Billinge Lump, a hillock on the flat plain, or Eccleston Mere, where you could row a boat and where one of the TB hospitals was sited, or Rainford, which was pretty enough and had hedgerows. But real country was in North Lancashire.

Then, the next day, the French women were treated to a visit to the Dick, Kerr's factory to see for themselves the bogie open-top, and learn about the industrial finesse that went into the creation of lamps which graced the railway carriages of the gentry. At a ceremony in the factory that morning, the visiting team was presented, at yet another do, with an engraved glass loving cup created by the same mechanical processes which went into the mass manufacture of the carriage lamps. St Helens, at this juncture, could have done better than Preston. My grandfather John, the glass-blower whose life consisted of blowing bottles and whose heart rebelled and stopped at the age of 60, could have blown them a chalice to rival the wonders of Murano. Alice knew this, just as I do. But Alice, along with the others from the Dick, Kerr's team, was gifted with a presentation also. After years of winning silver whatsits, she, along with the entire team, were given solid gold bracelets, from the munificence of one of the directors of English Electric.

The gift was a signal of the regard in which they were held as charity fund-raisers, and as footballers, and now as the central providers of an entente which was publicised in the national press of two nations. And, what's more, and what brought a lump to the throat of Margaret whenever she passed this story on, each bracelet bore the name of the player who received it. My father Jack, a Communist in his younger days, would have interpreted the gift as a ball and chain, but then he was brought up in St Helens in the Depression and his Communism was from the heart and from his bitter experience of being a graduate who couldn't get a job as a road sweeper because there were no jobs to be had. I, like Alice, and Lily who hardly understood the significance but had felt the value, would take the gift of the bracelets as a mark of respect.

So now, with bracelets or balls and chains in place, let's go gallivanting again with the girls in their new finery, even though a game of football intervened between the trip to the factory and this next, and best day out. We'll come back to the football later. First, it's a charabanc trip with the French girls to Blackpool.

To understand Blackpool, you really have to have been brought up in the sullen North West. Blackpool was our desert oasis. If it was sleazy, brash, filthy and deafeningly cacophonous, we hardly noticed. It was a city dedicated to all that is best in us – singing, marching in procession behind bands, laughing, eating, taking risks, dancing, drinking, being bluntly and offensively ironic to southerners who never got the joke, falling in love, and having a good time. 'Eeeh our Bar,' my grandmother Polly used to say when we picked her and William up after their annual week in Blackpool, 'it were reet good!' In a land in which working hard or looking for work was a daily struggle to survive, Blackpool let us dream that we, too, were toffs.

First there was the sea. I can't think of another town in which the sea itself is the star attraction, with an energy and an eccentric personality of its own. The sea didn't dawdle and drag its feet in Blackpool. It raced in like a late clocker-on in clogs, blown by the lusty and rain-sodden West wind, then threw itself in giant leaps against the cast-iron rails of the promenade. It was an Irish Wolfhound on tabs of sodium chloride. We used to chase between one salty geyser of its breath and the next, waiting to be drenched again. And then it would turn to race backwards, and where there'd been just a crumpled sheet of flecked grey, as far as the eye could see, there were suddenly the longest and widest and most improbable yellow ochre sands on which we could run and run towards the edges of the retreating waves and never catch them up. With the tide went all the rubbish, all the evidence of human waste, and what was left was clean and pure and huge, dotted with worm-casts, streams, ripples and wet footprints.

There never was so much sand in the whole world. And there never was, anywhere, so much sea. For children raised in homes without bathrooms, the expanse of water in which they could throw their entire body, over and over again, was a luxury they'd never encountered. For children from St Helens in 1920 who had learned to swim in the stagnant water of Stinky Brook and The Hotties, and had occasionally visited the Public Baths and may only once or twice had the tin bath to themselves without washing in the hand-me-down filth of every other family member, the Blackpool sea was pure joy, despite the numbing cold and the scales of crusty salt left on their bodies at the end of each day. And for the ladies of Paris, holding on to their cloche hats – especially Madelaine Braquemonde – and to the arms of their heftier opponents and friends, the Blackpool seafront, with the Blackpool sea lurching menacingly from beach to road across the rail tracks of the Blackpool trams, was a revelation. They had never, Alice Milliat said, seen anywhere quite so windy.

In fact they had never seen anywhere with such delights as the Winter Gardens with its Floral Hall, decked in a greenhouse display of aspidistra and potted palms and its Big Wheel, as its three wrought-iron white lace piers, as its rock-sellers, and its potted shrimps, cockles and mussels, sold from sea-front stalls and offered with nose-curling vinegar and a pin.

What they had seen before, in a way, was Blackpool Tower.

Just as I find the dissonant clash of cultures fascinating, I also find this assonance intriguing and ironic. Blackpool, twinned with Paris. The mind boggles at the metaphysics of these two cities being linked by an architectural oddity – an identical tower.

But the cultural statement which created the towers was couched in the same populist language. For the Parisians, the plan to build the Tour Eiffel was conceived to celebrate the centenary of the French Revolution with an edifice which would honour the industrial technology which had transformed France between 1789 and 1889, and would celebrate the *citoyens* who hadn't been instrumental in planning the Revolution but had been the means by which the Ancien Regime was finally toppled. It was a plan despised by the bourgeois because of its proposed skeletal use of an industrial process. There were calls for something more elegant and fitting than this populist monument to welding, but from the moment it was erected it became the most famous and best-loved landmark in a city of grace.

Blackpool wasn't by any means a city of grace. It was a Victorian hotch-potch of a sham showplace, founded by impresarios anxious to make a bob or two by helping the working class feel posh for a day. But in Blackpool the Tower stood for the same heart-felt emotion and pride as the Paris monument. It stood for industry and progress in the heart of the North West industrial landscape. It was something that Lancastrians could recognize as being factory-built, by sturdy people just like themselves. It was architectural finesse from foundry-made crassness. And there's another reason why both towers were an attraction for the working-class population – they could climb to the top and gain a vantage point, for once in their lives. Up there, they could look down, even those from the mining community who spent their working lives in holes under-ground.

So all the bravest of the girls, French and English, Thérèse and Madelaine, Carmen and Geneviève, Suzanne and Pascale, Lily and Alice, and Florrie and Florrie, and Jennie and Jessie, of course, climbed to the top of Blackpool Tower above the screaming gulls, and were, like the pigeon-fan-ciers of the Lancashire coalfields transformed for a moment into birds themselves. It was with a pigeon's or a gull's or a lark's eye that they looked down from clear air at the Fylde coast with its endless sands and the sea lapping the shores of the Isle of Man and Ireland, the distant blue mountains of the Lake District, and the pall of smoke lying across central Lancashire, all the way to the craggy Pennines and beyond, and were mistresses of all they surveyed. There was only London left to conquer.

By the time they left Lancashire behind, the French had already attracted an enthusiastic following, especially for their performance in Manchester when incessant grey stair-rodding rain had pelted down from kick-off to final whistle and turned the pitch into a quagmire. That the stolid English had kept their footing was to be expected. They had the big legs for it. But the little Frenchwomen had shown themselves to be undeterred by the conditions, and that they got stuck in, and never stopped to check that their *coiffeur* was still in place or whether the mud was only waist or neck deep as they ran fluently and tackled enthusiastically silenced those who had come to scoff. They left the pitch to rapturous applause, and had held Dick, Kerr's to a draw, despite being well-beaten in the earlier matches at Deepdale and Stockport.

The London papers had already been alerted to the progress of the tour and waited eagerly to watch this battle of French speed and elegance against the famous Northern oikish heft, and many of them had already penned their copy before kick-off. *The Times*'s correspondent in particular had unearthed a Greek myth of no relevance whatsoever with which to preface his stinging and sententious sneer at women's football and the spectacle of international matches of this, he said, hilarious and time-wasting nature being played at the Stamford Bridge, home of the famous Chelsea side. He missed the point completely and was totally out of step with the opinion of the nation as a whole, who were keen to pay to watch a match between ladies for a charitable cause. Sneering at these women was unpatriotic, surely, many claimed. They were doing their best.

What everyone expected was exactly what was presented to the whirring cameras of the Pathe News and the throng of press cameras. Initially. The English girls ran on to the pitch lustily, kicking the ball, in striped shirts which had been stolen from the men's game. They looked like everyone's big sister, or the woman who served in the pie and mash shop next door to the ground. They had big broad factory-girl faces and big broad thighs and arms, and you wouldn't want to meet any of them in a back alley late at night, especially not that scary-looking Lily Parr who was said to be only fifteen. They were Amazons, so unlike the tiny demoiselles from gay Paree. Instead of racing in and kicking in, they minced on to the pitch to the strains of La Marseillaise, in perfect formation, like little mannequins, their hands held at right angles to their arms as they swung their hips. They looked like a team of performing penguins. Their shorts were tiny, and just a little flared, so their every move was a sexy shimmy. And those berets! Lovely. Wolf whistles echoed across Stamford Bridge. Then the goal-keeper, petite Ourry, who had brought her man-sized rabbit to be in shot for the pre-match photographs, ran across to her goal with a posy of flowers with which she decorated the upright.

Actually, she did that at the behest of the press photographer who had handed her the flowers, but he knew that it would make a great photograph for the sports' pages. In the Press Enclosure the cartoonists were hastily drawing the match they hadn't yet seen and adding witty captions, *'These are neither Greek statues nor escaped sardines, but some of the players who seem to be strangely affected by the presence of the cameramen.'* The cartoon strips they produced were gently teasing rather than outrightly sneering like *The Times*'s correspondent. One saw the Dick, Kerr's goalkeeper pausing to powder her nose as the ball went into the net. Another showed the girls racing to the changing rooms at the discovery of a mouse on the pitch.

The game itself was perhaps not as good as it might have been from Dick, Kerr's perspective. Little Jennie Harris, the favourite with the French girls, was knocked out by one of the Laloz sisters in a shoulder charge which may have been a foul, and the game continued with the team reduced to ten. Annie Crozier scored an own goal, and Annie Hastie let in another, so despite a goal from Florrie Redford, the Preston girls were defeated in the one city that they'd hoped to set alight.

Yet, they did set it alight. After the prejudices had been duly satisfied, the game set off at a cracking pace, and the spectators were completely won over by the skill of the girls' game. They had expected to be bored or amused, but actually, it was good football. Very good football. The French women went tumbling to the tackles of Alice Kell and Jessie Walmsley, but they were flexible and agile and rode the challenges with their remarkable ability to turn complete somersaults and land on their feet and continue to huge cheers. The athleticism and the stamina of both teams was what surprised the scoffers in the crowd. And no one had seen anyone, man or woman, kick as powerfully as Lily Parr, or run from defence into attack as fast as Alice Woods. There were many in that crowd who went home to ask their daughters and sisters if they'd ever thought about playing football, and if not, why not?

The reviews of the match were gentler, and far more encouraging than the reporters had initially intended, although they did all mention the fact that Madelaine Braquemond had kissed Alice Kell at the end of the match. That took the male reporters aback. It also took Alice Kell aback. Lasses didn't kiss lasses in Lancashire, any more than they kissed lads, in public. It wasn't done. But apparently, in Paris, it was, so Alice duly smiled and returned the thank you with the same nodding sparrow pecks, one on each cheek, like the French, and within no time, everyone was kissing everyone else before changing and leaving for the hotel.

And a very impressive hotel it was, at that – the Bonnington, in fashionable Bloomsbury, built only nine years earlier and employing every modern industrial advance. There was electric light in every room. Lily and Alice giggled excitedly over the ornate fringed light-pulls hanging above their beds and kept switching the lights on and off with increasing volumes of whooping celebration. In the morning there was breakfast with real cloth napkins in napkin rings, tiny rolls of bread and Full English, or smoked haddock with a poached egg, or a pair of bloaters or omelettes, individually created by a chef in a big hat. There was fruit, too, and cereal. And cold cuts. Along the corridors were bathrooms with proper baths which they took for hours, and hot water coming out of the taps, and little bars of wrapped scented soap which had to be carefully purloined, packed and taken home for Sal and Margaret. Lily kept saying, 'Merde!' It was the only French word she had taken the trouble to learn and one of the Laloz sisters, Geneviève or Suzanne had practised it with her until her pronunciation was perfect. Alice just kept saying, 'Eeeh, would you credit it?' and shaking her head in disbelief at all these wonders. She was in transports of delight. None of them had ever been taught how to take the good life, if it ever arrived. They, sensibly, didn't trust it. But they loved it, anyway.

The next day it was all over bar the shouting, and there was plenty of that as the women, and photographers, set off on the obligatory tour of the tourist spots of London, with some notable diversions from the regular tourist route. One of these was to visit the statue of Edith Cavell, a mission which reduced most of the girls to tears, and which Thérèse Brule said was the most memorable event of the London trip. Edith was a British nurse from Norfolk working in Brussels, who was executed by firing squad for being a part of an underground movement which found safe passage for Allied soldiers who had escaped German POW camps.

The girls waved goodbye to the French at Waterloo in a tearful exchange of kisses which threatened to delay the train, and little Ourry and the giant rabbit made a last-minute decision to stay behind in Preston for extended work experience at Dick, Kerr's, and extra training to enhance her acrobatic displays as a goalie.

But their own departure as a team from Euston to Preston ran into a demonstration on their way to the station. The shop-girls of the John Lewis department store had gone on strike over the conditions in which they had to live and work, as residents of the shop's own hostels and filled the streets with their passionate demands for fairness for women employees. That women workers should withdraw their labour was unthinkable, pre-war, and this was the first time in British peace-time that it had ever been done. London was not, after all, that much different from the dissident north. It had even hosted a women's football match.

And both the striking shop-girls and the Dick, Kerr's Ladies factory football team from Lancashire, featured in the Pathe News, which was viewed in Kinemas up and down the length and breadth of Britain and in St Helens, too. Alice and Lily were film stars.

Four

Swank

It was easy for Alice and Lily to think that nothing had really changed in their lives, because talking about it was something you didn't really do, except to those who asked you, and that would only be family. Anything else was swank – showing off. They had to keep up the good manners which St Helens taught all its daughters, which was never to imagine yourself better than anyone else, and to accept good and bad with the same flat attitude. Swanking was the greatest crime against humanity, as was having 'side'. Grandmother Polly often described someone as having no side to her, and this always worried me as a child, how someone could slip out of dimensionality and be like one of those paper ladies I used to cut out and dress up in paper clothes, but I eventually realized that it meant someone who despite a difference in class or education had remained unaffected by these privileges. Alice, despite her successes didn't swank and had no side. But in the evenings following Alice's Great Adventure to Blackpool, Whalley and to an hotel in London, Margaret would follow St Helens convention by putting on a clean pinny, after all

101

the chores were done and the house cleaned and the step pumiced and whitened, and the women of the household would sit round the range in the kitchen, take out their sewing, crocheting or darning, observing the nightly leisure-time entertainment for women. Jangling.

Jangling is gossiping, chatting, and can allow any amount of scurrilous rumour, and any amount of the famous Lancashire sarcasm, skitting. Skitting is an art form. It allows everyone to put everyone else down and is poorly understood by posh people and southerners. There, trying to negotiate the skitting which would inevitably be heaped upon her if she tried to swank, Alice told them about what she'd seen when she'd left Sutton for ten days. Sometimes they'd ask her to speak French, as they thought it hilarious that they said Wee instead of Aye. But what they most wanted to hear about were the sanitary arrangements Alice had encountered.

In St Helens, there were no inside privies, let alone those with a flushing water supply and mains sewerage didn't reach the majority of the homes. It wasn't just in Gerrard's Bridge and Greenbank that sanitation was a low priority. Most of the outside privies were ashpits. These would be cleaned by the borough's night-soil men, who would arrive in the night in a wagon and empty the waste into a cart. Sometimes they would have to shovel out the solids, and might even leave these on the pavements for collection the following day. Miners clopping home from night turn would often fall foul of these pavement heaps in the dark which was where the clogs came in particularly useful.

That Alice had been somewhere with inside flushing toilets and with inside porcelain baths and wash hand basins with little towels was a matter of some family pride, and her repetition of this story was demanded whenever another family member came to visit. They never tired of it. And that she had brought scented soap home was proof of where she'd been and what she'd done. The tiny tablets of scented soap in their wrappers were carefully secreted in the drawers where the ladies kept their best vests and corsets, to make them smell sweet. They also wanted to know about the electricity, and the light pull over the bed, and the electric lights in the streets which must have made it look like Blackpool.

Alice had done something truly exceptional. She had travelled further and seen more than anyone in the family had ever done before, with the exception of John. But even John had never stayed at the Bonnington in Bloomsbury. Yet otherwise, life went on in much the same way that it always had, and Margaret still couldn't understand why playing a game of football could accord such treats and privileges. Alice couldn't quite understand it herself. She'd gone into Dick, Kerr's merely to get practice for her athletics. That she had entered a different sphere of life wasn't something that had occurred to her.

But she had. The French visit had drawn the nation's attention to the charitable efforts of this team of factory girls from Lancashire, and that was a seismic change in social behaviour. Until the Dick, Kerr's Ladies, working class women had never been admitted to the ranks of those who did good works of which the nation could be proud and for which the nation was deeply grateful. Charities and voluntary fundraising had always been done by the upper ranks of the wealthy leisured classes who espoused causes in order to give themselves something to do with the time which hung heavy on their hands. It was appreciated, of course. But that girls who worked hard for a living could have enough gumption in them to race round a football pitch playing quite good football on their half-day off, and give the cash they'd raised to men of their own class . . . consider what effect this solidarity in action might have on the Establishment which had always taken its own authority for granted. Somewhere in there is a shifting of power. And it could be thought dangerous, couldn't it?

For the moment, that thought had only occurred to a few who were canny enough not to put it into words, because that would have been seen as ungrateful. Those who had the thought kept it, just now, to themselves, and decided to bide their time.

The tour against the French did what Alfred Frankland had hoped it would do. It inspired other women's football teams throughout the country to rebuild the interest that factory football had engendered in the war years, and clubs were reforming or returning with renewed vigour and an enthusiasm to beat 'that team from Preston that played the French'.

One such team was formed from the ladies who worked for the Lyons Corner Houses. These were huge restaurants on several floors which served full meals, to orchestral accompaniment, as well as snacks, and had a shop at ground-floor level. Over 300 women were employed at each of the branches. Anxious to do their bit for the post-war effort, they formed themselves into a number of teams, and were offered the sports' facilities of the Lyons' organization to practise so that they could be worthy opponents for Dick, Kerr's. The world famous Strand Corner House had its own team. By targeting London, Frankland had inspired a new interest and vigour from the south of England. Bath then formed its own team, with the support of the Bath City AFC, and, again because there were training facilities and the support of the men's team, this promised to be a competitive side. In Plymouth, two teams fought against each other to be recognized as the major team in the area. Even in the Midlands, which had never had a munitions' factory team, a new club was formed in Coventry, and in Bradford the Hay's Brewery established a team which was at first dire, but which was able, after only a year, to hold the great Dick, Kerr's to a draw.

But perhaps the most interesting development was the formation of the Atalanta club in Huddersfield. Its name says it all, taken from the mythical Greek huntress. These women were from the same lower-middle-class origins as the ladies from France and had the same founding principles. They were essentially athletes with high ideals and as secretaries and teachers and students had rather looked down on football as a very common sport. Common was the term used to denote class disapproval. It was the word my mother always used to describe girls who had their ears pierced, chewed gum, ate with their mouths open, or who didn't wear their school berets on their way back home. The Atalanta Club, however, had to rely on a bit of common heft like their football captain, Ada Beaumont, to give the necessary grit and skill to enable the club to compete against Dick, Kerr's, and thereby raise money for charity. It was the only team I could find which took its inspiration not from its Lancashire sisters, but from its opposition team, the French Ladies.

However, when the Dick, Kerr's team returned from

their celebrity outing, they had their existing fixture list to attend to, and all arranged matches had to be honoured. Two of these, one following only two days after their return from the glories of London, were with St Helens Ladies.

Whatever the opposition drummed up in other parts of the country, it's clear that St Helens Ladies was establishing a special relationship with the team from Preston. It was the only team which had a similar male support and fanatical and dedicated women footballers to the Dick, Kerr's team. Alfred Frankland had tempted away its two best players, and there would never be anyone quite as good as Lily and Alice who played for the team. But, on the other hand, it was composed of girls who had learnt to play on the instruction of their older brothers, a toughness which refused to give up, and a genuine dedication to the game. St Helens Ladies was the team to watch.

And why did these women from St Helens play the game so passionately? I've already listed many of the reasons: soccer as a minority sport, women's sport as an acceptable and healthy thing for women to do, St Helens women being tougher than the boots in which they played because of the conditions which had given rise to their fight for survival. But it's worth considering the deciding factor. Poverty. St Helens was poor. And it needed charity. So if it could play a match against Dick, Kerr's on its own invitation, it would raise enough funds from cash-strapped miners and glass-workers to keep its own charities going. Dick, Kerr's was the crowd-puller, the team which ensured that spectators would turn up in their thousands, and St Helens needed the thousands to turn up so that it could raise money. It wasn't after glory.

In the months which followed, Dick, Kerr's would use St Helens as its worthy opponents when invited to play in a town or city which had no women's team of its own but needed to stage a match in order to raise funds for its own war-wounded and the unemployed ex-servicemen. Fixtures were requested by the mayors of these towns. So at Oldham, only two days after the departure of the French, and at Blackburn, later in May, St Helens Ladies played Dick, Kerr's Ladies to raise funds for both those towns. All the St Helens' players asked for was their expenses. They became the dependables on whom Dick, Kerr's could rely as the 'official' opposition, whenever they needed it. They knew that the St Helens team would give them a decent game of football, and that they wouldn't cave in and allow Dick, Kerr's to beat them by a silly margin with goals reaching double figures. Of the eight games played at the start of the 1920/21 season, four were played against St Helens, and three against the Vickers' team from Barrow in Furness, another old dependable. But the Vickers team was breaking up while St Helens' Ladies went from strength to strength.

It could be said that Dick, Kerr's was becoming an exhibition team, an act which was booked when alternative forms of fund-raising had failed to work. But that's both patronising and misleading and fails to account for the complexity of the interwoven reasons why these women played. They played because they loved football and played it supremely well. They used their skills, not to raise money for themselves as professional men's teams did, but to raise funds to help others. And, finally, they played in order to raise the profile of the game of women's football, and wherever they went, wherever they were feted in newspapers or on film more women came forward to play football.

And more would come forward after the return bout to play the French in late October, in France. Alice and Lily were to travel to a foreign country. No ordinary woman from St Helens had ever done that. In preparation for this terrifying ordeal, the girls had to fill in an application for a passport, yet more unfamiliar territory, and very amusing in retrospect. In 1920, the British passport consisted of a sheet of A4 size heavy laid paper, folded into eight. When unfolded, full details of the holder could be seen, and these full details had to be entered into the application form. Perhaps Alfred Frankland helped Alice fill this passport in, or perhaps it was Margaret and Jane, hunched over the kitchen table, gathered round an inkwell, and deciding which descriptions best fitted Alice Woods. My guess is that it was Margaret and Jane, and a really inadequate tape measure.

Apart from the measurable accuracies of her date and place of birth, her height in this passport is given as 5 feet 4 and three quarter inches. She was 5 feet 6 inches tall. Her 'round' face is accurate enough, but her fair hair is described as 'dark brown', her full mouth as 'small', her grey eyes as 'hazel', her rounded chin as 'sharp', and her nose as 'Roman'. Someone obviously ticked all the wrong boxes. Still, it carried a photograph, which was a blessing, and when it arrived in August, it was passed round from hand to hand in the family with reverence, like the precious document it was.

Press interest, which hadn't subsided in the weeks preceding the trip to France reached fever pitch during September when the women had important matches to play.

For them, the one which meant most was a game at St Helens on September 18th, the first time Dick, Kerr's had ever played in the town itself.

Five thousand St Helens people turned out, that night, to watch Lily and Alice running out with an internationally famous team, paying five pence, the cost of a Sunday roast, in a town which had the largest unemployment in Lancashire, to step through the turnstiles and support the girls of both teams. St Helens Ladies played well and even scored a goal, but Dick, Kerr's scored nine, with both of the local stars on the score-sheet. It was a wonderful night for the town, and all the money went to a good cause, the unemployed and disabled soldiers, and the crippled children. Crippled children was a charity which seemed to be particularly native to St Helens. A school was to be built for them, to cater to their specific needs, and it's a matter of speculation whether the chemical factories might have produced birth abnormalities in the population. I don't know. But I know that working in these conditions, and suffering the ill-effects of the fumes, can't have been conducive to the health of the prospective parents:

The gas given off cuts into their arms and rots their teeth. Most salt-cake men have teeth as black as coal. They also begin to suffer from chest complaints with deadly certainty after they have been some time at the work . . . Fancy working all day or all night in a fine mist of lime – lime particles about like a cloud of mosquitoes, with a far sharper bite, too. To protect themselves the men resort to a muzzle, or a piece of rag or flannel held tightly between the teeth. The exposed parts of the skin are carefully greased, and a sort of paper mask is frequently improvised in addition to the cap. In spite of everything, the lime gets in somewhere and inflicts its bite. All the time the work is carried on, breathing is a terrible effort. To breathe through the nose would have the direst consequences. A single inhalation and the lime particles would lodge there. So the air has to be inhaled through the muzzle and given out through the nose. Twenty minutes at a spell is as much as a man can stand; after that he goes out to recover himself and lay in a little air for his inside and some grease for outside lining.

That extract comes from a Trades Union report of the conditions in one of St Helens' chemical factories, before the war which turned Lily and Alice into fund-raisers for crippled children. By the time the match was played, most of the chemical factories had moved from St Helens to Widnes, a few miles to the south, where a new and cleaner process was gaining vogue and proving safer. But the names of the chemical factory owners were forever graven in St Helens history as sponsors of several wards which they had funded in the hospital and which bore their names afterwards. So, that made it all right, then.

Lily and Alice were interviewed for the local newspaper about their proposed tour of France at that St Helens match, and both of them admitted to one main subject of concern. The food. Specifically frogs. Both girls were nauseated by the prospect of having to eat them, as French people did. St Helens' frogs . . . perhaps I can see the point. The reporter suggested to them that they might prefer the other delicacy of France, snails. Both girls left hastily when

110

The Dick, Kerr's Ladies Football Team

Lily Parr

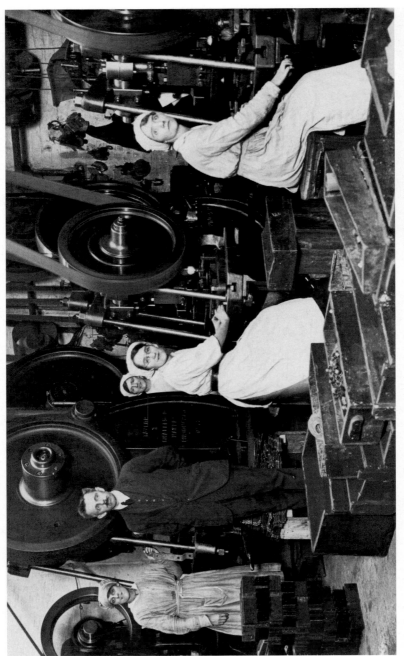

Women working in a Munitions Factory, 1918. *Mary Evans Picture Library*

Alice Woods in her running gear (with Union Jack)

Possibly Elaine Burton on the left, who would have been 13 or 14 at the time. In 1921 Alice had a bet of £5 with Elaine's father that she could beat Elaine again. Elaine was the first girl ever to wear little running shorts like the men. In her later years she became an MP, then a Peer

Alice proudly displaying her winnings (including her medal round her neck)

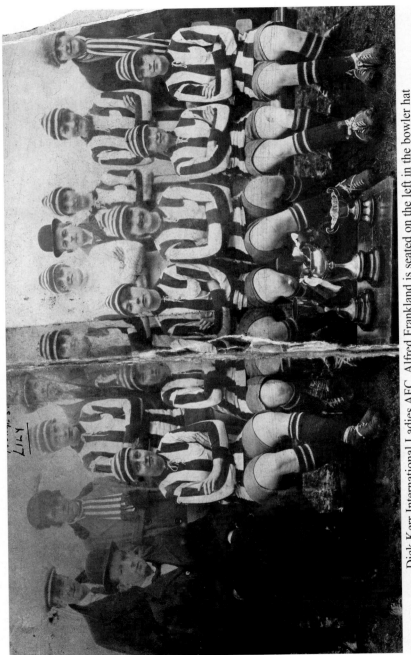

Dick Kerr International Ladies AFC. Alfred Frankland is seated on the left in the bowler hat

The French Team in 1920

The actual poster for the football match played by
Dick, Kerr's against France in Paris in November 1920

exposed to these stereotypes of French food and St Helens humour.

Before being exposed to French gastronomy, however, the team had a match on 29 September which allowed Lily and Alice to gorge themselves on whelks and malt vinegar. Funnily enough the similarity between whelks and snails didn't occur to them. This final pre-tour match was held at Blackpool, and it was to be, in a sense, the second international match Dick, Kerr's Ladies played. Interestingly, it was a match against a women's team from over the water, over the Irish Sea.

1920 was a turbulent time in Ireland. The country was about to be partitioned, leading to a bloody civil war. The battle of the Somme had caused huge casualties, particularly in Belfast, where some of the women put together a team prepared to travel across to England to try to raise funds for their own ex-soldiers. There was a natural connection between Preston and Belfast in the textile trades which had been the mainstay of both cities – cotton in Preston and linen in Belfast. My own great-grandfather, grandfather William's father who was an Irish Roman Catholic, came over to Lancashire from the Lough Neagh region There was also a clear connection between the Scottish managers of Dick, Kerr's and the Scots settlers in the North of Ireland who tended to play the popular Scottish game of soccer rather than Celtic football which developed in the south. Dick, Kerr's was to retain this involvement with Belfast, and to play a return match there, so although records say only that this was the Irish Ladies, I think it was most probably a Belfast team, and when the factory team from Preston got together with the lusty Irish ladies from Belfast, Blackpool must have been shaken to the core of its Golden Mile.

No one celebrates quite like the Irish side of my own family, and Lily would have been in her element, belting out a few songs in her inimitable husky voice – with the useful help of a packet of Woodbines – with the Irish Ladies. This one, the most popular Irish song always hurts whenever I hear it as I now hear it again in memory, hauntingly sung by the faultless high tenor voice of my grandfather William. There are tears in the music, said to have been carried to Londonderry by settlers from the Isle of Islay:

Oh Danny boy, the pipes, the pipes are calling
From glen to glen and down the mountain side
The summer's gone, and all the roses falling
It's you, it's you must go and I must bide

But come ye back when summer's in the meadow
Or when the valley's hushed and white with snow
It's I'll be here in sunshine, or in shadow
Oh Danny boy, oh Danny boy, I love you so

But when ye come and all the flowers are dying
If I am dead, and dead I well may be
You'll come and find the place where I am lying
And kneel and say an 'Ave' there for me

And I shall hear tho' soft you tread above me
And all my grave will warmer, sweeter be
For you will bend and tell me that you love me
And I shall sleep in peace until you come to me

It's the second verse I remember most clearly as my grand-father William could never get beyond it before he broke down in tears, along with everyone else, the strangely Irish use of the word 'it's', and that searing high call in the last line of that verse. I never fail to cry, as must some of those Belfast girls who lost their fathers and lovers at the Somme.

But if the mood in Blackpool was tearfully and happily sentimental, the mood in France was serious. And Lily and Alice had no idea that what was to face them in France would be beyond their comprehension. St Helens just hadn't prepared them for it, in anyway. They had expected more of the things they knew about – a good do or two, some rumbustious games of football, perhaps a procession, a visit to that other tower, and leaving the frogs legs on the side of the plate which Mr Frankland had informed Lily in particular was the correct thing to do when food was not to your liking.

Lily herself, prior to the tour, was acquiring some publicity in her own right. The *Daily News* gave Lily her personal headline

15-year-old with a Kick Like Division 1 Back

and the copy contained those words, 'a 15-year-old girl back who is said to kick like a First Division man'. That her skills had been noted, and that commentators had suggested she wouldn't be out of place in a men's team of the top quality is testimony to just how promising she was becoming after only six months under the training regime of Dick, Kerr's. There was a reference, too, in the piece, about Alice, saying that she was a sprinter. The other girls mentioned were Alice Kell, as captain, Florrie Redford, and the French girls' favourite, little Jennie Harris, described as 'Dick,

Kerr's box of tricks'. St Helens had as many stars in the team as Preston.

But St Helens was suffering again. The miners had been locked out of the collieries by the owners, affecting the entire economy of the town which was so dependent on its coal-fields and on those who worked them. With Alice's family all working in the mines, it must have been a wrench for her to leave them to it, and to take the trip to France, as she had promised, and for which she'd been preparing. But she did leave, to join up with the other team members in Preston.

There the tour began in fine Lancashire style with a Dick, Kerr's musical evening in the ladies' honour, then, the following morning they boarded the train in Preston for yet another night of luxuriating in the joys of the Bonnington bathrooms. And there was a special event programmed for them, a night out at the famous London Palladium. Variety shows were something the women of Lancashire loved in particular as the performers in variety and Music Hall traditionally came from just three areas – Glasgow, East London, and Lancashire. Performing in London around that time was the local lad, George Formby senior, an acquaintance of Alfred Frankland, and a man whose turns were often disrupted by violent coughing, as his lungs had been damaged by working in Lancashire forging factories as a teenager. Born close to St Helens, in Wigan, his style was typically Lancashire, as he played the northern geek, lost in the big city, henpecked and bullied by his oversized wife, the stuff of the Blackpool comic postcard:

SWANK

I'm a man that's fond of seeing life and my wife by the way,
She said to me: 'John Willie, you shall have a holiday'.
She took me up to London, the sights to let me see
And when we arrived at St. Pancras, the wife she said
   to me:

'John Willie, come on! Mind you don't get run o'er'.
A lady came to me and said, 'Have we not met before?'
My wife said, 'Miss, how dare you, that's me husband
   here be gone.
Y'know, it's mine, I found it first, John Willie, come on!'

She took me by the hand into a picture gallery
I saw a champion picture there, it fairly tickled me
It was a woman in the sea with long hair on her head
I was getting interested when the wife turned round
   and said:

'John Willie, come on! That picture makes you stare
It's only Venus rising from the sea, so don't stand there'.
I couldn't take me eyes off it when the wife she shouted,
   'John:
Tide's coming in – it's not going out, John Willie,
   come on!'

We went in Madame Tussaud's waxworks show and it
   were grand
And there we saw all t' waxworks kings and queens all
   shaking hands
There was Mary Queen of Scots and Queen Elizabeth,
   you see
They fairly took me fancy when the wife she said to me:

'John Willie, come on! It's closing time you see'.
The lights went out and all was dark and quiet as can be.
On turning round to my surprise, I found my wife had
    gone
And I'm sure I heard Queen Elizabeth say: 'John Willie,
    come on!'

It would be heartening to think that the Ladies might have
seen him on one of his final appearances at the Palladium,
as a year later, that cough which was so much a part of his
act, carried him off in the wings of the theatre, and his son,
George Formby Junior, the same age as Lily at the time,
went on to become a great star on the ukulele and in the
movies and married a famous Lancashire clog-dancing
performer. Pure Lancashire.

So after the variety show, and the night at the Bonnington,
it was off to France, with the Ladies still singing the show
tunes and 'John Willie' to Alfred Frankland at the start of
their foray abroad. The fare for a foot passenger on the
Dover Calais ferry, then, was fifteen shillings, the equivalent
of £150. Alice held on to that ticket for the rest of her life as it
must have been the most valuable thing she had ever possessed. And, because this trip with the most important event
of her life, she took a small notebook in which to record her
memories of the journey and what she saw. It's a curious
document, with a flat pragmatic style which lent itself
to making lists of the information she was given. It's clear
that between the lines was a culture shock of enormous
gravity.

The first shock came even before they reached Paris.
'Enroute for Paris saw soldiers graves at Etaples. One mass
of beautiful flowers on Hill Gloria Jesus Christ.' The girls

had been told what to expect. They had taken with them a wreath with a circumference of 12 feet to place on the grave of the Blackburn Rovers footballer, Edwin (Eddie) Latheron, who had been killed at Passchendaele, the third battle of Ypres. But thinking about war, and being made conscious of it from the pictures in the newspapers, and plunged into grief by the loss of loved ones, is rather different from re-treading the route of soldiers themselves. The Ladies weren't merely going to play football and have a light-hearted time wandering through in the country in a charabanc sing-song, they were entering a war zone. Etaples brought home to them the fact that this tour was going to be completely different in tone and kind from the frolics in Preston. Their visit would be regarded as an official mourning party and would be accompanied by sights and experiences many of them couldn't easily deal with.

Etaples, now a pretty fishing village, distant from the fighting, was where the Allies had their training centre, and their reinforcements, and their hospitals, in the sand-dunes. There were 100,000 troops there at any one time and 17 hospitals dealing with 22,000 of the wounded and dying. By 1919 11,000 British soldiers had been buried there on a site of 60,000 square metres on three terraces.

And this was the first thing Alice saw in France. Eleven thousand graves. For the rest of her life Alice would warn her family not to go to France, and she never re-visited. It was a country which she would always link with death.

Although Alice's diary on this first day in Paris reveals that the working class as ever loves to climb monuments and look down – she climbed up all the carefully counted 281 steps of the Arc de Triomphe – and included such touristic adventures as a boat trip down the Seine, a glimpse of the Louvre, and a tour round Notre Dame, war continued to make its presence felt. She found it necessary to mention that the French army had marched under the Arc de Triomphe on its way to war and that she saw a British soldier in the Bois De Boulogne saluting the Union flag flying there.

Not for these girls a day-long romp around the fleshpots like gaudy Blackpool. In the afternoon they were shepherded on a charabanc trip to Les Invalides, the military museum, to see several shot-down German airplanes, proudly exhibited in the museum. The tour was organized with military precision, and its object was militaristic, as the next morning, the women were rounded up at nine thirty and taken to St Cyr Ecole Speciale Militaire.

To put this in perspective, this would be similar to a visit to Sandhurst or West Point, as St Cyr is the training academy for the cream of the French military officers. Now imagine Lily Parr, 15, gawky, fed up, puffing on a cigarette, being escorted into this impressive Napoleonic building by officers with sabres, into the company of Colonel See, the commander of the training unit. Yes, I like dissonance, but it's a dissonance too far that the organizers of the French tour, presumably Alice Milliat and those she felt she might impress, had thought to have the girls treated to a lecture on the 'Analysis of movement in military gymnastics through moving pictures'. Because that's exactly what they were invited to undergo on that fine French Sunday morning.

Lily, after realising that there was nothing unguarded by a sabre which could be pilfered, nodded off, being prodded back to life for luncheon. The array of hierarchies of cutlery at each place setting must have, in itself, been a daunting prospect, let alone being waited on by soldiers who clicked heels, saluted and came to attention for our Lancashire lasses. Nothing could have been further from the rollicking good time that was had by all at the Bull and Royal and the Dick, Kerr's canteen.

The military connotations of this tour would have been reinforced by the stadium to which the Ladies were then transported for their first match – the Pershing Stadium, built on the orders of the American General Pershing who had an idea in January 1919 that the Allies should celebrate victory by holding a sports' tournament over several days, in a grim echo of that single famous football match on Christmas Day 1914.

The match, with the Ladies still reeling from their brush with the military, was kicked off by the French Minister for Aviation, and given the above restrictions, the crowd was huge. Ten thousand turned up to watch, among them many soldiers and workers from other countries, in Paris to help with the post-war rebuilding. It was a closely-fought contest in a crowd where patriotic fervour reached simmering point even before the match. The French were determined not to lose in front of their home crowd and the officials and functionaries, press-men and military who had turned out to see whether French women could resist the enemy. The German occupation of northern France in 1914 was a matter of some embarrassment still. Sections of the crowd were shouting lustily for Lancashire, but the majority was willing the French on with a passion, and when the factory girl, Genevieve Laloz, sprinted away in the first half and scored there was a huge burst of deafening applause. When, a little later one of Dick, Kerr's strikers, Minnie Lyons, went on to equalise for Dick, Kerr's, there was an equal cheer from the rather less restrained British Tommies and navvies, who had been drinking before the match. But tiny Ourry, her Lancashire training and good plain Lancashire food with gravy standing her in good heft, kept out the barrage of shots which Dick, Kerr's continued to pound at the goal throughout the second half. It seemed inevitable that Dick, Kerr's would score a winner, because since that defeat by the French at Stamford Bridge, the team had an unbroken series of victories. And then disaster struck.

With ten minutes left to go, Dick, Kerr's was awarded a corner, which the French disputed. So did the crowd, especially one section of French spectators who had been rowdy and very territorial. Suddenly, they burst through the barrier and on to the pitch, hurling themselves at the British women who had this last gasp chance of scoring. Lily Parr was in position, waiting to fire in the header, when suddenly she was bowled over by screaming French *citoyens*. The military and the sabre-carrying policemen gave chase in this unfortunate phenomenon which France had never had to deal with before – a classic pitch invasion. It was fortunate that both teams of women were exceptional athletes and could cover the distance back to the dressing-rooms faster than the men with the bottles. The French girls were all in loud tears. Lily wanted to get out there and punch someone and had to be restrained. Alice, remembering the incident while writing her journal that night was still so shaken that she made the only error in her diary, crossing out the word 'corner' which she'd mis-spelled and replacing it with another mis-spelling. The only bright spot in an otherwise bewildering and frustrating day was that the staff of the Hotel Beau Sejour had responded to the girls' calls for some decent food and had supplied a meal of steak and chips.

The next morning they were up at the crack of dawn, and had left Paris for Roubaix by 6.30. Roubaix was in the very centre of the northern industrial region which was very similar to Lancashire, with both coalfields and a textile industry. Football was a traditional sport in this area just south of Belgium, too, and the women would be warmly welcomed. But first, they had to cross the Somme battlefields.

In researching this book, I've had to look back at old photographs of the France these girls saw, which Alice recorded so flatly in her diary. I do understand that there was no easy way that the women could have been taken on a different route, but even looking at these 1920 photographs, made me, someone who has lived her life watching war unfold on television, desperately lost for response. On that battle ground, even in 1920, nothing had been left, not a home, not a tree, not even the undulations of the earth itself. And it wasn't napalm that had done this, or stealth bombing by computer-guided missiles, but all-out mortar and machine-gun fire from hand-held and hand-guided weapons, sometimes from low-flying planes, with real human beings pulling the triggers or calling the shots and dying in their thousands.

Bombed last night, and bombed the night before
Going to get bombed tonight
If we never get bombed any more
When we're bombed, we're scared as we can be
Can't stop the bombing sent from Higher Germany
They're over us, they're over us

One shell hole for just the four of us
Thank your lucky stars there are no more of us
'Cause one of us can fill it all alone

Alice lists the towns they travelled through, every one a
war-site – Amiens, Albert, Arras, Louvain, Vetry, Douai,
Lille, and she makes an interesting slip when she writes that
she 'landed' at Roubaix, rather than arrived at it. What she
had been through could have been a flight in a space shuttle
to the farthest cratered surfaces of the moon.

Here are some of the things she saw, two years after the
war had ended. She passed 'barbed wire entanglements' and
'shell holes' and 'trenches full of water'. And she repeats
'wire entanglements', 'ruins', 'woods demolished'. I saw that,
too in the frail copy of the Michelin Guide to the Battlefields,
published at the end of 1919. I saw a picture of something
that was supposedly Satyres Wood alongside a two mile
stretch of country road. There were just two stunted tree
trunks remaining of that wood. She passed over bridges that
had been 'temporarily built' and then she saw people trying
to live, in a tiny village called Blangy. 'Blangy small huts like
Eskimos live in made of all tins picked up from the dumps.'
In these villages, the rural communities were living in benders
made of oil drums which they'd salvaged from the ruins that
the armies had left behind them. That 'made of all tins'
touched me very deeply as it's such St Helens phraseology
that I can hear her saying the words. It was 1920 and still the
railway lines were blocked by derailed trains which had
carried soldiers. Alice found this hard to believe, 'Louvain
train bombed off rails still there.'

And then on to Roubaix after this four hour excursion
through hell.

Roubaix was one of the first towns taken by the German army advancing through to France from Belgium. This is the 1919 Michelin publication on what happened,

At 10 am on the 9th [October 1914], the first enemy aeroplane appeared, and dropped two bombs on the General Post Office. In the afternoon, all men from 18 to 48 years of age were ordered to the Bethune Gate [in Lille], with instructions to leave immediately.

A crowd of people from Lille, Tourcoing, Roubaix and the neighbouring villages, left on foot for Dunkirk and Gravelines. Several died on the way of exhaustion, others being taken prisoner by the Uhlans. The last train left at day-break on the 10th.

On the 13th, the German occupation started and was to last for four years. Taxes were imposed for the war effort, and the following year the entire population was issued with identity cards which had to be shown at all times. Then there were requisitions made, of machinery and even domestic bedding, and in 1915 the famine started. Bread cards were issued, and the tiny rationing amount allowed wasn't made of flour only, but of potatoes and rice. Townspeople were arrested, some people were shot by firing squad for hiding Allied troops, and then a curfew was imposed. Deportations began in 1916. Each night, within the three towns, up to 2,000 people were deported, and sent as forced labour into Germany – 25,000 in all. Meanwhile the textile mills were being pillaged and destroyed in an effort to undermine the French economy. Much of the equipment in the factories was relocated to Germany.

On October 17th and 18th 1918, the retreating German

armies finally left the area after first bombing the railways, and it was liberated by the British army. The mayor of Lille received the President of France. M Poincare, on October 21st, and said this,

> For four years we have been like miners buried alive, listening for the sounds of the rescuers' picks; then all at once the dark gallery opens and we perceive the light.

And so the Ladies played in Roubaix to a rapturous reception from a population whose life and liberty and pursuit of happiness had gone underground for four years, and for some would remain underground in the encircling cemeteries.

This was a town like Preston, so like Preston, with a passion for football, and a huge delight in offering to the women's football team everything it could salvage from the wreckage, but it has to be remembered that it had deep scars – collaboration as much as deportation and famine – which had destroyed the fabric of its common textile heritage. Nothing would ever be the same again in Roubaix, but it put on as much of a party as it could, even though its obelisk to the fallen was right there at the edge of the football pitch to commemorate the death of battle of the captain of the football team. A crowd of well-wishers cheered their entry into the town, many of them from the Lancashire mills who had been called in to offer machinery and help, some of them from the Lancashire conscripts who had decided to stay in Roubaix. Dick, Kerr's Ladies, exhausted, haunted by death and comforted by the presence of those they considered to be their fellows won the match 2–0. Then, the

next morning, aware that they would never find the grave of
Eddie Latheron amid all these myriad crosses to the Somme
dead, they placed the exaggerated wreath they'd brought on
the Roubaix War Memorial. They had suffered in their
lives. But not like these people.

Alice records,

Went to cemetery Roubaix and laid a wreath for the
fallen soldiers, then travelled in an ammunition wagon past Tourcoing cemetery of all the British soldiers
at Huryslines. Then went to dinner [lunch] at Hotel
Du Compte. Armentieres every house demolished.
Workshops being rebuilt. 3pm cross roads to Dieppe,
Croisement. Church demolished, Returned Roubaix
5.15, left for Paris 5.30. Arrived at Hotel 11.20 pm.

Listen, this is a St Helens' lass, writing a diary. Do you need
her to spell it out? Just look at what she reports and see the
poignancy and the disbelief in this journey out into No
Man's Land. Armentieres, 'every house demolished'. It's a
far cry from what she might have heard about Armentieres,

Mademoiselle from Armentieres,
Parley Voo?
Mademoiselle from Armentieres,
Parley Voo?

Mademoiselle from Armentieres,
Hadn't been kissed for forty years,

Hinky-dinky, Parley Voo?

The next day was a visit to Versailles. To us, now, a visit to Versailles means a visit to a palace with beautiful fountains and paintings and antiques, and it meant that to Alice, too. But there was something that happened in Versailles so recently and so notably that Alice had to mention it twice, 'I have stood where peace was signed', 'Table on which peace was signed 28th June 1919'.

And then there was more football, and more wreath-laying, first at Le Havre where Dick, Kerr's won 6–0, then at Rouen, where they won 2–0 and saw the tower where Joan of Arc was imprisoned. They didn't climb up there. In both cities it was incumbent upon the footballers to lay a wreath at a soldiers' graveyard before the matches.

It was too much. The essential quality of Lancashire women is a refusal to stand on ceremony, except perhaps when performing 'The Messiah' every Christmas and standing for the Hallelujah chorus. It's especially a quality of these particular Lancashire women who had been selected for the team because of their refusal to accept convention and their inability to sit still. That was the founding principle of their sport. And Lily Parr, whose blood-curdling threats to the opposing team were a feature of her game-playing, 'If you bugger come near me again I'll kick you over t' bloody cross-bar,' was expected to have, buried somewhere inside her, the formality and gravity which characterises French ceremonial. Not a chance. They shouldn't have done it to Lancashire lasses.

On Monday, November 8th their duties in graveyards and on football pitches was over, and they sailed back from Dieppe to Newhaven, then took refuge in the Bonnington for the night, where they all said goodbye to Lily Jones who was remaining in London where she was to be married.

She'd been with the team almost from the first, but, as Annie Hastie and others would do, soon, she had another life to live, as a wife and future mother. Tears were shed, and rice was put in her bed. Then, the train journey to Preston, and suddenly at six o'clock on November 9th, they were home to everything they knew and loved and everyone who knew and loved them and accepted them for what they were.

The Dick, Kerr's band was waiting to oompah them back to reality with a blast of 'See The Conquering Hero Comes', which was quite ironic considering what they had seen, and the memories which they'd hold for the rest of their lives, but the band was celebrating their footballing record, which is just as it should be. A charabanc was waiting for the team, and preceded by the brass band they were driven to the cheers of thousands to whom they waved the Union Jack, and the Tricolour, all the way to the Dick, Kerr's canteen where a lovely spread had been set out for them, and a welcoming committee stood with speeches at the ready.

Alfred Frankland was in a political mood, having been encouraged by the dignity he'd been expected to display in France. His speech was about the comradeship they'd noticed among the English soldiers and navvies in France, and he expressed the opinion that Lancashire should see more of this comradeship rather than getting involved in strikes and lockouts – the miners' lockout had only recently been ended. He felt that if nations played sports together all the bad feelings between them would be swept away. There were many hear, hears to that. He also expressed an opinion that although amateur football was becoming quite popular in Le Havre and Rouen, and very popular in Roubiax, the French hoped that professionalism would never make its appearance in the French game. Then the team was given over to the pierrots who gave a capital concert performance, and everyone sang along. It must have been such a pleasure for the girls to take off their coats and big hats and loosen their corsets, and get on with jangling in English while the chorus sang a specially rehearsed song for them:

> Roses are shining in Picardy
> In the hush of the silvery dew
> Roses are Flowering in Picardy
> But there's never a rose like you!
>
> And the roses will die with the summertime
> And our roads may be far, far apart
> But there's one rose that dies not in Picardy
> 'Tis the rose that I keep in my heart!

And exactly at the time the pierrots were singing, and the Ladies joining in while sipping sherry or milk stout and repeating 'Eeh, it's grand to be back home!' and becoming quite tearful, a coffin was carried across the Channel from France to England. This was the body of The Unknown Soldier due to be interred in Westminster Abbey in a specially ceremony on Thursday 11th, to commemorate the second anniversary of the Armistice.

The mood in Preston was uncharacteristically sombre after this trip to a war zone. The football was a joy, as ever, but some of the reason for it, helping their brothers and fathers to survive the post-war dysphoria had gone, and with it, the excitement. But in December, Dick, Kerr's was suddenly approached by the Unemployed ex-Servicemen's charity to try to raise cash for Christmas food to be distributed in Preston. At such short notice, what would make the crowds gather to feed the hungry children of the unemployed? Who was it who said, 'Let's play the game at night. Under floodlights?' My money's on Alfred Frankland.

The official website of the Football League claims that the first football manager to bring in night matches, under floodlight, was Herbert Chapman of Huddersfield, in the late 1920s. In fact, it had been tried before, in Birmingham and Lincoln but the lighting wasn't powerful enough to make the game visible, and maybe Herbert was the first manager to introduce floodlit football on a regular basis, but Alfred Frankland and a squad of engineers from Dick, Kerr's English Electric factory actually managed to make floodlit football a possibility. The unique relationship which existed between the company and the Army barracks at Fulwood was the key, and Dick, Kerr's engineers came up with the solution. Two Army surplus searchlights should do the trick. So, these were duly ordered from the War Office – can you believe it? – and were delivered to the Preston railway station the day before. To augment those, 40 carbide flares were put into position around the edge of the pitch, also supplied by Frankland's contacts in Fulwood barracks. Flares were placed at the turnstiles and to celebrate this extraordinary occasion not one, but three brass bands were requisitioned to lead torch-lit processions of spectators to the ground. And the Pathé News team was alerted to this experimental exercise in pre-Christmas jollity and turned out to make of it what they could.

As a spectacle, it was far more exciting than any of the previous Christmas processions and celebrations for which

Lancashire is famous. Men in flat caps, women in large hats, small children skipping along, processed to the Deepdale ground, so that later they could tell their own children, 'I was there when we played football by searchlight!'

The Ladies too, were excited, all of a fluster and a giggle. Back to their old selves. Lily did her Blind-Man's Buff impression, mimicking searching for little Jennie Harris through the dark by touch only. The opposing team was to be 'The Rest of Lancashire' and included two St Helens girls who had been tempted by the prospect of hunt the football. It could all have gone horribly wrong, but I doubt it, because even horribly wrong would have been funny.

And it was. Hilarious mayhem ensued. Picture it – on the touchline was the famous Bob Holmes whom I've mentioned before, throwing whitewashed balls on to the pitch, in the stands were scores of big lusty Lancashire lasses with their husbands, doubled up with laughter, and on the pitch were Lily and Alice and the others, wondering what damage they could do in the darkness. Except that it wasn't dark. It was glaringly bright, until one of the searchlights got an airlock and went out barely into the first half. Then one of the searchlight operators from the factory became very excited by a defensive tackle, and turned up his searchlight so strongly that both attacker and defender were temporarily blinded and keeled over. Then Jennie Harris, as willing as ever, kept making searching runs up the left, only to be halted by the sudden glare of flash-bulbs and skied the ball from 5 yards out. Everyone joined in the raucous madness. And when a free kick was awarded against an opposing player, a small crowd of Preston women started to chant 'Off! Off! Off!' to much laughter. When did women spectators ever take the lead on a chant? Amazingly, some goals were scored, eventually, and Dick, Kerr's won, and then a crowd of little boys raced on to the pitch to steal the football while the Ladies were entertaining the Press and rushed off with it, hotly pursued by the referee, a policeman, and the film crew. It was better than Charlie Chaplin.

The Ladies were then driven to that gourmet venue, the Dick, Kerr's canteen, for a hefty meal to put more roses in their flushed cheeks. The match cleared away the chill wind that had blown in from across the Channel. The gravy was pronounced gradely.

Less than two weeks later, Dick, Kerr's entered the record books again, in a match which demonstrated how far they'd come, and seemed to suggest that they would go much further than anyone had ever expected. They'd been invited to a 'Cup Final' match in Liverpool on Boxing Day (although the title is quite confusing, as there had been no preliminary rounds). The fact is that Liverpool had realized women's football could be a way to raise the cash it also needed to support its own charity endeavours. The 'Liverpool Ladies' team had been short-lived, so Dick, Kerr's provided the opposition by playing the team they considered to be their closest rivals – St Helens Ladies, led by the indomitable captain and goalkeeper, Waine, another player who had refused Alfred Frankland's blandishments to come over to Preston to play for his team.

Women's football had now started to attract the kind of following it could only have dreamt of at first, and the kind of carnival atmosphere at Liverpool had been dictated by the Dick, Kerr's love of good dos and mischief. Florrie Redford, the centre forward and one of the founding members of the team, the highest goal-scorer, would miss it all. She'd moved to Chorley, and despite a desperate effort to ride to Preston on her bicycle to meet the others for the early-morning departure, had missed the chara-banc, and the train. It was typical of Frankland's military style, and his confidence in the team, that he insisted they left without her.

So there was only one Florrie in the team that day, Florrie Haslam, who had fared better with her journey from Bolton, and Daisy Clayton – originally from the 'Liverpool Ladies' team but now a regular Dick, Kerr's player ac-corded the same stay-home privileges as Alice, easily man-aged the mile-or-so trip from her home in Walton to nearby Goodison Park, the home of Everton Football Club, where the match was to take place. St Helens' Ladies had only a ten-mile journey to make, but no one should think that this made them the home side. As I said, there's a huge gulf between Liverpool and St Helens, and generally speaking, the two communities loathe each other: there was wide-spread fury when St Helens became part of Merseyside.

Everyone knew that this was going to be a good match with plenty of support. Boxing Day morning is always the best time to go to a football match, and it's the one match of the year I always check first when I get my fixture list. If my team's at home on Boxing Day, there's no way I can be persuaded to be anywhere else but at the game. Christmas arrangements are made around it, and every other football fan in the country feels as I do. So expectations were high. And there was a little touch to the match that turned out to be a master stroke which would be adopted in future matches whenever possible – there was a celebrity to kick off. Although there had always been a 'someone' to do this job, it was generally a city worthy, a Mayor, or, at Deepdale, a famous footballer, like Bob Crompton, the Blackburn player who had kicked off at the search-light match. This kick-off was to be by the famous Ella Retford.

You may not recognize the name, but Ella, born in 1886, was one of the biggest stars of music hall and pantomime. At the time she was heading the bill at the Liverpool Empire. She was a great actress and did a good turn. By 1910 she was already the People's Favourite of the women music hall stars, eclipsing even Vesta Tilley and Florrie Fforde, and she later moved from the halls into British film, taking minor roles in the 1930s and 1940s. But for all of us in woolly-back country, the reason she was loved so much was that hers was the first and greatest stage rendition and recording of our song, 'She's a Lassie From Lancashire'. Get stuck in, Ella!

But even the high expectations for this match, prompted and encouraged by a letter to Alfred Frankland telling him that a match in Liverpool could possibly raise as much as £1,000, were a little exceeded. At a time when the biggest football grounds could pack in as many as 66,000 fans for a Cup tie, and Everton's ground at Goodison Park had a capacity of 53,000, 67,000 people turned out on Boxing Day 1920 to watch the match, and they didn't all come to watch the beloved and lovely Ella Retford. 14,000 of them had to be locked out. The police had to be called in to steward the crowd and deal with the disappointment of those who had to go back home. And the police also had to protect the Ladies as they made their way on to the pitch, and back to the dressing rooms.

In a city which loves its football and its stars. Dick, Kerr's Ladies provided both in a blistering game of brilliant football. The publicity machine, which had been cranked up since the visit of the French Ladies, was now whirring at full throttle, and the fans had got the message that women's football wasn't just a novelty. It was here to stay. If this standard could be maintained, then the men's game had a serious rival. Showered with flowers at the final whistle, pursued by crowds trying to get autographs or just touch these women from despised Lancashire, Alice, Lily and the girls with their cup presented by the Lord Mayor of Liverpool, and arm-in-arm with their 'rivals' from St Helens whom they had unsurprisingly beaten 4–0, had become almost as famous as Ella Retford, and they couldn't believe it.

Nor could the Lord Mayor of Liverpool. Because when the takings were counted, that match alone had raised over £3,000. That's over half a million pounds in today's reckoning. It's as much as was raised from each of the lengthy tours against the French, at home and away. It was unbelievable riches. All of it was unbelievable.

'I can't believe it, mam, I just can't believe it,' Alice said over and over again the next day, after the big do in Liverpool hosted by the Mayor of Birkenhead.

'To me, Alice,' her mam said, making Alice pace with the wet mangled sheet over the frozen yard. 'And we hope you're not going to show us up by swanking to all and sundry.'

'I wish Florrie had bin there to play t'match. She were allus good to me, and Mr Frankland should never have left wi'out her,' Alice said.

'Aar,' her mam said. 'And mebbe she shouldn't've bin late. Think on, our Alice. Allus be on time. Then you miss nowt, not even tha own funeral.'

These were the twin admonitions of St Helens – the inevitability of death and the fact that you should allus 'think on', an instruction which was inevitably accompanied by a wagging finger. Death was a part of day-to-day life. Intimations of immortality weren't. As for 'thinking on', I never quite got that worked out. It must have come from the repetition of Biblical texts, admonishing us to 'think on' these things, but in St Helens it means both think back to origins, and think forward to consequences, and doesn't really allow for any thinking in the present tense. That was called 'dwelling', and was something that you must not on any account do or you might go doolally, a mental state which all tried their best to avoid.

Alice had no time to dwell. Dick, Kerr's had received so many invitations to play football from town councils wishing to benefit from their largesse that they had to play mid-week as well as on Saturdays, throughout the season. A hundred and twenty invitations had to be turned down. And it was so exciting, too. The celebrations were bigger, the teas and sherries larger, the takings astronomical, the great and the good ever more fawning. Some of it was becoming competitive, too. In Liverpool, following the success of the Goodison Park match, Anfield had to try to go one better. There was always a fierce rivalry between the Catholic supporters of Liverpool Football Club, and the Protestants of Everton for the hearts of the Liverpool poor. So for Valentine's Day Liverpool Football Club offered Dick, Kerr's Ladies the chance – as if they could refuse – to play a team from the Rest Of Britain for the Harry Weldon cup. Harry Weldon was, like Ella Retford, one of the most popular actors and comics of his day, the singer of such unforgettable songs as 'Bailey. Why Don't You Go

Home?' 'Daddy, You're My Father' and 'I'm Going Home To See If I've Gone Home', which used to knock 'em dead in the aisles in Lancashire, he'd brought his famous panto, *Dick Whittington and His Cat*, to Liverpool where it was going down a storm, as it always did. The game was conducted in the atmosphere the Ladies knew and loved. It started with a fancy dress procession (plenty of brass bands, lots of bogie open-tops and charabancs), was kicked off by Ella Retford again, and concluded with both teams having stalls seats at the panto. The cup was presented to Alice Kell at the end of the show. Dick, Kerr's had knocked the Rest dead in the aisles at 9–1, as predicted. It's just as well Alice Woods didn't have to collect the cup. She couldn't stop laughing, as Lily Parr kept repeating the funniest lines in the show in her loud husky whisper.

Alfred Frankland wanted to give the girls more good times like these, but he was swamped with administration. The sheer physical effort of arranging the matches was taking its toll, and he needed help. So he had to take on an assistant secretary, someone who could do the books, make team-lists, list the contents of the kit skip, keep everyone's address on file, keep score- and scorers'-lists, and generally be a gopher. So he engaged young Herbert Edward Stanley.

Before the war, Alfred had lived on Taylor Street, next door to Mr Herbert Frederick Stanley, and the two families had become close friends. Herbert had been a gardener, which was how he met his wife, the formidable Sarah Anne, who was then in service to a solicitor in Preston. Sarah Anne was from Abertillery, and Welsh girls were very much valued by well-to-do families, as they were reliable and efficient servants, very clean, very trustworthy, or so it was said. Sarah was certainly all of these things. She was also very shrewd, keen for Herbert to make something of himself, as he was a 'Stanley'. The Stanley name is famous in Lancashire, as it's the family name of the Earls of Derby, the local aristocracy, and all Stanleys feel that they are distantly related, although not many of them made quite so much fuss about the possible connections as Sarah Anne did.

With her encouragement, Herbert Senior had taken on the rental of a neat detached house on the outskirts of Preston, and set up in business as a market gardener and nurseryman. There were large greenhouses behind the house, and an allotment at the side for vegetables and fruit trees, from which Herbert sold fruit and vegetables to the shops of Preston. Sarah Anne took in washing, as many married women did. But it wasn't just any washing. She was appointed, by Alfred Frankland in 1917, to launder the strip of the Dick, Kerr's Ladies. So when it came to needing a willing young man to help out with secretarial matters, it was suggested that perhaps young Herbert Edward, Herbert Junior, might like to take on the job.

At the start of 1921, when Herbert became involved in the running of the team, he was only 18 years old, and a trainee accountant. Like Alice, he was good with figures, and his handwriting was deemed 'economical', too, which was how he obtained his first position at Pratt's, an oil company in Preston, after he left school, four years previously. He was everything his mother was – shrewd, meticulous, hard-working and dedicated. From the age of eight he had been a part of his own family firm because as the only son this was expected of him, so he'd rise at dawn to help with deliveries. He was a keen footballer, but a better cricketer. He cycled all over Lancashire with his best friend Percy Hardacre, who was also a confirmed bachelor. Tall and rangy, he had eyes that could light up a room, if he chose to, and a laugh that was more infectious than most.

But he was also very quirky. There was something quite unconventional about this young man with the neat clothes and the bowler hat, which defied his upbringing and his choice of career. He was a gifted watercolour artist, who spent his summer holidays painting in Cornwall, and had even considered opting out completely, moving to Cornwall and indulging his passion for the arts. He wrote stories, gave recitations, told wonderful anecdotes, had a huge store of jokes and tried his hand at verse:

> Here's to the team without a defeat
> Watch them play – they are a treat.
> A reverse to them is a great unknown
> In Ladies' football they stand alone.
>
> They have played in nearly every town,
> Indeed they're a team of great renown.
> For charities' sake they play the game,
> And never think of personal gain.

Herbert Stanley was not only the gopher of the team, he was also a fan. Alfred Frankland had chosen wisely, and it was Herbert Stanley who kept some of the few records of the team's achievements, expenses and line-ups. Most of what we know about them can be deduced from his carefully completed notebooks, and something of what we know about him, too. In the notebook in which he marked down the match-by-match reports, there's one entry, crossed out as all were when dealt with, which appears a little mysterious:

Entries close for 100 yards N.E. championships May 26th.
Run June 4th.

Herbert Stanley was not an athlete, so why would he write the entry details of a sprint race? The answer is that the memo wasn't for him. It was for Alice Woods.

This is the only non-team memo in the entire notebook. So we can safely date the start of a relationship between Herbert Stanley and Alice Woods as between January and May, 1921.

It was an unlikely romance. Herbert was 18 and Alice 21 when they met and romances generally didn't occur between older women and younger men. Alice was a well-travelled women of the world who had been to France. Herbert had been to Cornwall. Alice was from the mining community of St Helens and Herbert from the lower middle-classes of Preston. Alice lived in dust, Herbert in a home surrounded by things which grew out of the ground. They even spoke differently. The accent in St Helens is as harshly flat as its despoiled landscape, but there's a warm burr in the cotton-mill towns which rolls the 'r' gently, like the sound of water on a wheel.

And yet there were certain similarities. Both were far more intelligent than their education had provided for. Both loved lists, especially if numbers were involved, and both had artistic gifts – Alice's being her needlework. Both were good at sports, although Alice's mastery far exceeded Herbert's, and perhaps that was where his initial fascination with her came from. She was someone famous, someone he could look up to. Was it love? It was pragmatic, and dogged and unspoken. But, right from the start, it never wavered. It was there in exchanged glances. It was there in shared jokes – Alice had a rich deep laugh. It was there in sudden silences. And it was there in the memo in his notebook, made for his new best friend.

Alice certainly needed a friend and an escape from the difficulties St Helens was facing. 1921 was a year of strikes and lock-outs in the mines, which had been returned to the owners from the government control of the war years. Demand for coal had reduced, and the mine owners decided that the men could work for longer hours and less pay. Miners in St Helens refused to take a 50 per cent cut in wages, and were locked out from their jobs. St Helens was feeling the pinch, as it had done for a couple of months in 1920, but this was worse, since the lock-outs stretched on for months and months, and more people were forced to turn to Public Assistance. But, once Margaret had agreed to the new arrangement, Alice lodged with Sarah Anne in Preston for the Saturday and mid-week matches, where she could enjoy good food, and hospitality, and laughter. Alice in Preston regularly meant one less mouth for the Woods family to try to feed during the miners' lock-out, while Sarah Anne was delighted to have a famous Dick, Kerr's Lady in her home. She had taken to the girl immediately.

The miners' lockout had an effect on women's football, too. It politicised it. Taking heart and inspiration from the success of the Dick, Kerr's Ladies' efforts, local women in the mining districts around St Helens formed themselves into makeshift teams and put on spontaneous exhibition matches on any piece of waste land they could find to entertain the locked-out miners. There was another purpose, apart from providing a reet good laugh, though. At these 'pea-soup' matches, collections would be taken from the onlookers, and the money raised was used to support the miners and provide them with food after the strike funds ran out. Women's football had come to be associated with charity, and had its own credibility. Now it was used as a tool to help the Labour Movement and the trade unions. It had, it could be said, become a politically dangerous sport, to those who felt the trade unions to be their enemies.

The Dick, Kerr's Ladies, of course, weren't playing the game for political purposes, at least not overtly. They went to play in the towns to which they'd been invited, and continued to raise huge sums for local charities. But their example, as women who went out to support their menfolk, a Lancashire tradition, was causing ripples in a society which wanted women to revert to their prewar roles as set down by their masters, of keeping their place, that place being in the home and kitchen. Lancashire lasses were upsetting the social order. It wasn't acceptable.

Did they care? Not at all. And moreover they cocked a snook at convention by deciding to set up their own holiday fun and frolics. They deserved a break in August, and no one fancied another trip to France. The French Ladies had visited again, this time playing only one match, in Staffordshire, against Dick, Kerr's, but setting their sights generally lower, playing the newly formed teams in the South West. Not that the entente was over. Far from it. On that visit, in May, Carmen Pomies – the dental student – decided to give up her studies and live in the warmth of Preston for the foreseeable future. Immediately, and perhaps surprisingly she formed a close friendship with young Lily, which would last a lifetime. Carmen was one of the few people whom Lily ever took back to St Helens with her, to visit Sal and George and the children. Goodness knows what the educated middle-class Parisienne thought of the St Helens welcome and the bacon and eggs and black pudding.

After much debate about where to go, the Ladies decided on the Isle of Man, and decided to take the St Helens Ladies with them for a break from poverty and politics. The St Helens' team was delighted. None of them had travelled beyond Blackpool, and their home life was depressing and hand-to-mouth. The lock-out had affected glass production, which meant that neither of the working communities was actually working. So this trip could be taken at any time by the unemployed girls from St Helens, and they went along with the Dick, Kerr's plan to take the trip during the Preston Wakes Week, when Dick, Kerr's factory would be closed.

Wakes Weeks are a particular feature of the Lancashire cotton industries – one week each year when the boilers which drove the machinery had to be inspected and the mills shut down. The word wake actually means vigil, and was the night before a saint's day (Holy Day or holiday) when everyone was supposed to stay awake to pray, but in Wakes Weeks everyone usually stayed awake for an entire week to play. Burnley, Bolton, Accrington, Preston, Blackburn, Bury, Darwen, Oldham, Shaw – the streets of those towns were silent, while entire families decamped to Blackpool, Rhyl, or the Isle of Man.

The Isle of Man was the closest most of us got to going abroad. A holiday there was the most expensive option because of the ferry fare, but every year my school went on the horrendous trip across the North Sea to this tiny fairy island. The crossing was worse than any I've ever been on.

142

SWANK

There's something relentlessly angry about the Irish Sea, and the ferry boats weave and duck to try to ride the same furious tides which throw themselves across the promenade at Blackpool. We travelled from Liverpool, our nearest port, but the Ladies must have travelled across the easier route from Fleetwood, close to Blackpool, with hordes of other Preston holidaymakers. Even now, the thought of that trip brings the old retching feeling into my throat.

The problems, as the Ladies will have discovered on that August Saturday, are caused by the occasion as much as by the fury of the waves. Everyone on that ferry is in holiday mood, and if they imagined that the trip would be as pleasant as, if a little rougher than, the crossing to France, they would have been disabused of the notion very soon. Everyone over the age of 15 makes for the bars, the moment the ship sets sail. It's Lancashire holidays, Lancashire mischief, Lancashire good dos. The families have saved up all year for this booze cruise, and won't stop until they arrive at Douglas harbour. Everyone under the age of 15 is given holiday pocket money which is immediately squandered on ice cream, sweets, and buns. Halfway across, the entire passenger list begins to vomit, some merely because they see others doing it. The ferry decks have to be hosed down before the next happy holidaymakers embark at Douglas. Lily Parr with her prodigious appetite would have been, I think, the first to succumb to the throwing-up orgy of that trip. The stalwart Jessie Walmsley would probably have been the last. Alfred Frankland and Herbert Stanley and perhaps Alice Woods would have passed the journey healthily on deck, as all of us are strenuously advised to do by seasoned travellers. 'Don't look up, don't look down, don't go inside, stand on th'deck and look ahead.' But the

Ladies would have arrived in Douglas happy and emptied. Because everyone's on holiday, no one cares very much about being sick. It's all part of the fun.

The Isle of Man is tiny but green and rolling, with all the silly superstitions and air of mystery which make us wriggle with foreboding and hope. In the Isle of Man you have to say hello to the fairies as you cross over bridges, and in all too many places there are wishing wells, magically dark and deep and filled with pennies. St Helens likes a wishing well almost as much as it enjoys doing the Pools. Promises of riches are always attractive. Then there are the miniature railways – Jennie Harris would have enjoyed those, and the Laxey Wheel, a huge waterwheel formerly used to power the zinc mines, but so much prettier than a pit-head, and everywhere there are tunnels of sun-speckled foliage, dipping to head height. The Ladies went home with three victories, in Ramsey, Douglas and picturesque Port Erin, and the thanks of many more delighted mayors. Alice Woods went home to strike-hit St Helens wondering if the strange feeling in the pit of her stomach was to do with the return crossing or with the love-pact she'd made with the fairies as she sat quietly with Herbert Stanley, watching him sketch the beauties of the island in careful watercolour.

Alice really did need that week of football and Herbert and quiet reflection. All the women did. Since Christmas they had been on a punishing schedule, playing the length and breadth of the country, sometimes three matches a week. They'd made several forays into Scotland, including Kilmarnock, no doubt encouraged by Dick, Kerr's management, and had beaten the Scottish national side. They'd travelled into Wales where they'd played both Cardiff and Swansea in a four day mid-week tour in

March, and had beaten the Welsh national side twice, on two successive Saturdays. They'd played against some of the newest clubs like Atalanta and Bath Beauties and Hay's Brewery and had beaten them embarrassingly well. Sometimes they'd had to take St Helens along with them, especially in January and February when no one else seemed to want to play. Sometimes they'd had to stay overnight, sometimes for several nights. They were playing far more matches than most men's professional teams.

For those girls in employment, this frequent travelling required understanding employers, willing to accept that the footballers were only part-time workers. Florrie Redford, the highest goal scorer in the team was training as a psychiatric nurse and had to miss many shifts, or make up her time by working nights, then cycling to the next match. Alice had to talk Margaret round to the idea that she may not be at home as much as her mother might need. And Alfred Frankland had to keep reminding Dick, Kerr's that these matches were strictly necessary, and persuade them to take on any latest 'star' he discovered, like little Alice Mills, who wasn't quite as small as Jennie Harris, but had similar pace and goal-scoring abilities.

And they'd become media darlings with the Pathe cameras following almost their every move. It was fun, but sometimes it did involve playing up to the cameras. In one hilarious afternoon, Pathe filmed what it claimed was a training session to show how the girls were actually all-round sportswomen. This session included a boxing match between several girls, and finally a horse was found from somewhere to illustrate the fact that Alice Kell could ride a horse round a football pitch.

But for Alice, star of that Pathé film shown at every St

Helens cinema, to rapt audiences, there were more important things in life than a boxing match staged for the
camera, with her old friend Lily. There was love. It was
almost as important as football, and certainly more important, if you weren't swanking, than celebrity.

Five

Booted Out

Celebrity, although sought by Alfred Frankland to aid the team's charity-raising, is a double-edged sword. Especially when, as happened in mid-1921, press columnists began to cater to the followers of this new sport, women's football. While this meant that the team and the game generally had good coverage, not all of it was positive.

Football Bits the periodical, started a 'Miriam' column which took joshing side-swipes at women's football, and published many cartoons with titles like 'Those Girls Again'. It was gentle enough banter. *The Football Special* went one further, and started a column written by 'Football Girl' specifically dealing with the issues raised by women's football. This was a particularly mealy-mouthed column, and I doubt very much that it was written by a woman player, as it purported to be. It had its own agenda, which seemed to be that Dick, Kerr's were fair game.

Are Dick, Kerr's So Good?

There are rumours that Dick, Kerr's are not as good as
they used to be. People who have seen them play, both
this season and last, seem to be pretty unanimous in
saying that their play has deteriorated. Perhaps we
can't tell really, for they are still winning their matches
by comfortable margins, so that it is probable they do
not exert themselves to the degree they would if they
were in danger of losing. We shall perhaps see keener
play when the other clubs who play fewer matches
have got more into their swing.

Hmm. Is this really a lady footballer writing this column, a
supposed expert on the sport, who claims without having
seen the side play, and allowing that they have been winning
their matches by a considerable margin, can suggest that
their play has deteriorated? How exactly? And did a women
footballer actually write the following?

It is an interesting question as to whether girls' schools
should take up football. Personally I should hesitate to
introduce football among very young girls. It has been
done, however, in one or two schools and with success. Football is more strenuous than the usual games
played at schools, and for very young girls to play
might involve the risk of doing them harm internally.
Most ladies' football clubs, I know, have young
players and often they are very good. The Dick, Kerr's
star player, Lily Parr, is only 16; and Miss Chorley, the
clever little centre-forward of the St Helens team, is 16.

Indeed there are few clubs which haven't 16- and 17-year-old players.

On the other hand, the Atalanta club have a rule that no girl under 18 may play football, and I think such a rule is wise. The girl may seem to stand the strain all right, but it is probable that she will suffer later in life. On the whole, if football is to be introduced into schools, I think it should only be played at the colleges where the girls are usually in their late teens or early twenties.

Oh dear. So let's hear it for hockey, that similar game where women not only have to race around at full pelt, and tackle, but are also supplied with an implement which can be whacked against another's flying body if internal damage is an object of the play. Or lacrosse, where the implements are held at head height and woe betide any head that gets in the way. Or netball – surely leaping so high whilst propelling a ball into a ring might pull a few internal muscles?

'Football Girl's' voice is the voice of the 'Lady Correspondent' of the *Guardian* back in 1887. It's the voice of Middle England, bristling with moral indignation and moral rectitude. It's the voice of the Establishment. And it's the voice of the backlash. While giving column inches to women's football it displays its own prejudices: a deep southern bias, a middle-class agenda, and plans for the reformation of the game. 'Football Girl' is very much in favour of women's football being established along League lines and the country divided into regions, under some central control, which will compete internally. But is it forgetting four years of history which made the women's game slightly different from the men's and therefore not in need of such rigidity? 'She' couldn't absolutely turn her back on the reason for playing, as that would be unpatriotic, so she manages a sentence about it at the end of the column.

> Charitable institutions have benefited considerably since girls' football got into its stride, and this, surely, is the answer to the many rather unkind things that have been said about the girl players.

This leaves me to ask the essential questions – what many rather unkind things? And why plant that suggestion? And why does 'Football Girl' know nothing about the mind, heart and motivation of Alice Woods?

Alice won a beautiful leather-bound and gilt-edged autograph album for her athletic achievements that summer. She was rightly proud of something which had a practical use. In November she managed to remember to take it with her when the team travelled to Manchester to play, at the invitation of the City of Manchester, against the newly formed Lyons Ladies. Now you know something of her mind, heart and motivation, you won't be surprised by this unsophisticated and star-struck behaviour. This is one of England's top women athletes, a woman whose generosity of spirit and superb skills have made her known all over England. Yet she carries with her to an important function a new autograph album, which, on its first page, carries a tender little painting of a child feeding a begging dog, and opposite that picture, the most valuable entry in her new book from the man who painted the picture:

When this you see
Remember me,
And bear me in your mind.
Let all the world say what they will,
Speak of me as you find.
Best Wishes
Herbert
30/10/21

The match itself was a great success, yet again, and the autograph book was carried round with her at the do, afterwards, at which they were offered several very moving votes of thanks by Lord Mayors from the entire region. Here is one of the entries in the book made that night by a grateful member of the Mayoral teams:

Excuse me on this occasion but foregoing entries are so good that I feel I cannot improve. One thing I can do is to give my testimony to a good game of football in the match
Dick Kerr's Ladies
v
Lyons Ladies
at Manchester Nov 23/21
at which £500 was raised for Manchester's adopted town of Megicies devastated by the
Great War 1914–1918

WA

Doesn't that say it all about what these women were doing? And doesn't it make Football Girl look like a spiteful little cow (or bull)? And this is Alfred Frankland's entry for the

same night, showing his twinkling humour in the light of
the increasingly barbed comments about women footballers
expressed by the football referee, John Lewis, in his weekly
column in the *Lancashire Daily Post*:

> To our Miss Woods
> Allow me to thank you for all your great work for our
> Team. You have at all times conducted yourselves in
> such a manner as to bring Credit upon yourself and
> your great Team which we are so proud to belong to,
> John Lewis being an exception.
> > A Frankland
> > Hon Sec
> > & May you live long and die happy

We would all wish that for Alice, wouldn't we? Apparently
not. The night of the long knives was about to begin.
'Football Girl', John Lewis, 'Miriam' and others were
now permitted to speak because Dick, Kerr's Ladies had
become successful, and there's nothing quite so satisfying to
the British psyche as iconoclasm, providing the iconoclast is
truly conservative and is hitting out at someone who has
'got above' their station in life. Miners, the Mayor of Cork
on hunger strike, the girls who served behind the counter in
John Lewis's stores, and the Dick, Kerr's Ladies – who did
they think they were?

The anti-women's-football voices were loud and proud in
the North East, which might surprise those who sketch
everything north of Watford as the North. The North East,
despite its similarity in industrialisation and poverty to the
North West, has always had a different attitude to its

women, a macho quality, a tendency to downgrade and downplay 'the missus'. This is in direct contrast to the Lancashire John Willy tradition of George Formby Senior. Lancashire is famous for its matriarchal society, the influence on the family being through the mother, despite the apparent domination of men in mining communities. Big Lancashire women have always been seen as the power in the county, the men hen-pecked and fearful, but that's an exaggeration of what is actually a form of mutual respect and a refusal to conform. It's that dissident tradition. Men and women just rely on each other, much as the women of Dick, Kerr's relied on the management and Alfred Frankland and Preston North End to help them out. And as for the men, they actually refuse to see why their women should be of less value than they are.

My father was typical of St Helens' men in refusing to conform to a stereotype in my upbringing. For him, I was a person, not a girl. From the moment I was able to under-stand the concept of games, I was taught to play rugby, because that was the game my father coached. Every Satur-day I stood with him on the terraces watching the Saints. Most summer days I played cricket, with the boys. I spent my summer holidays at our caravan bare-chested until I was thirteen. When my mother intervened in my upbringing and sent me to ballroom-dancing lessons when I was twelve, it was only because my cousin Mike was going and had no one to dance with. My father never saw me as vulnerably female, and habitually smacked me across the head with the back of his hand, until when I was fifteen. I said to him, as a friend and fellow ironist, 'Go on, show what a big man you are, hit a woman!' and he laughed with me and realized that it might not be appropriate. Most of my friends were boys and most of us girls were regarded as 'one of the lads' who could sink a pint or two. I was brought up to think of men as my equals and good trustworthy pals, as Lily and Alice were, and I'm still confused when some men treat me as less or more than that, and believe that as a woman I'll have a hidden agenda and be manipulative, because this is the way 'women' are supposed to operate. We don't have those hang-ups in St Helens. We're as direct and dissident as our men. St Helens created the wysiwyg woman before the acronym. I never met sexism in any form until I left home and went to university, and was always confused about why feminism was necessary until I saw and was amazed by male chauvinism in action, in my early twenties.

Therefore the refusal in 1921 of the directors of Newcastle United to allow women to book St James's Park again for their matches is beyond my understanding, and why they, and other members of the Football Association, should have complained and complained again and again about women's football bewilders me. Just what was their problem? The women of the North East were as good as the Lancashire women in supporting their men through the miners' lockouts, putting on football matches to raise funds for food. And there were some truly outstanding and keen players in the North East, like Winnie McKenna. But in Newcastle their man wouldn't back them all the way, as Alfred Frankland backed and respected his women's team. Just look at his entry in Alice's autograph book again and see his insistence on solidarity – 'your great Team which we are all so proud to belong to.'

The Football Association listened hard to the complaints, and decided that it was time for some strong-arm tactics. In October 1921 it laid down a rule that no football club in the

Association should allow their ground to be used for women's football unless it was prepared to handle all the cash transactions and do the full accounting.

That edict alone implied that there might be some fraudulent jiggery-pokery going on in women's football, and that those who organized it might be less than honest. I'm sure that suggestion must have gone down well with the Mayors and Aldermen who arranged the matches, and with Harry Weldon. And Dick Whittington.

The voices which had been raised against women's football grew even louder after this. The forces of conservative good began to do something to stem the tide of liberal generosity flowing only from the weaker sex, so in London, the men's clubs decided to show willing and arrange a series of charity matches, just to prove their hearts were in the right places. In 1921. What a shame no one had thought to do that earlier.

For a while the women of Lancashire held their breath. The Manchester game had been played at the City Ground under the new ruling, but no one had done anything wrong, surely? Look at how they'd been thanked for raising the cash.

The Football Association, too, held its breath, and wondered whether to make its feelings properly known to Alice Woods and Lily Parr and the other Lancashire lasses who were threatening its authority. And then it decided that enough was enough.

On 5 December 1921, at the behest of some of its members, particularly those in the North East, and following its own gut feeling, the Football Association issued the following decree:

Complaints having been made as to football being played by women, the Council feel impelled to express their strong opinion that the game of football is quite unsuitable for females and ought not to be encouraged.

Complaints have been made as to the conditions under which some of these matches have been arranged and played, and the appropriation of the receipts to other than Charitable objects.

The Council are further of the opinion that an excessive proportion of the receipts are absorbed in expenses and an inadequate percentage devoted to Charitable objects.

For these reasons the Council requests the clubs belonging to the Association refuse the use of their grounds for such matches.

In effect, the FA said that in future women's football should not be played on a decent football pitch which was used by any affiliated team – and every football team in the country was affiliated. It also made it impossible for any FA-related official to referee or act as linesman at any women's football match. The Football Association was effectively banning women's football. Kicking it out.

And where to begin to dissect the collection of uncorroborated gossip, scurrilous whispers, and unreconstructed male chauvinism in its statement? From what we have learned about these ladies, and some of the men who supported and encouraged them how could anyone suggest that they'd done anything even remotely reprehensible? And more to the point, how could the beautiful game be under the jurisdiction of an Association so childishly vindictive that it could say, in effect. 'If we're not winning the game we're taking the ball home'? This Association had been formed to decide on rules and regulations and to set up templates for games. It had overseen professional and amateur football from its origins fifty years earlier. It was the body set up to disseminate the British attitude to its sport which all other nations looked up to – fair play. That's what Baron de Coubertin wanted to aspire to. It fuelled his own notions of a world fraternity of sportsmen bound by the loftiest ethics handed down from a phoney Hellenistic ideal. It was Britain alone, according to Coubertin – and Sir Henry Newbolt – which could show the way to fulfilling every man's moral duty.

> There's a breathless hush in the Close to-night –
> Ten to make and the match to win –
> A bumping pitch and a blinding light,
> An hour to play, and the last man in.
> And it's not for the sake of a ribboned coat.
> Or the selfish hope of a season's fame,
> But his Captain's hand on his shoulder smote –
> 'Play up! Play up! And play the game!'

> This is the word that year by year,
> While in her place the school is set,
> Every one of her sons must hear
> And none that hears it dare forget.
> This they all with joyful mind
> Bear through life like a torch in flame
> And falling fling to the host behind –
> 'Play up! Play up! And play the game!'

So what happened to the women in this glorious fair-play ethic? Why is it only sons and men? According to Newbolt and Coubertin and the Football Association, women didn't count. According to my dad and St Helens, we do.

So let me unpick the fabric of untruths created by the Association set up to protect the game. First, that football was an unsuitable game for women. Throughout history, as I've said repeatedly, women had played it. It's hardly a contact sport. But the FA brought out its tame doctors to verify that, in fact, football did terrible things to women's bodies. Mr Eustace Miles had a scientific reason for believing this, or so he said – 'The kicking is too jerky a movement for women and the strain is likely to be severe.' So are we to assume that women's bodies are unsuited to jerky movements? That's put paid to sex, hasn't it?

Thank goodness for the wisdom of a lady doctor, Dr Mary Lowry, called in to watch the game being played by the Dick, Kerr's Ladies: 'From what I saw, football is no more likely to cause injuries to women than a heavy day's washing.' Or a day on the pit brow, washing and grading coal. Or a day filling shells with TNT. And this is the view put forward by Dr Elizabeth Sloan Chesser – 'Women should be allowed to choose their own psyche. If football will make a woman a better citizen, then let her play it. A woman should be free to choose.' Most women can't choose their class or gender, both of which help determine their psyche, but Dr Elizabeth was on the right lines.

I wonder if the Football Association would have had the nerve to dictate what was or was not suitable for women to Lady Florence Dixie or Nettie Honeyball or the Duchesse d'Uzes? Or to a lady tennis player, or one who rode to hounds? Or to Alice Milliat, who was a rower? What the

Football Association actually meant was that it was an unsuitable game for certain women because their class determined that they should go back home and procreate (without jerking) to provide a workforce for the future, which could also be locked out of their jobs or left unprovided-for when they returned wounded from another Great War. There was no medical reason whatsoever why the game of football was unsuitable for women. 'Jerky movement' just doesn't quite hit the correct note of scientific infallibility. But here is a wonderful riposte from the Letters page of the *Daily Herald* in December, from a woman calling herself Centre Forward. I couldn't have done better myself.

I am not sure if I'm a womanly woman and I can't ask George Robey because we haven't been introduced. But I do like a man to be a man. I should not like him nearly so much if he were an elephant or a dromedary or anything like that. I like him to be manly. I cannot bear to see a clean-limbed Englishman in immaculate flannels stand about in a field doing nothing, sometimes for hours and hours, while he might be brightening cricket up and at the same time toning up his virility by wrestling. And why does the 'referee' wear spotless white linen and blow a whistle instead of rolling in the mud or hacking somebody? He might be a womanly woman. And it reduces me to despair when I see a man playing the violin. Why doesn't he bash somebody over the head with it to prove he is a man?

Cannot the rot be stopped in our nation's manhood? There is a way but so revolutionary that no other paper would, I am sure, print it. Why not leave the men to decide what's manly and what isn't?

I am afraid, however, that this is a very silly suggestion or, of course, the FA would have thought of it.

That is pure St Helens' skitting.

But, strangely, several people were uncomfortable, not
about women playing football, but about them playing
football in public. Lady headmistresses in Newcastle felt
strongly about this. The headmistress of the Central High
School for girls said, 'Men attended these football games
because they were novel and provided them with amusement, and that was objectionable.' Presumably if the
matches had not been entertaining, it would have been
acceptable? But the headmistress of the other Newcastle
girls' school has a more interesting view. 'I have no objection to girls playing football in the school playground.
Football played in public, however, encourages betting,
and it is on this ground that I object. Hockey and tennis
are far more suitable for girls. I would not let my girls play
football on any account in public.'

As well as being totally illogical – would she object to the
building of Blackpool Pier because it might have slot
machines on it? – that is a far more obvious class-based
objection. Betting at matches, as I've said, was not wide-
spread but was very much a mining and working-class
occupation. In fact in St Helens betting was so much a
way of life for the miners who drank at one pub, that the
publican arranged different contests for them – who would
be the first to speak, to sip their pint, to say yes, or no – with
forfeits taken from the loser. These forfeits, collected in a
jar, would pay for an annual trip to Blackpool for the
miners. The headmistress was merely showing her class bias
in objecting to side-betting, although it has to be said that

women's football, with its difficult-to-predict scorelines, as opposed to professional men's games, would provide far more interesting odds. All the ingrained class prejudices could finally be aired by those who were seeking, in the post-war backlash, to re-establish their position as natural leaders and moral arbiters, even though their arguments lacked logic or reason. 'It's right (or wrong) because we say so, and we know best' has never cut any ice with St Helens' dissidence, and never will.

And the same bias shows in the argument put forward by the Football Association that some of the money may not have gone to Charitable objects. Presumably they had heard about the 'peasoup' matches played in some pit-villages, and presumably this wasn't a Charitable object they approved of, so they reclassified the feeding of miners as non-charitable? This brings a whole new meaning to Neuro-Linguistic Programming.

What about their arguments that the expenses were too high? From the notebooks kept by Herbert Stanley, and from reports in the newspapers, we know that between £28 and £38 was taken from the profits of every match – for both teams. I've said before, but it bears repeating that this amount genuinely did no more than cover the cost of laundry, transport, pay in lieu and staffing – although what the FA would have thought about the provision of Lily's 100 Woodbines (37 pence) on Herbert Stanley's expenses' list, we can only speculate.

At no time during the four years of Dick, Kerr's charitable efforts did any money go missing, nor was any siphoned off. Herbert Stanley recorded all profits where the sum taken was passed over to Dick, Kerr's for their distribution to Preston. He didn't record, because he didn't know, all the amounts taken at matches organized by individual cities for the relief of their local poor. Nor did he record the takings at matches where Dick, Kerr's were the 'away' side. These takings went directly to the charities sponsored by the 'home' side, like St Helens Ladies, which in a little over twelve months of being understudies and bridesmaids to Dick, Kerr's raised £2,000 for St Helens charities alone.

But there was something in the wording from the FA which may have passed most of us by. It didn't pass Alfred Frankland by. He asked why the FA had thought fit to question the fact that the Ladies were often treated to a meal by the host city or club, given that professional footballers were often accorded this same provision after travelling long distances. And that, as Alfred Frankland so acutely noticed, was exactly what the FA was objecting to. The dos. The Bonnington. All the ranting about expenses and some things not being Charitable objects was a veiled reference to the dinners, pierrot shows, speeches and dances, and an occasional night in a decent hotel, which followed the matches played by the Ladies, the cost of which would have been set against profits from the games.

And why not, we'd ask in Lancashire? The whole point of football, the whole point of life for a Lancashire lass, was and is elation. The games of football were a celebration of their exuberance, and the after-match dos were an essential part of that exuberance. The FA didn't want to foot the bill.

But they weren't footing the bill. In fact, the FA had done sweet FA about the plight of the poor, and had made a profit from leasing out its grounds. That the FA saw fit to question how much money was being spent on sherries and milk stouts and over-cooked beef and tinned-peach trifle was a bit rich since, as Alfred Frankland also pointed out without the women there would have been no charity money for the FA to call to account. Nothing.

The Newcastle United directors, however, were giving their heartfelt thanks that women's football had at last been given the boot.

The game of football is not a woman's game and though it was permitted on professional grounds as a novelty arising out of women's participation in war work and as a novelty with charitable motives. The time has come when the novelty has worn off and the charitable motives are being lost sight of, so that the use of the professionals' ground is rightly withdrawn. The women's games have developed into commercial concerns and the expenses they reckon it would cost to play would not have left much for charity.

It is questionable whether Mr Frank Walt, the secretary of Newcastle United who made the above statement, actually knew what the word 'commercial' meant. It means when the money earned by something goes back into the pockets of those who run the business, and the motive is profit. At least that's how most of us define commercial. Try applying that word to the match held at St James's Park when the Newcastle Ladies met Dick, Kerr's. The match earned £1,200 for the city of Newcastle. And on 8 December 1921 three days after the Football Association banned women's football and the macho men of Newcastle United's Board of Directors applauded, the Newcastle War Relief Committee announced that unless further charity was received by the Fund, they would have to immediately halve

the amount of relief distributed to Disabled and Unemployed ex-servicemen.

From their formation until the FA announcement, Dick,
Kerr's Ladies had raised over £60,000 for charity, and the
same amount had been raised by all the other women's
clubs combined. That's, in total for the years 1918 to 1921,
£120,000, or, in today's reckoning, 24 million pounds. And
the FA? I think we can safely call the scoreline 24 million to
nil.

Liverpool, unlike Newcastle, was angry, and so it should
have been. In the two matches played for the city at the end
of 1920 and the beginning of 1921, Dick, Kerr's had raised
£4,350 (£870,000) for Liverpool charities, even after the
expenses of the bun fights, processions, pantomine seats
and fancy dress and Lily's Woodbines had been deducted by
the grateful Mayors. And Major Cecil Kent, of Liverpool, a
former football club secretary, sent the following letter to
the FA, which was read out at their meeting.

I may mention that in present and past seasons I have
watched about 30 ladies' football matches between
various teams and I have met the players. I have
travelled with them frequently by road and rail and
I have attended the various functions to which they
have been invited, and I have met the local Lord
Mayors and also the officials of the local charities
and football clubs concerned. On all sides I have heard
nothing but praise for the good work the girls are
doing and the high standard of their play. The only
thing I now hear from the man in the street is 'Why
have the FA got their knife into girls' football? What
have the girls done except raise large sums for charity

and play the game? Are their feet heavier on the turf than the men's feet?'

And as soon as his letter was read out, the FA read out their ban. Cecil Kent's plea had made no difference to their decision. So why did they make it?

Certainly, it wasn't for the reasons they gave. That football is a dangerous game for women is obviously ludicrous. Why, even those tiny mademoiselles from France could play the game without suffering the ill-effects of 'jerky movements'. That expenses had been fiddled is a non-argument, something about which the FA knew nothing as they had never tried to raise money for charity – although they probably resented the likes of Lily Parr being instructed in the art of peeling a grape by the illustrious Colonel Sée, and allowed to sit down to tea with the luscious Ella Retford. Lily Parr was a non-Charitable object if ever they'd seen one. But no, the fiddling of expenses was just a rumour which was a straw to which they clung. In fact, all three of their reasons maliciously played to the prejudices of the Establishment.

For the FA, the psychological reason was that women's football was something they were powerless to control. It had sprung up as a spontaneous expression of free-spiritedness by the lower orders, in a totally different way from that in which men's football had developed. Men's football had initially been a game for gentlemen which had only later, after its control by the FA, turned into a rough-house performed for the working classes by the working classes, which they and they alone paid to see while the owners and investors pocketed the proceeds. This was the natural 'All Things Bright And Beautiful' order of things, in which the rich man in his castle and the poor man at his gate were arranged neatly by the Deity who chose to make each of them either high or lowly. It behoved the rich man to teach the poor man about rules and manners and fair play because these were things that the rich knew all about, as they had the leisure time to develop decency and the cash to buy it. But in women's football there were very few rich men, just a lot of common factory women. There was no League structure, no hierarchy, no fees paid to accountants, no skimming off dividends, no affiliation to a professional body. Women's football was random and organic, and its popularity suggested that people other than those selected by virtue of their birth could do something noble, fair, generous and joyful. It was out of control, and it was a bad example to set the nation as a whole, which was already rebelling against the old power structures.

But psychological reasons apart, women's football was doing football itself a commercial disservice. And this was the immediate and uglier truth, which was why the secretary of Newcastle United made that Freudian slip of mentioning commerce. If women's football, which had shifted slightly from its factory roots and begun to establish itself as a sporting means of raising huge sums of money for charity, were to continue, how long would it be before the man in the street, to quote Cecil Kent, and the woman on the London omnibus, the London clippie, started to ask – where does the money raised in men's football go to?

Lily, Alice and their like, and their male friends like Alfred Frankland, had managed to operate on a shoe-string, hiring football grounds and filling them, had paid nothing for publicity, had no huge Board of Directors, and had even played Internationals on both sides of the Channel, and were becoming media stars. And in the process, this tiny shifting power-base made up of clubs which formed and disbanded had raised the equivalent of £24 million for charity over four years. So? If they could give this kind of money away from this small, co-operative and fluid organization, just how much money was going through the turnstiles of professional football every week, and whose pockets was it lining now that Entertainment Tax had been abolished? Not the poor's. Not even the government's to help out the poor. In fact, it could be said to be a means of bleeding the poor even drier, as they formed the bulk of the spectators. It's worth thinking about. And the FA had thought about it. This was the reason women's football had to be stopped. The FA wasn't primarily opposed to women playing football, even though they were old-fogeyish enough to take a scandalised stance when it suited them: what they were really opposed to was anyone playing football for charity on a huge international scale, and thus demonstrating how easy it was to make money out of the professional game.

And that was the chief reason Alice and Lily weren't ever again allowed to run out into the roar of the big Deepdale crowd, to kick in on that famous ground, stand on the charmed circle like their heroes, surrounded by thousands of fanatical supporters singing their names, singing 'She's a Lassie From Lancashire', and cheering every magic pass, every brilliantly struck goal, every searing tackle. Class and control were factors, but commerce was the main reason the FA took the crowds out of women's football, and denied the girls the hugeness of their athletic dreams and the adoration of millions.

Sir Frederick Wall, who was the chairman of the Football Association which imposed the ban in 1921 said in his memoirs:

We are the guardians of the game, but our zeal as trustees must not over-ride our sense of justice and our responsibility to the public. We must always do our duty without fear or favour and retain the confidence of the public. That is the spirit in which all inquiries and commissions have been conducted and the basis of all findings.

Tell that to the girls of Dick, Kerr's, Sir Frederick, and ask them if they can see a sense of justice and responsibility to the public (which includes women as well as men) in the action taken by the FA on 5 December 1921.

And tell it to their daughters and granddaughters, too. Because I saved the best till last. Here's the punch-line, which comes in the true tradition of Lancashire music hall, after the music.

> You might forget the gas and shells, Parley-voo,
> You might forget the gas and shells, Parley-voo,
> You might forget the groans and yells
> But you'll never forget the mademoiselles,
>   Hinky, dinky, parley-voo.
>
> Mademoiselle from Armentières, Parley-voo?
> Mademoiselle from Armentières, Parley-voo?
> Just blow your nose, and dry your tears
> We'll all be back in a few short years.
>   Hinky, dinky, parley-voo

That ban on women playing football on any ground under FA jurisdiction remained in place for the next 50 years.

Six

Uncle Sam's Soccer

If the FA's decision took Alice, Lily and Dick, Kerr's by the throat and shook them into what it hoped would be total surrender, it also took Meg Foster with them.

Meg Foster was a trail-blazer cut from the same fabric as the Preston girls, as she was the very first football heroine to find her way on to the bookshelves, appearing just in time to hear the FA tell her that she wasn't wanted. For some time, Amalgamated Press had published a series of fourpenny novelettes about footballers, and in 1921 the comic-book publishers, realising that women's football was becoming a force to be reckoned with, commissioned a series of books featuring girl footballers, to set beside those about men. It seemed to be a shrewd move at the time. Women tend to read more than men, and the novels about women's football could play on the successes of various 'heroine' serials currently showing at local cinemas – *The Perils of Pauline* had been going down a storm since 1914. Apparently vulnerable but secretly tough women are every writer's and every man's dream. And so the fictional Meg Foster was born, to immediate popularity.

Meg lived and worked in a mill town, and it was her determination and feistiness which set up her factory's football team. Naturally there were pantomime villains, who are much easier to write if they're men embittered by the fact that the woman they fancy won't look at them – as Meg's villain was. There's the 'Ugly Duckling' character, in this case a tiny factory girl called Titch, who is the butt of the factory jokes until, one day, she stands in for the absent goalie and proves to be the finest goalkeeper the team has ever seen. The writer must have been impressed by the tiny French goalkeeper Ourry. There's the wicked woman, the absent goalie who is jealous of Meg and plots to bring the team to its knees, but fails because of the secret brilliance of the Ugly Duckling, and there's the love-interest, in this case the son of the factory owner. It's a wonderful novelette, with much heftiness, much rolling-up of sleeves, and a continual refrain of, 'Well, we'll see about that! No one's going to put one over on us girls!' Even when there's trouble down at t'mill.

Naturally, writers being mostly men, there were credibility gaps in the story – lady referees for instance – and a League with knock-out cup runs which were what men's football was all about, but not women's. But in many ways, *Meg Foster, Footballer* was the future of women's football as dreamed up by the media. On the last page of this piece of tough frippery was an advertisement for the next book, *Captain Meg*, due out in the middle of December. After the FA ban. The further commissioned novels duly appeared after *Captain Meg* – *Bess of Blacktown* and *Nell of Newcastle*. But by 1922, sales were reflecting the turmoil into which the ban had thrown the women's game.

Inevitably, at Dick, Kerr's, there was the obligatory

sleeve-rolling, and the pragmatic Northern spirit which refuses to take no for an answer. The Ladies rescheduled their big post-Christmas game against Fleetwood from Deepdale to Ashton Park, and invited a group of doctors to be in the 3,000-strong capacity crowd and give their opinions about the suitability of football to women's bodies after the match. Lily wasn't particularly interested in what the doctors had to say: she was a five foot ten woman fed on black pudding, and more than a match for a five foot five St Helens man with TB or black gums or asbestosis or pneumonoconiosis. She just revelled in the fact that she could at least have her Christmas run-out, and score goals, which she duly did. The medical opinion, as suspected, backed up the girls' assertions that football wasn't damaging their tender frames, and the following day, playing St Helens at New Brighton in front of a crowd of 7,000 on a festival pitch which wasn't affiliated to the FA, Alice Woods got her goals, and her own satisfaction. The St Helens girls had shown what they thought of the FA in their own inimitable style. Members of the FA panel had been invited to attend this game, but apparently found that they had been booked to appear elsewhere on that date.

Alice needed the boost of goal-scoring. The FA hadn't merely got its knife into her, but into her brother, John. John had been talked into playing a game of Rugby League, at the behest of his girlfriend, and had been paid to make up a team on a day when the squad in his girlfriend's home town had been hit by flu. It was against FA laws for a professional footballer to play a different game for money, and John had lost his career. The FA banned John, just as it had banned his sister. Neither of them was given leave to appeal.

Meetings of the women footballers and their committees were called throughout the next few months as they tried to set up their own Leagues, but it was impossible. The plain fact was, as Lancashire and the North East showed in their conflicting ways, that unless those with experience of the game, men, were willing to support and encourage these relative novices, and take over the organization until they'd trained their female successors and the women officials who could run the lines or referee, there could be no sustainable future for a game which had developed in a haphazard manner in response to a national need for charity funds. And although teams like Dick, Kerr's and St Helens, Hay's Brewery and the Atalanta club, which had their own factory grounds or a municipal facility, could go on playing, saddled by the ban on playing the big grounds they would never raise the monies they'd managed to raise before. Ashton Park had a capacity of 3,000. Goodison Park, as we know, had a capacity of 53,000. Meg Foster and her kind had lost. That was all there was to it.

'Football Girl', who had been negative, to say the least, about the game she was purportedly reporting, disappeared. She was the author of her own demise, continually telling her readers that charity football matches had had their day, and that it was time to organize Leagues.

As far as I can see there are two alternatives. The first is that inter-club matches be abandoned altogether, each club having two teams of its own and playing privately: the other is that matches be arranged to take place between neighbouring clubs on the practice ground of one of the clubs.

'Football Girl' never had quite understood what women's football was about. To Lily and Alice it was showbiz and razzle-dazzle, posh frocks and milk stout, music hall and pantomime, fun and Blackpool, running hot water and pink soap all wrapped up. Take that element away, put the girls in some corner playing in front of one pensioner and her Jack Russell, and what's the point of having heft? Those who work hard need to play hard, and need to perform for and delight others – as big a sing-songing crowd as possible. What comes out of Lancashire is always thus. It's the Gracie Fields effect, and Gracie, born above a chip shop in Rochdale just one year before Alice Woods, would have approved of the girls' decision not to be shoehorned into a recreation ground in the shade of Billinge Lump. The team had bigger plans than that. They had been to France and had been inspired further by the big dreams of Alice Milliat, who was currently stepping up her own battle for women to come out of the closet and star on their own stage, whatever stage that might be.

For Alice Milliat it was the Pershing Stadium. In 1921 she'd been encouraged in her efforts to start a women's international athletics movement after successfully holding an International women's meet at Monte Carlo. In 1922, as the Dick, Kerr's Ladies were planning their next move, she came up with the biggest idea she'd ever had. She booked the Pershing Stadium, the scene of the pitch invasion at the match between Dick, Kerr's and France, and staged the first fully supported International women's track-and-field meet.

It was an audacious move, and one in the eye for Baron de Coubertin (although he and his committee had her remove the name 'Olympics' from this women's event).

Nevertheless, that's how it was regarded by the press and the 20,000 spectators who packed into the stadium to watch the finals stages of the meet. There would be teams from Germany, Czechoslovakia, Switzerland, Great Britain and France, and for the first time in its history the USA sent a team of women athletes. All were very much the products of the well-to-do families who could afford to sponsor their well-educated and well-trained children to attend and compete. And in today's terms, most of them *were* children, Lily's age – 16-year-old kids like Maybelle Gilliland and Elizabeth Stein let loose on their first transatlantic voyage on the *Aquitania*. There was little Kathryn Agar, who didn't make it into the finals but who describes the excitement of just being there, in Paris, at her first athletics meet:

Last night we just stuffed ourselves with cake and candy and stayed out as late as the chaperons would permit. Just imagine fifteen peppy young American girls going to bed at 9 o'clock every night in training for that Olympiad, and not eating sweets more than once a month. We didn't think it was possible, but we felt wonderful.

The team from Britain was mostly made up from the newly-formed London Olympiades, whose members were graduates of various London polytechnics, not the likes of Molly Walker, Alice Woods and Jennie Harris, who might have welcomed the chance to show off their athletics' skills at international level. Nevertheless, the graduates did Britain proud, with Nora Callebout winning gold in the 100 yards – in the same recorded time as Alice Woods' North of England record – and Mary Lines

174

winning the 300 metres and long jump, and Hilda Hatt the high jump. Britain won the meet, with the USA second, thanks to a gold medal in hurdles from 19-year-old Camille Sabie. Another member of the British team was the legendary Sophie Eliott-Lynn from County Limerick, who shares my grandfather William's Irish surname, and who helped found the Women's Amateur Athletic Association in 1922, and went on to become a leading aviator. The French girl who won Bronze to Camille Sabie's Gold in the 100-yards hurdles was Geneviève Laloz, Alice Woods' good friend, and the girl whose occupation was listed in the newspapers as 'machine-minder'. So she can stand in for those from Dick, Kerr's, who were deprived of their chance to compete at this high level because of the accident of their birth.

But there was something that even factory girls could do to retain their star status, despite the machinations of the Football Association. They could tour America.

It was a thought which had occurred to the team management back in 1921, but had been put on the back-burner because of the constraints of a packed schedule. With women's teams now rethinking their status, the fixture list was decimated in 1922, and there was only the annual tour from the French Ladies, in March, to provide a touch of the glamour which brightened their lives. So the idea of a tour through North America was resurrected, and passed by the committee with the same wilful optimism that had carried the team through to international glory. The combination of pragmatism and excess, they hoped, might just work again, but there was also a touch of naivety in this latest plan. It reminds me very much of the Marriott Edgar-penned monologues, which all capture perfectly this

Lancashire trait of reaching for the impossible on a whim, and a wing and a prayer.

> I'll tell of the Battle of Hastings,
> As 'appened in days long gone by,
> When Duke William became King of England,
> And 'Arold got shot in the eye.
>
> It were this way – one day in October
> The Duke, who were allus a toff
> Having no battles on at the moment,
> Had given his lads a day off.
>
> They'd all taken boats to go fishing,
> When some chap in t' Conqueror's ear
> Said 'Let's go and put breeze up t' Saxons.'
> Said Bill – 'By gum, that's an idea.'
>
> Then turning around to his soldiers,
> He lifted his big Norman voice,
> Shouting – 'Hands up who's coming to England!'
> That was swank, 'cos they hadn't no choice.

This is one of my favourite recitations, performed at family parties and on talent shows at Happy Valley on Llandudno's Great Orme, and contains my favourite Lancashire phrase – 'By gum, that's an idea!' And perhaps America wasn't such a bad idea.

Many of the factory workers in Lancashire had relatives in the weaving and spinning mill-towns of Rhode Island and Massachusetts. As the textile industry died in Lancashire it took new roots in the countries which produced the cotton crop. For years workers had been emigrating from Lancashire's unemployment to the new opportunities across the Atlantic, and sending letters home about the new lives they'd made for themselves in the home of the brave. Most of the Preston women had some relative who had settled on the north-eastern seaboard. Some of them had family in Canada, where the immigration policies were attracting young British factory workers to swell the population. And the port of Liverpool was one of the biggest exporters of human cargo to North America, with its daily sailings to New York, Quebec and Montreal.

And this is where, in the tradition of the fourpenny novelettes, the two inept but superficially convincing shysters appear. These are the men with the apparent know-how who are supposedly working in the hero's best interests. They are the men who sell the goose which lays the golden eggs or the beans which they exchange for a cow, and everyone in the audience knows that our leading man, or woman, has been led astray, not by the forces of evil, but by someone who knows much more about the workings of the world than they appear to, and that it will all come right in the end because good always triumphs over the used-car salesman and the real-estate agent. So, meet those who claimed that they could organize this tour, and had the contacts to do it: Abe Zelickman and David Brooks, who swore that they could pull off the deal to arrange a Dick, Kerr's tour of Canada and the USA.

Had this been anywhere but Lancashire, these two would never have been entrusted with the task of negotiating a fixture list, arranging the finances, sorting out accommodation, and doing the necessary PR for the job. Let's look at each of these men in turn, and try to understand why it's only in the land of the naive at loose in a big city that their vaunted skills would get beyond the selection committee.

Abe was slightly out of his depth, and quite honestly, he never made any pretensions to being anything other than a clothes' salesman from Brooklyn. The Zelickman family was originally from Russia but had settled in England in the late nineteenth century. They were Jewish tailors who chose Sheffield as their refuge from Russian anti-semitism and political crisis, and were hard-working and ambitious. Abraham, born in Sheffield, was more ambitious than most, and as a young teenager emigrated again, this time to the USA, where his family skills and determined nature led him into the textile business as a salesman. He had been keen on football in Sheffield, and soon became involved with the game of soccer in his newly adopted country and city, New York. With many in the Russian émigré population he settled in Brooklyn, and was an influential member of the organising committee of his local football team.

How he met Alfred Frankland, or came into contact with the Dick, Kerr's Ladies, is a mystery, but may have something to do with Alfred's previous contacts in tailoring in Preston, as Abraham travelled to Europe to sell American manufacture to a depressed British market. Perhaps he was someone in Alfred's contact book, and perhaps the mutual love of football drew them together. He may even have exaggerated his influence in the fledgling sport of soccer in the USA, where it was always a minority interest. Soccer was played by college boys or working-class European immigrants, and was never regarded as an 'American' sport, like the other British-exported sports, rounders (baseball), and Rugby (American football).

So this is the first of our two organizers, a man with little influence in a minority sport, but a well-intentioned man, who genuinely wanted this tour to work out, and who would work for nothing to make it happen.

The second man, David Brooks, was more problematic. All we know about him is in Herbert Stanley's records, so if I question his motives, Herbert is to blame, not me. And yes, Herbert did go on the tour to the USA as Alfred's sidekick, missing out on weeks of salary to have this trip, and to be close to Alice.

Herbert implies that 'David' Brooks' Christian name wasn't David at all, and that he wasn't English, but Irish. Herbert tells us that Brooks, who was officially in charge of the tour, was a famous footballer who represented his country internationally, and was centre forward and captain of a North of England football club in the year before the tour. It's possible that the man referred to as David was actually Ned Brooks, who played for several Irish teams before spending a season as captain and centre forward for Stockport County, and who left Stockport at the start of the 1922–23 season, went missing for a while, then reappeared in Ireland.

He may have been Ned, or he may have been someone else, but there's no denying that this man had more than his fair helping of blarney. He was, as grandmother Polly would say, 'fawse as a ferret'. According to Herbert, he had a hidden motivation for leading the tour to Canada and the USA – the impossibility of Irish divorce. Brooks left behind a wife and family who may never have known about his secret mission to disappear to North America. Can we trust what Herbert tells us about him? Perhaps. But we also know that Herbert had a wicked sense of humour, which was the reason Alice Woods, at first reluctant, had been slowly falling in love with him. And he had a wonderfully inventive streak, and was a brilliant raconteur. So Herbert may have invented this story to amuse the woman he loved. However, it does fit the facts, and we'll allow Herbert the benefit of the doubt, and allow ourselves to be amused by the antics of the wild and devastatingly handsome young Irishman, Mr Brooks.

We have only to look at the fixture list and the itinerary of the North American tour to realize that this tour was arranged by either a madman or a man with a romantic soul but little perception of geography or the constraints of time. The tour was to start in Quebec, the disembarkation point, and then proceed to New Jersey, the Eastern seaboard, New York, back to the Eastern seaboard, then Washington, Philadelphia, Detroit, Ackron (Ohio), St Louis, Chicago, Pittsburgh, Baltimore and back to Edmonton, Toronto, Ottawa and Montreal in Canada. Find an atlas and follow that route with a piece of string, and when you have you'll discover that you've made a cat's cradle. It's impossible. The tour was to start two days after arriving in Quebec, on 24 September, and finish sometime towards the end of November. The return journey was not yet finalised by the time the Ladies, shrieking and giggling and playing up for the cameras on the deck of their liner, the *Montclare*, were preparing for the biggest adventure of their lives.

It's a shambles, but it's wonderful, and that must have been exactly the mood in which Alice and Lily, in another new set of home-made outfits, kicked a football to each other and the rest of the team, and posed holding lifebelts on deck, prior to departure. Goodness knows what the sensible Parisienne Carmen Pomies, now the regular goal-keeper of the team, must have thought of it all. But she'd come to Lancashire for all the fun of the fair, and this helter-skelter of a tour must have seemed to her to be just the antidote to a life of formality sobriety and mourning in postwar France. One of the things she'd learnt in Lancashire was allus to keep looking on the bright side, and refuse to be put off by negatives, just like Tommy Thompson's Owd Thatcher:

> 'Don't thee preich at me. Ah don't apologise for meself an' Ah don't need anybody else to apologise for me. My past is one o' high endeavour an' no heeltaps. Yours is full o' inhibitions. Don't do this an' don't do that. Yo' cannot knit a full life o' negatives. If ever Ah get to heaven Ah'll fly theer on positives.'

And there was one thing the lasses noticed as soon as the ship was out of dock and heading for Ireland, while they unpacked in their cabins and went to inspect the dining facilities. It was that, for once, Lily wouldn't be clemmed. 'Clemmed' is starving, and it's one of the most popular words in the Lancashire dialect, because most of us had a life which was characterised by being hungry. I remember being clemmed for most of my childhood, in my case not through grinding poverty, but through postwar rationing, and the high points in my childhood were when I was treated by my grandmother Polly to the rare occasion of a restaurant meal. We'd have roast spring chicken, a luxury usually reserved for Christmas, and then Polly would sit and watch as she insisted on my having the ultimate in self-indulgence, a Knickerbocker Glory, with three different flavours of ice-cream, jelly, tinned Fruit Cocktail, and chocolate sauce. Oh and a swirl of fresh cream on the top. That was the sublime treat, as, in my childhood, cream only came in tins, and that rarely. Food was our obsession and we gave thanks every time we had what was called an adequate sufficiency:

> Bless all on us, Lord, wi' this gradely stuff,
> An' nudge me when ah've 'ad enough.

So Lily and Alice must have been in raptures when they saw the menu on that extraordinary liner, which had only made its corporate maiden voyage on the Liverpool-Quebec route a month before. There was tripe simmered with tomatoes for breakfast, pandering to the tastes of the Liverpool passengers, as well as pancakes and maple syrup. There were between seven and fifteen choices for each course, and, what astounded Herbert and Alice, and something they would report to an incredulous Lancashire, there were little cubes of ice in the drinks. And because this was only the second voyage the ship had made from Liverpool, and the first one in which all the passengers were paying passengers, special events and treats were laid on. There were dances every night, celebratory meals, card-schools where they could play the Lancashire favourites of solo and whist, speeches and lectures – all in all the kind of programme normally reserved for pleasure cruises.

On the first day, however, there was a sombre moment as Alice, supported by Herbert, and many of the other passengers, gathered on deck at the point at which the *Lusitania* had been sunk in May 1915 by a U-Boat torpedo, just south of Queenstown in Ireland. For all the Ladies, this was a chilling reminder of the war which had killed so many of their relatives, and a memory which would stay with Alice for the rest of her life. Although later the *Montclare* passed through the icebergs which sank the *Titanic* and she was upset by that tragedy, it was the story of the *Lusitania* which distressed her deeply, seeing, as she had, the war zone of the Somme battles. For her the *Titanic* was an accident of nature, not an example of the inhumanity of war.

For the next two days the ship was battered by storms. Only Lily Parr had the constitution to appear in the lavishly panelled dining room, claiming to be clemmed, and only little Jennie Harris could maintain her balance as the *Montclare* rode the storm. During those days Herbert, sick to his stomach, spent many hours jangling between retches with his cabin-mate, the mysterious David Brooks, and listening to his stories. Herbert was barely twenty, and David wanted to educate the young man in the ways of the world, spinning him yarns about the number of women he'd had in his life, the way women tended to throw themselves at footballers, and how he, Herbert, should grab some of the action while he could. After all, David pointed out, wasn't this too young for him to be thinking about settling down? Yes, Alice was a good-looking lass, and she was famous, which always helps a man's sense of self-worth, but hadn't he looked round the passengers, and chalked up the one or two who might provide some decent entertainment for a single man on his first big outing in the world?

David had weighed them all up, all the desperate widows, all the likely young girls. He had his eye on a wealthy elderly woman travelling back to her home in Canada. She, David reasoned, would soon fall victim to his charms and help him out.

'Fact is, I don't have a penny piece to bless meself with,' David confessed.

'I'm doing a runner. Had to arrange all this on the quiet, so the missus wouldn't find out.'

'So how're you going to pay your way? And how're you going to find the £25 we need to get through Customs and Immigration? They won't let us through without our stake money.'

'You got yours?' David asked.

Herbert shrugged. He had. Just.

'Lend us a couple of quid, then?' David grinned, smiling like a ferret.

And Herbert did.

David went missing overnight for the next few days, while Herbert did his appointed job, which was to satisfy the other cabin passengers' fan-like adoration of Alice and the Ladies by getting them to sign photographs of the team. The girls were regularly feted by their fellow passengers, drinks were bought for them, and somehow David Brooks was always around to demand a small whisky when there was a round of drinks ordered for the Ladies and their management team. Herbert carried with him a set of photographs that had been specially ordered from a top Preston photographer, showing the girls posing in their new 'England' kit which they'd assumed after the cup final at Goodison Park, and wore when they played against France – white jerseys with a crest topped by a red rose, as well as striped knitted hats, blue shorts and black socks. Lined up in front of a goalmouth the Ladies in the photograph were almost the identical team brought on this tour. Fronted by 17-year-old Lily Parr holding a football, there were Jessie Walmsley, Carmen Pomies, Alice, Florrie Haslam (whom Lily always mistakenly knew as and referred to as Florrie Aslam), Florrie Redford, Alice Kell, Daisy Clayton, Jenny

Harris, and the new girl, Alice Mills, who was almost as tiny as Jenny. Of the girls on the tour only Lily Lee and Molly Walker were missing from the photo, and the newest recruit, May Graham, who had come along as reserve. Each day the Ladies sat with their drinks and cigarettes, autographing more photographs. The First-Class passengers were all given one. Herbert had orders to hand them out to important people.

Then David reappeared. Not that he'd wandered far. In fact, he was seen regularly on deck or at meal-times with his very elderly and very wealthy paramour, who had been entertaining him in her First-Class cabin, and buying his drinks. This reappearance signalled his first tutorial to Herbert. 'Want to see how it's done, Bert?' he winked at him. 'Just follow me out on deck and walk between the rail and the row of cabins, come over when I call you, and I'll teach you a thing or two.'

Herbert duly obeyed, walking where he'd been instructed while David Brooks canoodled at the ship's rail with a woman old enough to be his grandmother and wealthy enough to buy his favours. He watched, as he approached the pair, David extracting from his wallet a photograph of the team, and then he was called over. 'Herbert here will see to it that the Ladies sign this photograph for you, won't you Herbert?' he asked, smiling and winking. 'I'll just sign it first,' and then as he extracted a pen and tried to hold it in the same hand as the wallet, or appeared to, he flicked his wrist deftly, throwing his wallet into the sea.

Herbert, standing where he'd been told, was the only person to have seen the wrist flick. To anyone else watching it would have seemed like a terrible accident. The dismayed widow, several of the crew, a crowd of passengers,

185

summoned by David's stricken cry, 'My wallet!' gathered to watch the empty wallet being swallowed by the waves. David was distraught, it appeared. All his money, his savings for the entire tour, were in that wallet, he explained tearfully to the crowd.

'What am I going to do?' he kept asking. 'How will I get through immigration without my money?'

The Purser, sympathetic and efficient, immediately put his mind at rest, telling him that this was an accident which could happen to anyone, but it was very sad that it had happened to the manager of this renowned team who was about to lead them to victories across the North American continent, but that sir shouldn't worry, as he, the Purser, was sure that something could be done about it.

'How much exactly was there in the wallet, sir?' he enquired.

'A little over fifty pounds,' replied the fawce guy.

And so a collection was taken amongst the First Class passengers for this poor unfortunate, although sadly only £45 could be raised. Herbert, standing incredulously at David's side while the presentation of this sum was made to him, with many apologies that the total was a little lacking, heard David's graciousness as he shrugged off the loss of over £5 from his original worldly goods, and later, in the cabin, was given back his £2. 'It's what you can do with just a little planning and a way with words,' David told him. 'You ought to learn from this, Bert. There's nothing that can't be done, if you know how.'

In telling this story, years later, Herbert Stanley said that for the most plausible rogue, David Brooks took the cake. And it was this plausible rogue who was leading the Dick, Kerr's Ladies tour around the USA, and who had briefed

Abe Zelickman with the pre-publicity which should get them the matches they needed. Which was why, in the cities they travelled to, the Dick, Kerr's Ladies were billed as Newcastle United. Perhaps it was done as people would know the name of Newcastle, and the girls did dress in the same strip, but was it a totally necessary bit of blarney? Perhaps the well-known name of a leading English team had been acquired for financial reasons, because the costs of the tour demanded that any team volunteering to play the Ladies had to be able to guarantee them a fee of $1,000 for each game. That's $20,000 in current terms, £14,000. Or perhaps Brooks or Zelickman had just got it wrong? We have to wonder how much of this cash was going to pay the wages of the worst tour organizers since the lemmings.

But there were more disasters in store when the team disembarked from the ship to find the other half of the Mutt and Jeff team of co-conspirators, Abe Zelickman. Their arrival must have been a: 'Wadda you wanna know – the bad news or the bad news?' There wasn't any other kind of news available. First, there was the cancellation of the entire Canadian leg of the tour. Given a cautionary note by the FA, the Canadian ruling body of football, the Dominion Football Association, decided that women's football should not be allowed. In fact they announced, 'a woman was not built to stand the bruises gotten in playing football' an interesting statement which would have tickled our Lily, as the Newcastle player she was the one on the pitch most likely to be giving out the bruises. Nothing ever stopped her, as Minnie Lyons and her plait could testify. Lily loved Minnie Lyon's plait, which gave her a unique tackling opportunity. She just yanked the plait, pulling the player to the ground. And earlier that year, Dick, Kerr's Ladies had played a match against a men's team at Chorley, and with usual macho pride, the goalkeeper had invited Lily to try to take a penalty against him. The 16-year-old had asked him if he was sure she wanted him to try to do that but the goalkeeper had insisted. Lily had taken the ball, placed it on the spot, and with her usual devastating accuracy and rifle-bullet speed had placed it in the back of the net – along with the goalie. In trying to stop her shot with his arm, he had broken it. The story was already one of the team's great after-dinner anecdotes about their teenage legend.

But the Dominion Football Association had never seen Lily Parr, and rarely seen women's football – just like the FA – and were in no position to judge the fortitude of women's bodies and the tendency of truly athletic women, like the French team, to roll and slide and somersault their way out of crunching tackles and land on their feet. This time the Ladies had landed, in Quebec, on their bottoms. Canada just didn't want to know. The entire final month of touring had to be wiped from the schedule, which devastated Florrie Redford, as her sacrifice of time from her nursing training had been specifically so that she could explore Canada and discover what openings, if any, there were in the Dominion for a nurse who played football in the odd hours she could absent herself from her career. Everyone rallied round. Alice Kell, Florrie's best friend, told her that there'd be other chances for her to see Canada, and why didn't she emigrate there, one of these days? It was something Florrie had never thought about, but now she did. She would emigrate to Canada one of these days, why not? Lancashire women ride the tackles and bounce right back on to their feet.

And the next bad news?

'Er, Mr Frankland, their ain't no girls' football in the

USA, so I've had to book the team to play men's teams,' Abe Zelickman announced.

'What?'

'They're the only ones who could afford the expenses,' Zelickman explained. 'But you'll get real good publicity because these teams I gotten, they're the best damn teams in the USA. I guarantee! The League winners! From Ohio, Illinois, New Jersey, Philadelphia, Massachusetts, Washington, NYC – the very best.'

Everyone looked at Lily. She huffed and blushed, and hunched her shoulders, and dropped her head to the left.

'I hope your goalies are ready for her,' Jennie Harris giggled, as Lily struggled to light up a Camel.

'We don't play men as a rule,' Alfred Frankland insisted.

'We're in America now, Mr Frankland,' David Brooks reminded him with a disarming smile. 'The rules stop here.'

And Herbert, remembering the scam over the lost wallet, could only squeeze Alice's hand and look upwards. Was there anything else that this pair of schemers could do to daunt the already flagging spirits of the team which had arrived to the popping of so many champagne corks?

'And we better be leaving, now, Alfred,' said Abe Zelickman, 'because we gotta make New Jersey in forty hours for the first kick-off. This schedule's real tight.'

Tight? It was punitive. In the twenty-first century, the rail journey from Quebec to New York State takes a total of 28 hours. And the Ladies had disembarked, even those like Alice Woods who hadn't partaken of a little light refreshment to celebrate the first new continent they had ever seen, with sea legs. They were expected to play a decent football match against a top-quality Paterson team which was riding high in the Soccer Leagues, and prove to the USA that women could play football, despite their exhaustion. It was a tall order and one requiring Owd Thatcher's words of wisdom, 'Yo' cannot knit a full life o' negatives.' They just had to crack on.

They arrived to play Paterson, at Clifton in the heartland of the New Jersey textile district, on Sunday morning, having travelled throughout the previous day and night, and after checking into their hotel, had to play within three hours of their arrival. And the hotel wasn't exactly what they'd expected. Not that they were prima donnas, far from it, but that first hotel was a cheap lodging house in a rough area, with the smell of grease permeating the corridors, and four- and six-legged intruders skipping across the dank carpets and up the walls. From the first moment they arrived Lily was at war with the bugs, although there was little time for her to do much more than throw her football boots repeatedly at the crawling and scuttling things before Abe Zelickman picked them up to take them to Olympic Park where a crowd of 5,000 waited to see 'Newcastle United Ladies' Team from Preston, Lincolnshire'.

The girls astounded the spectators, even before they had kicked a single ball. New Jersey just wasn't used to women competing in public, and the shorts, shirts and caps were a revelation. Among the US women athletes who had travelled to play in the International meet at the Pershing Stadium, most wore their hair bobbed, as was the new fashion among the young educated middle-classes, but in the immigrant centres like Clifton NJ, the women kept the waist-length hair which had been traditional in their original homelands, and many commentators were surprised at the bobbed hair sported by most of the Ladies. In reporting on the kit and the hair, the *New York Times* and the Pawtucket newspapers weren't as overtly titillated by the unconventional dress as the London newspapers had been when they watched that match against the French at Stamford Bridge. In the USA the match report was placed on the sports' pages, rather than the news pages, as had happened in England, and the comments about the hair and kit were admiring, rather than excited. It was clear that the women, in the USA, were to be objects of curiosity, but also subjects of respect, even though they were roundly defeated by eight goals to four.

The play was analysed as being 'English' rather than as being 'girly', which again made a change from some of the commentaries in the British newspapers, and the match reports emphasised the open play, speed of the play, and the accuracy of the passing. Attention was drawn to the clever link-ups, as it appears that the US game was altogether a rowdier free-for-all, with little teamwork and much personal expression. The style was therefore admired by those who saw the 'English' game as a template to which others should aspire. It was little Jennie Harris who, yet again, caught the eye, but Lily came in for her fair share of praise too. 'Her driving from the wing and the accuracy of her shots left little to be desired.' Tell that to the cockroaches at the lodging house. And Alice's muscular athleticism was also noted:

There were few falls, McGuire, the noted one-armed forward from Brooklyn, being the first to measure his length on the green-sward. For this Annie *(sic)* Woods, the sturdy centre half-back, was responsible, and seemed just a little proud of it.

191

So Alice Woods proudly showed New Jersey the meaning of the word heft. And then it was back to the cockroaches. Alice didn't get a wink of sleep that night, the second sleepless night for her. Sharing a room with Lily, she was disturbed all night by Lily's refusal to admit defeat against the bugs, sitting up all night shouting obscenities at them, and throwing her shoes until the light of daybreak made them scuttle off home.

It was hardly a pleasant introduction to the USA. The Ladies were weary, dirty and dispirited after the pampering on board ship, and the imminent departure for Pawtucket meant that although they could escape from Bug City shortly, they had somehow to get their hearts in the right place before moving on.

Pawtucket was far more to Lily's liking, and the other women agreed. It was home from home. It even looked like the best of Lancashire, although on a much grander scale, with tall mill chimneys and moist but very warm autumnal air, a river estuary like the one in Preston, and townspeople who traced their roots back to Lancashire's industrial heartlands. As well they might, as they'd been tempted here by jobs in the cotton industry, founded on this side of the Atlantic by a very interesting British entrepreneur, Samuel Slater, in the late 1790s. Now there was a fawce guy if ever there was one. Slater had been brought up in Belper in Derbyshire, the son of a wealthy landowner, and decided to make his living as a cotton magnate. He learnt the trade as an administrator in Jeremiah Strutt's Derbyshire factory, but he knew the secrets of the Arkwright machinery which was enabling British cotton manufacture to take a lead in the world's production. At only 21, he disguised himself as an agricultural labourer and set off the conquer America –

illegally. This was just after the War of Independence, and emigration was bound by strict limits. In particular, no one with the secrets of the British Industrial Revolution was supposed to travel to the USA to hand over the cotton trade to the nation which grew cotton. America had been trying to set up mills to rival the British cotton industry for many years, but their machinery was much slower. Slater, with blueprints of the Arkwright spinning machines memorised and an awareness of how much they were worth, landed at New York, moved to Pawtucket, and found work at a mill there, introducing the secrets of British machinery to America, and sparking America's industrial revolution, a move which eventually destroyed the Lancashire cotton industry. If the Ladies but knew it, Samuel Slater, the industrial defector, was the main reason Lancashire was unemployed. However, he did provide them with this recognisable landscape and these warm-hearted people from Lancashire and Scotland and Yorkshire and Derbyshire, who did everything they could to offer a warm New England welcome.

They provided luxury accommodation, and the YMCA gym for practices, and showed Lily how to play basketball, a skill she immediately mastered and which became an obsession. Jessie Walmsley was delighted to discover that the man responsible for the arrangements was a Mr John Walmsley, the president of the J&P Coats' factory team. And this was another connection which made the girls feel comfortable – they were to play a factory team. In the USA many of the soccer teams were factory teams, just like women's football in Britain, as immigrant workers from Britain and Scandinavia brought their national game with them and played in their break times in the factory yards.

And the immigrant population had the same Lancashire

hedonism which demands a knees-up, with speeches, at every opportunity. A reception was arranged the night before the game by the British-Canadian Great War Veterans, and everyone had a chance to make welcoming speeches, or reply to a speech, before the vocal selections and recitations were performed, and this was followed by the usual buffet and dancing. It was just what the doctor ordered, despite Prohibition and a distinct lack of sherry. But of course the Veterans knew that the women would enjoy a variety show and dancing, because that's what they enjoyed, more than anything. The greatest name in American Vaudeville had been born just up the road in Providence, RI. George M. Cohan was to the USA what George Formby and Ella Retford were to Britain, and when the Ladies, led by Lily, started up a sing-song at the end of the evening with 'She's a Lassie From Lancashire' their hosts responded with a Cohan song and with a Mary instead of a Sarah, and Lily and Alice and the others sang along.

> My mother's name was Mary,
> She was so good and true;
> Because her name was Mary,
> She called me Mary too.
> She wasn't gay or airy,
> But plain as she could be;
> I hate to meet a fairy
> Who calls herself Marie.
>
> For it is Mary, Mary,
> Plain as any name can be.
> But with propriety, society
> Will say Marie.

But it was Mary, Mary,
Long before the fashions came,
And there is something there
That sounds so square,
It's a grand old name.

There was something else of interest at that night's good do. It was a speech from the Reverend Arthur J. Watson, and it made headlines in the *Pawtucket Times*. The good Reverend said that if women devoted more time to outdoor sports, there would be less need of powder and paint, and that women should make a practice of getting out in the air more and taking part in regular exercise.

Why was it only in America that this was the view taken of the game of football? Not once at that function, or anywhere else the women played, did anyone say anything different from this. For the USA, this tour was a demonstration of glowing, healthy womanhood as opposed to the floozy life of loose-living and indolence, so it's ironic that in Britain the opposite stance was taken – that football was an unhealthy activity for women to indulge in, even though it was the most popular working-class women's sport.

So the Ladies ran out on to that pitch in Pawtucket with good food, good music and encouragement, and several good nights' sleep fortifying them, and drew the match 4–4. Nine thousand people paid to watch them, more than double the usual attendance for a football match. But even at the end, when they left the field having captured the hearts of their hosts and the huge crowd, they were still referred to as Newcastle. Thank you, Brooks and Zelickman. Then they had to leave for New York and another flea-pit hotel, and another brief rest before they were to take the pitch to play a top-of-the-league fixture against Centro-Hispano.

The gloves now came off. Alfred Frankland had never been one for asking, 'Don't you know who these girls are?' but their treatment at the hands of these under-experienced publicists and Zelickman's fellow-committee members at Brooklyn F.C. had everyone at breaking point. While Pawtucket had been wonderful, New York City was as bad as New Jersey, and something had to be done, as he told Thomas Bagnall, head of the National Association, the organising body of soccer in the USA. He was present at the Centro-Hispano game to listen to the complaints from the girls and Frankland, and agreed that this tour had been mismanaged from the start, especially when he saw the fixture list, which was impossible. There was little he could do to rearrange the tour so that this to-ing and fro-ing across the Eastern seaboard could be rationalised, but what everyone saw, especially the accountant Herbert Stanley, was that if the team continued to make these long rail journeys between fixtures, the expenses' money they had demanded would run out, and wouldn't allow them decent accommodation.

They had asked for $1,000 expenses from each club, but this money had to pay for their return crossing, as well as all travel and accommodation within the USA. There were 16 players and Alfred Frankland, Herbert Stanley, and David Brooks to accommodate fully, and Abe Zelickman would need travelling expenses and accommodation in some cities and towns. Allowing half of the total to cover their Atlantic crossing, if one match were played each week, each person on the tour would have a budget of $25 per week, the equivalent of $500 in today's terms, to cover hundreds of miles of internal travel and hotel expenses and food. If the

196

travelling wasn't curtailed, it couldn't be done. Someone somewhere had seriously underestimated the costs of this tour, which is why the Ladies were, yet again, living in a downtown flop-house.

Thomas Bagnall did his best to salvage things. The first action he look was to truncate the tour. The final four weeks, which should have seen them play at New Bedford on 7, Washington on 8, and Detroit on 14 October, followed by Akron, Ohio, on the 15th, St Louis on the 21st, Chicago on the 22nd, Pittsburgh on the 28th and Baltimore on 29th, was an itinerary made in hell. So the programme was cut and the Ladies moved to a decent if unimpressive brownstone hotel in New York. Provided they didn't overspend their pocket money, they would just about be able to eke out a living on the tour. The temptation not to eke out their spending money was great. The New York shops and department stores were full of goods the girls had never seen – electrical devices, strange-looking tubs that did the washing, radios, ready-made clothes, dolls which moved when you pushed a lever, and exotic lingerie the like of which had never been seen in Lancashire. Of course it was pointless their buying any of this equipment to take home to a Lancashire town which had no electricity to plug it into, but they did, nevertheless. They had marvelled at London, but New York had been modernised beyond their expectation. People drove round in cars, all the time. And there were Vaudeville theatres and shows everywhere.

Lily was much taken with Vaudeville. And Vaudeville was much taken with Lily. Or at least, the manager at one of the theatres was besotted. It was strange. Lily was as gawkily uncomfortable as ever, chain-smoking her way through New York, although she didn't particularly like the roasted taste of the cigarettes, and she was still what my grandmother Polly would have called 'as okk'ard as Dick's hatband'. On the other hand, and this was something she rarely recognized in herself, she was an extraordinarily beautiful young woman, with a strong, square Lancashire face but huge eyes and a wide gentle mouth. He was an Italian American, with sleeked greased hair and a liking for the big peasant women in his homeland of Lombardy, and after their first meeting, at the Centro-Hispano match, he pursued her with a passion, which was wonderful for Alice and the others, as this gave them free entrance to the nightly variety shows which kept their spirits up. Even had she wanted to shrug him off, or give him a swift shoulder-charge, Lily had no option. Without her beau, the others couldn't have the best seats, so the adoration was encouraged. She was embarrassed by the attention, especially as no one would leave it alone.

'Will yer bloody shurrup about 'im?' she'd beg.

'Ey oop, Lily's got a cob on! She's gone all mardy!' Jennie Harris would giggle.

'Just stop bloody mythering me will yer?' And she'd flounce out, throwing a boot and a 'Why don't yer pick on Alice and that bloody Bert!' over her shoulder.

But they wouldn't stop mythering her. It was the team's standing joke. Everyone was highly amused by Lily's first romance, and more highly amused when, on the morning of their departure for Washington, he sent her a large bunch of roses, a replica of the Statue of Liberty, and a photograph of himself in a tuxedo, looking every inch a worthy gent, worthy enough to carry off the child star of the Dick, Kerr's Ladies. Throughout the journey someone would start up, and they'd all join in . . .

She's my lady love.
She is my dove, my baby dove.
She's no girl for sitting down to dream,
She's the only Queen Laguna knows.
I know she likes me,
I know she likes me, because she said so.
    ('*No I NEVER!*' from Lily)
She is my Lily of Laguna,
She is my Lily and my rose.

The girls drew the match at Washington, and Lily was named in the *Washington Post* as the best player on the pitch, credited with having played a 'very aggressive game', which is hardly surprising in the circumstances.

And in New Bedford there was more aggression. And the team's first victory. And it was all without Lily Parr. She'd been so aggrieved by the non-stop teasing that she'd gone to the gym to burn off her anger in a game of basketball, and twisted her knee so badly in too surging a run and too rapid a take-off, that she was on the subs' bench wrapped in a large bandage. In all those years of playing football she'd never been injured, and now, as if to prove the FA and the lady headmistresses wrong, here she was bruised and battered by a game of netball. Irony strikes when you least expect it.

The largest crowd that New Bedford had ever seen turned out to watch this match, and Lily could only sit and glower and watch the Ladies dominate the men, although the local newspaper didn't dare see it that way.

Chivalrous New Bedford Team Before Biggest Soccer Crowd in City's History Was Too Proud to Fight Dick, Kerr's Girls Who Won 5 to 4

was the newspaper's excuse. And there was an interesting side-view from the *New Bedford Evening News*, too. 'Most of the players on the All Stars are married men, and yesterday their better halves were out there strongly rooting for the girls, willing to bet their boxes of candy on the members of their own sex winning the outcome.' This was strong stuff, even if it was softened by candy. Before the tour, US women just didn't go to soccer matches, even if their partners were playing, and in New Bedford suddenly the Ladies were there, and so were women supporters. This was vitally important. It was the reason the Dick, Kerr's team had been invited to the USA, to try to drum up support for soccer – perhaps not to other women as players, but to women in general, as supporters. This was the important thing. Though the women were officially the ambassadors for the health and hygiene of leading a vibrantly sporting life, Thomas Bagnall among others, had decided on his priority.

If this team of women footballers could get the untapped American female support behind this sport, it could actually take off in the USA. He was looking to the commercial value of the Ladies, and what they could do to rescue soccer from the minority immigrant sport it was at the time. At the time, women didn't attend any sporting fixtures, let alone soccer, any more than they had done in the UK before the advent of the Dick, Kerr's Ladies and other women footballers. Now, if Bagnall and the National Association could be the first to break through the barrier of female spectatorship, then this was worth money, real money.

How it would happen was a problem. But everyone knew that the race for sports' funding would be won by those who could appeal to the entire family and put women and children up there on the bleachers. Women had never shown any presence in sport, but it wasn't because they had no interest: it was because while the men were spectating, women were supposedly at home, doing the shopping, the cooking, the cleaning, and the child-minding on Saturdays and Sundays. The secret of success would be if one sport above all others could appeal so much to the housebound women that they would come in their droves to watch it, as they had done to every match the Dick, Kerr's Ladies had played in the USA. Hard commercialism was in the minds of this nation of entrepreneurs as it had never been in the UK, where class leisure activities were seen as manly only, perhaps because men and only men had a few hours of spare time between the Saturday lunchtime klaxon which announced that the morning shift had finished, and the religious observances of Sunday morning would begin shortly.

After New Bedford there were now four more matches – at New York, Fall River, Baltimore and finally Philadelphia. But by the Fall River match, at which seats were specifically reserved for women for the first time ever, the job had been done. Women had been given permission by the Dick, Kerr's Ladies to get out there and make their voices heard and their presence felt in sport as a national pastime. And maybe it didn't work out as Thomas Bagnall may have wished, and maybe it wasn't soccer which came out of this as the main contender among those who manned the turnstiles and pocketed the cash, but it was the Ladies, leading the charge on sports, who helped make sport a spectator activity for both sexes in the USA. Women in America said, why not? And they had the time to spend on standing on the terraces and sitting in the bleachers because, unlike their Lancashire sisters, they had money.

At Fall River, a city similar to Pawtucket, with much the same overwhelming support for soccer and many immigrants from Lancashire, Alice's warm smile and glowing, healthy demeanour impressed a local woman so much that she was presented with a special doll which had a Native American beaded skirt, and eyes and hips which moved at the touch of a lever. Lily wanted one too, so another was found for her, Margaret, on Alice's return, put the doll under a glass dome in the parlour, stultifying its movement. Occasionally the lever was pressed, for friends. But the motor died anyway, from the coal dust which squirmed under the glass and clogged up the mechanisms of healthy movement and progress.

At Baltimore, the Ladies were called upon to demonstrate their skills to college girls, who, it was said, wanted to extend their sporting prowess and believed that soccer might be a way to do that. The idea didn't go down too well with their educated parents. Soccer, they said, was an immigrant game played by roughnecks, and it would be over their dead bodies that decent American girls ever learned the sport. Tell that to the USA Women's World Cup winners. During the tour of the colleges, Lily Parr discovered that she was unique. A rugby-shaped ball came flying from a pitch towards her, and she casually kicked it back, perfectly, to the male student footballers. The game halted. Every man, most of them on sports' scholarships, stood transfixed. It was a fact, surely, that women couldn't kick footballs, and it had taken these men many years of tuition and practice to master the art of the oval ball.

'Bet you couldn't do that again! It was a fluke, right?' one of New England's best and brightest sons shouted.

Someone had said 'bet'. Within seconds odds were being shouted. This was Lancashire as they all knew and loved it. Challenges were being set. The men had never heard the like before – all these laughing and screaming women making fun of them and collecting the dollar bills. But they accepted the bet and stood by it, and stood by as Lily, trained and honed on the gravel at Chessie's, not only did it again, but sent it beautifully over the cross-bar, then shrugged and blushed and got okk'ard again, almost embarrassed by her own prodigious talent.

At Philadelphia, there was a farewell ceremony for the English Ladies who had given some credibility to the game of soccer. But first there was a race. Around the pitch was a running track, and Philadelphia, hearing about the miracles of clean-living and athletic prowess which the Ladies were said to possess, had a treat in store, one scheduled to restore American faith in the American woman as a similar role model. They had managed to entice the four national championship USA relay-team members, lovely well-brought-up girls similar to those who had so ably competed in the Pershing Stadium in Paris and brought the silver medals back to the USA, to enter a pre-match relay race against the Ladies. Alice, under the weather that day, didn't take part. But Jennie Harris did, and Lily, of course, and Mollie Walker and Florrie Haslam. Dick, Kerr's won by a whisker.

Then it was on to the match, which they lost by a whisker at 5–6. But of all the matches throughout the tour, this was the one which created the biggest stir in the press. The skills and team-work of Dick, Kerr's had the locals on their feet, and even the sports' reporter was lost for words of fanlike

203

approbation, making almost purple prose of the skills of Lily Parr.

This Parr girl, however, simply electrified the spectators in the manner she dribbled, tricked the Phillies' defense and then generally finished up with a submarine shot that compelled Ness to get down on his knees to stop the ball going in the net.

And there was equal adoration for Jennie Harris, who, from the *Philadelphia Inquirer*'s sports' reporter received both drooling praise and a new nickname – 'Kid' Harris. The report finishes in the way all sports reports should:

With the score tie away at three-three the crowd were with the English girls almost to a man, woman and child.

Now, that's what we like to hear, men women and children, all except the headmistress from Newcastle who actually didn't think that women should amuse a crowd. Perhaps she, like many others, had mistaken the reasons why the women got the support they did. It wasn't titillation: it was because these women were actually exceptionally good at what they did.

Anthems were played, flags were raised and lowered, folded and exchanged. A football signed by President Harding was presented to the Dick, Kerr's Ladies, who had not brought charity funds into the USA, but had validated a sport, and had offered up an extra potential 50% in revenue. At every game, the Ladies had doubled the highest takings. This was impressive.

The Dick, Kerr's Ladies sailed home in early November,

having played nine, lost three, drawn three, won three; having conquered only the Yankee East Coast. Some, like Lily Lee, had met up with cousins from the USA. Some had fallen in love, like little Alice Mills who met her future husband in Pawtucket, and would return to marry him and become an American citizen. Others had been loved, like Lily, and decided that the kind of love offered perhaps wasn't what she wanted. Alice Woods knew that the slow-burning love she had with her friend and fellow-joker, Herbert Stanley, just might last.

There's a moment, in a love affair, which tells us all we need to know, and which, in revealing ourself to ourself, gives an indication of the future self we two may become. The love affair between the Ladies and the USA was such a moment. It was the point at which the bud flowers and before the bloom dies, just as the roses bloomed in the florid words of the Philadelphia press. It had taken the entire tour for the Ladies to take the USA by storm, but they'd done it with panache, every one of them, including the Parr girl and Kid Harris. The women factory workers had crossed the Atlantic to demonstrate what Lancashire women are about, and America saw that and thought it might be able to profit from it in some way, some day, but meanwhile it held them in its heart.

And meanwhile the Ladies had done what no other women in football had ever done: they had played professionally, taking their earnings exclusively from football for the entire duration of that trip. Professional women's football in 1922? Would you credit it?

The women were greeted with the usual do in Preston – charabancs, sherry, processions, pierrots, potato ('prater') pies with short-crust pastry, carved ham with barm cakes, speeches, Victoria sponges and Valetas. But, strangely or not depending on your level of cynicism, the Works Manager, and the Mayor, and the President of the club, and everybody who really ought to have been there to welcome them besides the crowds in the streets who knew in their hearts that Lancashire lasses had conquered America, was unavoidably detained. The bloom had died.

Politics is a nasty game, as played by those who know their position within hierarchy of a postwar backlash. So it was left to the ex-Mayor of Burnley, who had retired and didn't give sweet FA, to offer the speech of thanks to the conquering heroines for the sterling work they'd done in the land of the free. Perhaps Marriott Edgar, the poet and versifier who wrote all Stanley Holloway's 'Lancashire' recitations could have done better in welcoming them. Perhaps he did, because this is how his 'Battle of Hastings' verse continues, after the 'By gum, that's an idea':

> The kick-off were sharp at two-thirty,
> And soon as the whistle had went
> Both sides started banging each other
> 'til the swineherds could hear them in Kent.
>
> The Saxons had best line of forwards,
> Well armed both with buckler and sword.
> But the Normans had best combination,
> And when half-time came neither had scored.
>
> So the Duke called his cohorts together
> And said 'Let's pretend that we're beat.
> Once we get Saxons down on the level
> We'll cut off their means of retreat.'

When the Conqueror saw what had happened,
A bow and an arrow he drew.
He went right up to 'Arold and shot him.
He were off-side, but what could they do?

And after the battle were over
They found 'Arold so stately and grand,
Sitting there with an eyeful of arrow
On his 'orse with his 'awk in his 'and.

Seven

Alice and Lily

The verse brings us back to the equivalences which have been made throughout history between war and team games, and football in particular. Orwell likened football to war, saying that football is war without the shooting – although of course, as Lily Parr attests, shooting, and firing the bullet header or the rifled shot still play a part in winning the game. The languages of war and football are interchangeable. The Dick, Kerr's Ladies, though, had made the equivalence more humane and charitable than their male counterparts. Unlike Sir Henry Newbolt, they hadn't imagined metaphorical war on the playing fields of Eton, but had, like Francis Tolliver and the discharged unemployed ex-soldier, actually played the game in No Man's Land, and behind the lines in Roubaix, in the immediate aftermath of that Great War.

But in 1923, perhaps it was time to forget about playing football for the victims of war. At least that was what the FA had said. Lancashire women, though, are made of sterner stuff than to go down under a hail of elegant fluff from Baron de Coubertin, Charles Hamilton Sorley, and

Sir Henry Newbolt, and our ladies decided that despite the ban, they'd continue to play on whatever village green or waste tip or Old Bonk they could find, if people wanted them to, which they did. So Dick, Kerr's resolved that despite the set-backs and the truncated tour of America, in which they'd had a chance to examine a foreign species of cockroach and some fawce ferrets, they were up for it, and wouldn't give up their reputation and the chance of some decent functions and sing-songs. A blind eye was turned to them by the FA, which had at least brushed them into the corners of the newspapers.

Alice Woods, like Lily Parr, came home from the USA with some wonderful stories and with every determination of playing football until she dropped. She was an athlete, and needed to find some self-expression away from the housekeeping duties at Sutton Road, and as she was now courting Herbert, it was necessary to play as much football as she could before they settled down, which was why in early 1923 she was again lodging at Preston, at Mrs Stanley's home, after playing a tough game for the team. She was due to leave the following morning to return to St Helens and Margaret, but in the night was struck again by a pain which had irked her on and off for a year or two, and which had stopped her taking part in that relay race in Philadelphia. She'd blamed it on Coca Cola and ice cubes, then. This time, though, it was different and intense. The pain became searing, unbearable, and Alice began to vomit uncontrollably. When Sarah-Anne was called in to look at her, she realized that Alice was seriously ill, and would need to be taken to hospital. In the days before the National Health Service this wasn't easy, but Herbert was woken and sent to find a doctor, who declared that Alice had

209

appendicitis, and needed an immediate operation. Transport was arranged to take her to the hospital.

It wasn't merely appendicitis. It was peritonitis and a strangulated hernia, and the emergency operation was lengthy and risky. For weeks Alice lay in hospital, unable to stir, and when she was finally taken back to the Stanleys' house, she was too ill to move for two months.

It was the longest period of inactivity in her life. All the girls came to see her and give her the latest news – two Tiller girls had asked to join the team, St Helens' Ladies was disbanding and the best players were moving to Dick, Kerr's, Lily was missing her, and Alfred Frankland sent his best. But it was Herbert's company that she enjoyed the most. He'd bring her jokes that he'd written down so he wouldn't forget them, fetch her tea and the Lancashire cure-all remedy of pobs – bread soaked in warm sugared milk – and tripe and onions. This is what we always had in St Helens when illness struck, but on that front I was what my grandmother Polly called 'bred out', some kind of weirdo who didn't belong in a decent St Helens' family, as both pobs and tripe and onions made me throw up violently.

Alice was probably fed egg and sherry in milk, and fresh vegetables and fruit from the Stanleys' greenhouses, as she made her slow progress to health, worrying continually about how Margaret would be managing without her. But back in St Helens, the family had been called in to compensate for Alice's illness, and Elizabeth Anne's eldest, another Margaret, was old enough to help out with the laundry. She loved visiting, just to see the American doll, and was sometimes allowed to take it from under the glass dome, switch the lever, and watch its eyes flash and its hips swivel. No-one in Sutton had seen the like. 'Would you credit it?' they'd ask as the little skirt shimmied from side to side. 'They're fawce, them Yanks! And did you know that they have little lumps of ice in drinks?'

By the time Alice was well enough to return home, she and Herbert had an 'understanding' that once he was fully trained, and bringing in a decent wage and could afford to rent a house, they'd get engaged and married. But the wait was longer than either of them anticipated, because although 1925 had seemed the best time to get engaged, that year and the following one was crunch time for St Helens and the failing mining industry which had under-pinned its growth.

In 1925, the coal industry in St Helens and throughout the country was in crisis. Germany, one of the biggest coal-mining countries in Europe, finally had the postwar restric-tions of coal output lifted, and flooded Europe with cheap coal. The response of the coal-owners in the UK was to offer wagecuts to British miners, and at the end of July, a national coal strike was temporarily averted when the government decided to offer a nine-months' subsidy to the owners. This merely postponed the inevitable. Grumblings, like Alice's appendix, turned to rumblings. The subsidy ran out the following April, when the miners were again, as they had been in 1921, offered a take-it-or-leave it option – work longer hours for less pay or we'll shut the mines down.

In 1926, 1 May fell on a Saturday. It was a traditional Walking Day or Maypole Day or Workers' Day in many of the mining towns like St Helens, but in 1926, disrupting the processions and the silver bands and the banners and ribbons of the maypoles, there was brawling in the streets, and impassioned speeches were made on every soap-box in the Lancashire coalfields. The miners were locked out by

211

the mine-owners, who had threatened this for years and had done it before in 1921. Other unions had agreed to back the miners if this happened again, and that's what they did. Gradually, in the first week of May, one union after another called its workers out on strike, leading to the General Strike. While the government had had nine months to work out what to do if the mine owners shut the mines, and had contingency plans put in place, and had carefully plotted the probable moves which might be taken by the opposition, the trade unions were disorganized and, after a fortnight, ordered their members back to work. Only the miners remained, locked out and without support. And St Helens was brought to its knees.

The St Helens' colliers wouldn't give in. They knew that their mines were mostly unproductive, but they also knew that they were doing their damnedest to try to earn a living. Some of them had to walk five miles underground before they could begin to hew coal. Oh, they knew, all right, how impossible this task really was. Some miners, including Smack and Cute, took rashers of bacon down the mines with them, because by the time they got to that day's coalface, it would have cooked in their tin. The work was hot, deep, relentless and pointless.

Miners are traditionally careful with their money, saving it up week by week for their annual trip to Blackpool. And many of the miners had a small cache of savings. So those early strike weeks in the days of late spring and summer took on the characteristics of a holiday. They knew, in Sutton as in the rest of St Helens, that the mine-owners and the government had laid in huge stores of coal. Every confrontation with the miners started this way, and was usually timed for late spring when coal stocks were at their highest, and demand at its lowest. The miners had to sit out the summer. Gathering at The Pickled Egg opposite Alice's house, amusing themselves with matches and races on the Old Bonk and dominoes, and betting with spent matchsticks, this is what they did. Those who could spare a penny had the odd money bet. But some, particularly the single men were in trouble from the start. Single men weren't entitled to any benefit whatsoever from the strike fund. Some young men from St Helens decided to take their summer in Southport, to sleep rough on the beach and spend their days ferreting rabbits, or plundering the potato fields at night for something to eat and to sell. The police came in droves and those who tried to stay alive by these means were jailed for six months or more. At least in prison the miners got three meals a day. So they didn't mind too much.

Back in Sutton young women, including Alice, collected the scraps of food donated by, among others, the local Co-operative stores. By doing this the Co-operative stores earned a respect from St Helens which never faltered for the next fifty years. Like all St Helens women, I can remember our 'divvie' number, the number we quoted when we bought anything from the Co-op, which eventually re-housed itself in the luxurious Helena House, and was always the biggest department store in St Helens. No one dreamt of shopping anywhere else. Another benefactor was the Salvation Army, which through its steadfastness and its care of the starving during the dark years of the lock-outs and Depression earned its own respect, even from those miners who now, in their droves, joined the Communist Party. At the start of the miners' lock-out there was one Communist Party branch in St Helens. By the end, there were thirteen. My atheistic father was later to join one of these, and yet he, like every other Communist I knew, would buy the *War Cry* or give to the Sally Army collecting boxes without demur.

Having collected a donation of meat and vegetables, Alice and the other women in Sutton would prepare and cook huge hotpots in the family washing boiler, and these would be ladled out to anyone who hadn't had a meal that day. In Sutton, that meant almost all the adults. Children were provided for. Every church rallied round, and all children were given breakfast at school, and a filling dinner, so that all that was needed at night was a slice of bread and dripping. Those with gardens or allotments, not that there were many, would give away the contents of their vegetable gardens to the wash-boiler stews to keep others alive, and the pubs, too, played their part despite their subsistence-level takings. They would buy bread and margarine in bulk, and make thin sandwiches to be given away to all their regulars. Pigeon-fanciers with racing pigeons which had won prizes and rosettes strangled their pet birds and added them to the stews.

As autumn approached, and the mine-owners showed no sign of backing down from their demands that the men should work an extra hour a day and revert to several per cent lower than their prewar pay, the hedgerows were scoured for blackberries, and as brambles were the major feature of hedges in St Helens, many baskets of these were gathered by Alice and her family, who then sent out urgent requests for sugar, so that they could make jam in big pans over the fire.

Not an hour on the day, not a penny off the pay.

The rallying cry was powerful, but little use when you were clemmed. Some were worse off than others.

Coal-picking, searching for nuggets of coal on slag heaps or in open-cast mines, was a daily activity for some, and the sacks of coal they found could then be used or sold to other industries in the town which were trying to keep going. Without coal, no miner's house could function, as there was no electricity, and no other way to cook except on an open range in the kitchen/living-room. Some even went to the extreme of cutting down, quite illegally, any trees which had managed to survive in the caustic St Helens air. Others hunted and salvaged what they could from the rubbish dumps, all day, picking over the left-overs of those who owned things, and who could afford to throw a jar or some rags into the midden. The miners were locked out until the end of the year. The St Helens' miners consistently voted against capitulation and held out the longest. Finally, after two million working days had been lost in St Helens alone in the months between May and the end of November, work was resumed.

For Alice, as for all St Helens, it was a bleak year. Everything she had earned from football and saved towards her trousseau had to be sacrificed for food. For Lily, the panic in St Helens was not so personal and devastating. Her father was working for Pilkington's Glass, but even glass workers suffered, some by the most foul means. Any worker who went on strike during the General Strike, which lasted only a week in the glass industry, had a shilling per week of his pension fund confiscated for the rest of his life. For George, a labourer, this didn't count. Only the engineers were involved and lost their pension contributions. Anyway, George had his chickens and his pigs and could get by, which was just as well as Lily's contribution to the family income was suddenly put under threat.

Because the strike had its ramifications, all the way to Preston.

Preston suffered, too, through the short-lived General Strike, and the longer-lived miners' lock-out. Fuel crises always have a knock-on effect on industry, even one so apparently solidly built as English Electric, which, let us not forget, is what Dick, Kerr's now had become. Being part of a conglomerate is good for corporate profits, but can destroy the sense of community and initiative which small profitable companies encourage. As I said in the early chapters, the essential ambience of Dick, Kerr's had been laid down by the Scottish Presbyterian ethic of its founders, that feeling that anybody can do anything, and that all initiative is to be rewarded while the weakest are protected. Paternalism like this can stifle or encourage, and it was a combination of both paternalism and entrepreneurship which allowed the factory women under the leadership of Alfred Frankland to set up the football-for-charity initiative which was so effective and which gripped the public mood.

However, the mood had been changing subtly for some years. There was that business of the top brass absenting itself from the reception party for the Ladies after their glorious tour of the USA. And why should English Electric fight to keep alive the name of a firm which had been swallowed by its maw many years ago? And why, it had to be asked in the board of directors, were the Ladies still playing football against the wishes of the ruling body of football in the UK? And why was English Electric still, in these years of depression and cut-backs, allowing its employees time off in lieu and paying good money to workers who were passing their profits on to worthy causes? Should English Electric continue to subsidise charity football when the FA had banned it?

The question was bound to come up some day. That English Electric had continued with its subsidy, through its provision of Ashton Park and its payment to absentee workers, some of whom had the gall to be missing for more than two months at the end of 1922, was surely enough contribution to the general good. Times were hard. International trade was faring badly. The miners' lock-out showed no signs of ending. English Electric could no longer carry the can for the poor and the absentee workers, especially not Alfred Frankland, who was surely spending useful working time, it was suspected, organising fixtures for this team of women footballers. The team would have to go. It was surplus to requirements.

Duly, Alfred Frankland was called into the office and given his notice. He'd been a drain on company profits for too long, as had all these dead-beat women who needed time off at the drop of a hat. He needed to realize that charity was no longer needed, and would no longer get the support of the directors.

'Lose the team, Alfred, and do a full-time job for English Electric, or sadly, we'll have to thank you for your sterling work, and say goodbye. Several redundancies have to be made, and you're expendable.'

It was the end for the Dick, Kerr's Ladies, the board said, as Alfred took his redundancy. But he wouldn't let his Ladies go. They were his girls, who depended on him. So he called them all together in the yard in which he'd first seen them play, and tried to explain what had happened –

that he'd been given his notice to quit, and that their futures with the firm were in danger, but if they wanted to remain a team, then he would back them.

Lily listened to this announcement as confused as the rest of them. No one quite understood the implications, especially those who had recently come to Dick, Kerr's (English Electric) from St Helens. Some of the girls believed he'd done something wrong, to get them all sacked when they'd only been in the job five minutes. What had he done?

He'd done nothing except lose his job. But how to explain this to girls who didn't have a grasp of corporate economics? Some of them, he knew, would be able to hold on to their menial jobs, even after he'd gone. But some of them, like Lily, would have no chance. She was never on time. She was always in the back having a crafty ciggie. She filched anything that was left lying around. And with Lily gone he had no hopes of keeping his team together, because the exceptional Lily Parr was the star who made everything happen. Alfred Frankland wasn't going to allow the team to disband, and Lily, he knew, was the next employee under threat. If she was made redundant, the team would flounder.

'I'm going to set up in a little shop,' he explained to the girls. 'It's something I've always wanted to do. And I want to keep this team together, even though we're not allowed the facilities of Ashton Park. Some of you may be able to stay here, some of you won't. But I want you to know that the team isn't going to be defeated!'

(Cheers)

It was just like a scene from *Meg Foster, Footballer*.

'I've got some plans. And if any of you need another job, I may be able to get you one. I don't know. I just hope I can.'

'Like what, Pop?' Lily asked. They always called Alfred Frankland 'Pop'.

She had told no one that she'd been called in to the office and given her last warning that her work was unsatisfactory, and that she must stop taking time off or she'd have to go.

'My sister's in charge of one of the wards at Whittingham. I'll see what I can do,' Alfred promised.

Whittingham was the local mental health institution, the loony bin as it was called in those days. Florrie Redford had worked there for several years, and had almost completed her training as a mental health nurse. But it was a tough job, a really tough job – holding patients down for ECT and charging them with electric currents to 'relieve' their distress. Many vomited or wet or dirtied themselves after this brutal treatment, and emerged mesmerised and bewildered.

'I can do that,' Lily said. 'Ask yer sister to giz a job?'

'I will,' Alfred said. He knew that Lily had the heart and the strength to do it. He'd speak to his sister.

Within weeks Lily was working as an orderly and trainee at Whittingham, and Alfred and his wife had rented a house and a shop from which they sold fish, and greengroceries supplied by the Stanleys. He did all that he promised, re-named the team The Preston Ladies (formerly the Dick, Kerr's Ladies) and continued where he'd left off, arranging tours against the French and for the team to play Belgium, when Belgian ladies too caught the football bug. And Lily, as he had known, was the vital member of the ever-changing team, earning plaudits wherever she played, as the one woman in England who could have stepped into any top-division men's side.

Her job at Whittingham went surprisingly well. There she

had the right balance of responsibility and supervision, and took to the job with the hefty practicality she'd inherited from her powerful mother, who was now doing a coal round to help tide the family over the Depression. Whenever Lily went home for a day or a weekend to a house awash with feathers and coal-dust, she took a football for the children and a basket of food she'd helped herself to from the kitchens at the Whittingham, but no one seemed to mind about her tendency to take anything that was left lying around, because she was a damn good nurse, strong and yet quietly compassionate when she sensed that someone needed her. Her patients adored her. The other staff loved her unexpected dry St Helens' witticisms, expressed under her breath in that husky flat voice, and no one cared that she always had a lit Woodbine held between thumb and first finger and hidden in her palm as she did her rounds. Her eccentricity and capability were valued off the pitch, as well as on it.

As for Alice, she had to wait until September 1928 to marry Herbert. Margaret had died in 1926 at the age of 75, and the official period of mourning, and the requisite arrangements, had taken their toll on Alice. She had wanted her mother to see her wed, but hadn't been able to leave her side as she slid into sickness during that dreadful year in St Helens. Alice was 29, and Bert was 26, and they married in Preston, not St Helens. She wore brown chiffon, a dress she'd made herself with her sister's help, and carried bronze chrysanthemums. Shortly afterwards Herbert found a better job at Esso, in Stockport, where they rented a house with a cricket and tennis club behind it so that both of them could continue to play some sport. She had four children – Bert, Lynn, Edward and Claire – and like her mother went on having babies into her forties. Everyone who met her was drawn to the natural warmth and motherliness which characterised her whole life. 'A warm, athletic type of girl' was how the New Bedford newspaper had described her, and she remained exactly the same until her death in 1991 at 92 years old.

Her grand-daughter Gaynor, Bert's daughter, inherited her natural athleticism, and became an international breast-stroke swimmer, captaining the England side and winning medals, just like her grandmother.

Lily continued to play for the team until 1951, and remained close friends with Carmen Pomies, who stayed in Preston until the outbreak of the Second World War, when she went back to Paris and joined the French Resis-tance, returning to Preston when the war ended. The team outlived Lily's reluctant retirement, and even managed to outlive the death of Alfred Frankland in 1957, but fixtures were hard to come by, and in 1965 it finally folded, a year before the England men's team won the World Cup, and five years before the FA finally lifted its ban on women players.

Lily's working life gave her almost as much satisfaction as her football, and while she worked at the Whittingham, rising to the position of Ward Sister, she met her partner, Mary. Together they bought a house in the Goosenargh district of Preston. She was the first and only member of the family to have owned a house, and the excitement went right to her head. She never had been any good with money, it was always easy come, easy go, and Mary had to be the one who handled finances, but after successfully buying her home, she decided that she would buy the house in Union Street where her family lived. She entered into a mortgage arranged which she never paid, but the house was condemned and no one cared. It was finally modernised in 1955 when electricity was installed downstairs, and by running a cable up the wall from a downstairs socket, one of the bedrooms could be lit. It was as haphazard a house as it had always been.

Her sister Doris had a baby, Roy, in 1940, and Lily doted on the boy, offering to adopt him when Doris left briefly for the USA to marry an American serviceman in 1945, but Sal couldn't bear to be parted from him. Lily still regarded the boy as her heir, and when she died of breast cancer in 1978, it was Roy who travelled to Preston to sign her death certificate, and it was Roy who inherited her only possession, a car she had won in a raffle. She chose to be buried not in her adopted home, but in St Helens, a fact which surprised the women who had played with her for all those years in Preston, and had never heard her talk about her family. Except Carmen. Lily was a deeply private person, right to the end, but her heart was still in the town she'd left at fifteen, and with the family she loved to her last day.

During her career, Lily Parr proved herself to be one of football's greatest goal-scorers ever, scoring over 900 goals during her long career. In 2002 she was inducted into the Football Hall of Fame at the National Football Museum in Preston.

Roy Parr's grandson, Martin Cox, entered the Academy of Liverpool Football Club, aged 13, in 2003. He is reputed to have the most powerful shot the club has ever seen in one so young, but he has a serious problem with his deportment. He stands round-shouldered with his head down, pointing slightly to the left, just like his great-aunt, to whom he bears an uncanny resemblance.

✻　　✻　　✻

While researching this book, I had to travel back to St Helens. It was my first visit for almost 20 years. The town had changed beyond all recognition, and is now little more than a shopping precinct ringed by four large supermarkets, one on each of the entrance roads to the town, and several straggling industrial estates. I stayed in a four-star hotel, one of a national chain, next door, of course, to a supermarket.

I was disoriented and lost. In front of the hotel, the only one now in St Helens, was the St Helens canal. Next door was The World of Glass. And opposite, I slowly worked out, was Canal Street, the route I took to my grandmother Ellen's house. I knew that I would have to walk that route again, but I couldn't face it. There were too many memories attached to that journey, and the new St Helens had wiped my mind clear of them all. I missed the smells. From my hotel window I saw some chimneys rising into the sky, but only one, a part of the museum, was the old brick-built blue and black and red chequer-board chimney of my remembered childhood. The others were taller, more elegant, slim and metallic, suitable for a minimalist age, yet still, at dusk, the smoke emerged from them, almost as pale as summer clouds in a coal-free town.

Hoping to cling on to something from the past, I paid to go into The World of Glass, and saw the neatness and efficiency with which both my grandfathers' deaths had been excised from the life of the town. Yes, there were little notes attached to the impressive exhibits and the working models, describing the temperatures in which the labourers worked, but nowhere was there any indication of the human degradation and financial need that could make men work so close to a boiling furnace, shovelling up glass dust which invaded their lungs, or blowing out bottle after bottle

over a nine-hour shift, clad only in singlets and answerable
to the demands of a ear-splitting siren which announced the
start of each of those shifts. They were called turns – 'Your
grandad's on night turn this wik,' my grandmother Polly
would tell me – and this was hard for me to understand, a
term used to confuse a variety act with an act of work. He'd
go off to shovel his cullett on his bike, with his snap tin, and
when he came home he would always put a tin plate on the
gas cooker and fry up bacon and tomatoes in lard or
dripping for his breakfast or supper, cutting off huge doorsteps of bread to soak up the dip, and handing me small
torn-off pieces of this fat-sodden tomatoey bread. The tin-
plate cooking was something he'd picked up on the Western
Front, and he never changed his routine. I still have the tin
plate.

I found the visit to the Glass Museum very difficult. But
that evening, my cousin Pete and his wife joined me in the
hotel, and we sat for hours, talking over the old times
when he and I would sit under the chenille covering of the
dining table at my grandmother Ellen's house in our 'den'
after the men of the family had come back from watching
the Saints, and Ellen busied herself getting the tea, which
was always spam and salad with slices of boiled egg,
quarters of tomato, sliced bread and butter, and either
tinned fruit or a selection of fancies from Pimblett's, the
cake shop, while the sports results came on the radio.
Then, in the dark of our den, Pete and I would have to be
really quiet because all the men would systematically
check their Pools coupons. None of them ever won.
Betting, eh? It's a fact of life in St Helens. I remember
so clearly the fusty dark under the table, the smell of
green chenille and rag rugs, the crackle of the fire, and

whenever I hear the music which started *Sports Report*, I taste spam again.

'Do you remember the smell?' I asked Pete, 'and the sand dunes out the back that were all pink, and the cinder patch we used to play on, and that outside toilet with the spiders and the Izal toilet paper or newspaper, and Hatchie the dog, and how dirty the air was, and all that pollution?'

'No,' he said. 'It was home to me, and it was warm. It was always warm. I loved it.'

Part of me is still, like Pete, profoundly Lancashire at heart, and deeply, sometimes cloyingly, sentimental, just like our songs. My father and his younger brother Jud, the one who had run away to sea at 18 and been captured by the Japanese at 19 and held in a prison camp on the Burma railroad for the rest of the war, often burst into song later on Saturday night, after the spam, duetting on:

> My brother Sylvester
> He had thirty medals on his chest
> (Big chest) . . .

and then the ladies would sing:

> A North Country maid up to London had strayed
> Although with her nature it did not agree.
> She wept and she sighed and so bitterly she cried.
> 'How I wish once again in the North I could be
> For the oak and the ash and the bonny ivy tree
> They do flourish and grow in my own cou – oun-oun-try'

That one always confounded me, although I always asked for a repeat because I loved the tune and the sentiment, but I didn't understand how someone from St Helens could sing about oak and ash and ivy – was that really a tree? – because we didn't see many trees except in the park or when we went on holiday.

The day after the night of the meeting with Pete and his wife, I went with the Woods' family to look around Sutton at the places which had been important to Alice. In the graveyard of St Nicholas's Church was the family grave, but Billy, Alice's cousin, now in his sprightly late 80s, pointed to other graves as we went by. 'She used to play football an' all,' he'd say, pointing to another grave, 'and her!' Houses and sites of houses were pointed out, 'That's where Annie Salt lived, and that's where Sarah Pepper lived, and they were both in the same class as my mother,' Lynn told me. 'She used to say there was salt and pepper in her class at school! She never forgot that!'

We saw where Alice's house used to stand on Sutton Road, and the Methodist Church, now boarded up and used as storage. And the Pickled Egg was still standing, and selling pints and pickled eggs. Together we climbed the Old Bonk. There were no railway lines up there now, behind the neat row of miners' cottages in which Billy still lived, and in which John, Alice's brother, had set up home after his marriage. There was just a wild expanse of scrubby grassland, a huge plateau, on which Billy demonstrated where the football pitch and the running track used to be, and over there, below us, were the demolished engine sheds, and beyond, the Sutton Glassworks where Alice had worked in munitions. It was now some kind of industrial unit, but then, all St Helens has been turned into units. The colliery pit-heads once visible from the Bonk had been pulled down. There wasn't a plume of smoke in the air. It was almost possible to imagine that this was once countryside, albeit rough and treeless. And then back to the road, where colliers had sparked and clomped to their turns in their studded clogs. It brought back for me the memories of my first school, in the shadow of one of those pits, and the street outside which the miners, still unwashed and in their helmets, would trudge down with a clatter, some of them carrying ice-creams in cones sold from a cart at the colliery gate, held like white ostrich feathers against their black faces and white eyes.

Then it was on to visit the Parr family, to look at the huge framed oval portrait photograph which Sal had invested in at a time when hand-tinted photography cost the earth, and from there to see Bill, Lily's youngest brother, still alive and almost ninety. He'd been a professional sportsman in his time too, playing rugby for Oldham, among others, and was still, as we say in St Helens, 'all there'. 'I said you'd come at dinner time and mess us up!' he called as we walked in, but it was just a demonstration of the Parr straight-faced joshing. 'It's just what our Lily were like! You never could tell if she were being serious.'

Bill had collected together all he could find of Lily's mementoes, and his memory was faultless. 'There was a Susie Chorley from St Helens played for Dick, Kerr's an' all,' he said, 'and married one of the Owen twins from Haresfinch.' He was right. In fact, Dick, Kerr's also took Lydia Ackers, Lizzie Ashcroft, Emmie Grice, the Fairclough sisters and others from St Helens as well as Susie Chorley and Alice and Lily. Everyone in St Helens knew someone who knew someone whose lass had gone up to Preston, in the end, to play, or had played for as long as possible in St Helens before getting married and settling down to have a family.

So the rumours about how women's football destroyed female reproduction and female attractiveness to the opposite sex were as baseless as we'd always known them to be, but it was good to have confirmation, and real examples of grandchildren coming forward to show me their grans' photos and medals and cups, and to hear more stories about the esteem in which these women were held in my own home town. Only the local historians hadn't heard about the phenomenon of women's football and the part it had played in the social history of the town. Still, it was hardly surprising. St Helens isn't short of a role in social history.

'Have you ever thought of a blue plaque scheme?' I asked the woman at the press office of the St Helens Council. No she hadn't.

'Have you ever thought of campaigning for a blue plaque scheme?' I asked the local newspaper. They couldn't see it going down with the readers.

'Have you ever tried to set up a blue plaque scheme?' I asked the local historians.

'They'd only get robbed,' they said. Nice one.

On my last day in St Helens, I forced myself to take that long walk along Canal Street. The town planners had left one recognisable building on the corner of the street and Grove Street, the now-listed former Pilkington's Head Office, a curved Art Deco building with steel-framed windows, and the usual penny-pinching construction of St Helens brickwork which is neither Flemish nor English bond, but consists of five rows of stretchers to one row of headers – the cheapest possible way to ensure that a building can stand for a little while. Almost all St Helens has this pattern of brickwork, and this, in a town which actually made bricks, is an indicator of how little attention was paid to the town's own future. Like an American frontier town, it was regarded as a place to come to, then run from. I remember seeing the gates of this Head Office building teeming with human traffic and bicycles when the sirens went for the end of turns. Now, the place was silent, as was Canal Street. It was a hot sultry day.

On the left was the new Pilkington's, the longest float-glass conveyor in the UK, placed in St Helens as a placatory gesture to the workforce which had kept it alive. On the right, where there had been the train lines running into the second sector of the Pilkington's works, there was a new housing estate, privately built, no doubt to provide some customers for the acres of empty supermarket aisles. These pared-down houses, some with gables, all with patio doors and a choice of bathroom fittings and kitchen appliances, were laid out in curved streets. It looked like a pleasant place to live, if you had the money to do so, but it had an eerie stillness, quite unlike the lively activity in the older estate where Roy Parr lived, and where my cousin Pete and his parents had moved to after leaving my grandmother's home. There was something anti-communal about it.

At the end of this stretch, by the troll bridge, the estate continued, behind what had been the sandbanks and was now a grassed hump. There was a distribution unit on the left, where we'd once turned into the area of the fluorescent ponds. I decided to walk in that direction, past the speeding cars, and soon came to a sign announcing UGB Industrial Estate. That had to be the road to take. Here, the landscape had been transformed into scrub. There was all the vegetation which grows on slag – buddleias and meadowsweet and elder – as I trailed round the edge of the distribution unit towards the car lot which had been placed to mark the end of the street where my grandmother Ellen's house had once stood. I could see the site of the street, dwarfed by the brash expanse of second-hand cars, and the second bridge which we'd played under, Pete and I, behind the house. There was the UGB entrance. And on my left was one of the fluorescent pools.

Except that it wasn't shiny with oil and effluent. Under its surface, little fish appeared, and gulped and swam down again. There were bulrushes and water-lilies and a single lolling tree shading living waters. It looked alive, and it shouldn't have done. It was not what I expected.

I stood in an apex, a time-warp, caught between memory and reality, and between what I felt and what I saw, between the post-industrial soullessness of this compromised attempt at human economics which was clean and pointless, and the historical industrial filth and stink of a community struggling, together, to survive. And I wondered, I really wondered, about whether I should write this book because if I did, I knew that it would bring to the surface some of the recidivist sentimentality in me. I would have to write about me, as I, like Alice and Lily, am a Lancashire lass, with all the weight of hefty cultural baggage that entails, and I would have to reveal my soft underbelly.

So I hesitated, looking at the pond on my left which was no longer deadened by pollution, and at the tacky and deserted display of cheap cars on my right, now available on easy terms, and at the line drawn in front of me under the small former foundations of Ellen's house and the modern housing beyond, querying my motivation. I wanted to show how these women from my town were denied their right to be themselves, and to go with their curious combination of toughness, pragmatism, reckless enthusiasm and hedonism, and God-given ability, against the odds. Could I do that?

And, this is beyond my reasoning and beyond my scepticism, so bear with me. As I stood there, on what had been the foul playground of my childhood, I saw a heron, standing beside the pond, its grey and white observance, its beaked curiosity, its exotic presence startling me. Its appearance was as apposite as a nightingale in Berkeley Square, and as likely.

I had never seen a heron at close quarters, and if anyone had put heron and St Helens in close proximity, ever, I would have shot them down in flames. St Helens doesn't do herons. It's not in the job specification. But there it was and as I watched it took off into the sky, grey-white as smoke, soaring above what should have been effluent.

So this is why I wrote the story about Lily and Alice. I sensed the heron louder than a siren as he rose into the clear air, and he, although I don't know why, brought to mind one of the songs my Irish grandfather William used to sing, about love, and about doing what's in your heart. William's pure clear voice, and this perfect song, performed at all tearful family get-togethers, drifted into my head, and seemed a message from my St Helens family, who had all climbed Blackpool Tower for that liberating bird's-eye view of Lancashire and the angry Irish Sea. It was a message from the ladies, too.

This book is for Lancashire women past and present – Lily, and Alice, and the Dick, Kerr's Ladies, and the unnecessary battles they had to fight, and the relentless resources they brought to them – hope, and generosity, and heft, and fun.

Ex Terra Lucem, Lily and Alice. Raise your glass of milk stout to the Ladies, gentlemen.

Dear thoughts are in my mind
And my soul soars enchanted
As I hear the sweet lark sing
In the clear air of day.

It is this that gives my soul
All its joyous elation,
As I hear the sweet lark sing
In the clear air of the day.

GLITTER ON THE GARLAND

by Helen Juliet

Glitter on the Garland

Copyright © 2016 by Helen Juliet

ISBN-13: 978-1-9997067-0-8

DEDICATION

This first one's for Mommy, John, Dan, and Alyson, who are all totally brilliant.

Also for Colin, for his part in bringing the story to life.

Here's to many more joyous Christmases to come.

ACKNOWLEDGEMENTS

This book would never have happened without the all-hours beta reading of my brother John and the thorough and unrelenting editing of Alyson Pearce from Between The Lines Editing.

The beautiful cover is credited to Natasha Snow, of Natasha Snow Designs. Extreme kudos to her for not only getting the artwork right on the first attempt, but also turning it around in just three days.

The line '-because nothing says 'Christmas' like Bruce Willis in a vest-' is from my friends' original Christmas song 'Christmas Films Again' by Belly Of The Steal Beast, and is used in homage to them.

All my love goes to Dan, who gradually tricked me into writing at a real desk, in a real chair, with a real computer. I, and my back, thank him. Also, thanks for all the cuddles and support babe x

Final thanks go to the UK (and beyond) LGBT+ Fiction community, who made me feel so welcome this year. Especially to Alyson, who never stopped believing I could do this.

CHAPTER 1: MERRY CHRISTMAS

Matt couldn't say that his bedroom ceiling was all that interesting, but he was staring at it anyway. It was brightish-white in the weak sunshine that filtered around the edges of his curtains, and while there weren't any cracks in the paint or cobwebs in the corner, that was all it really had going for it.

He sighed and rested his arm under his head. This had to be the longest he had ever lay awake in bed on Christmas morning, but he couldn't seem to find the motivation to get up. It didn't really have the same appeal as the Christmases from his childhood, but he tried to tell himself it was going to be a fun day anyway.

When he and his sister had been little, they had camped out in the same room together—either his or hers—and eagerly kept each other awake trying to catch Father Christmas coming in to fill up their stockings. They never did.

This small bedroom had been his for just over a year, and he couldn't say it held any special memories like that for him. It didn't hold much of anything, really. His mum had encouraged him to hang up some of his posters once they'd moved in, but it hadn't felt right to try and recreate

7

his old room. His pictures and silly nick-knacks that had seemed so important at one time or another had either remained in boxes under his bed or had got lost in the move altogether.

He frowned at his own melancholy and squirmed around in the sheets and duvet that he had wrestled in to a sort of nest around him in his sleep. It wasn't like the room was completely boring. Over the past year, Matt had decorated it with a few new things—a couple of postcards featuring his favourite Reading F.C. players (a birthday present from Tilly,) a shot glass from their holiday in Tenerife, and a decent collection of books lined up on a shelf he'd been proud to hang himself. All things considered, it could have been worse.

He stretched and ran his fingers through his hair, ruffling where sleep had stuck it to his head. Maybe what he needed was new memories, not reminders of the past. Perhaps today he'd get some fun presents to liven up the space. Just because this Christmas was going to be a different sort of experience didn't necessarily mean it would be a bad one, and it was about time he started celebrating it. His phone said it was gone half nine, so he shuffled to the edge of his mattress with a grunt, then let gravity help him in flopping to the floor.

Once untangled from his bedding, he jumped a few times to get the blood flowing, then slipped on his dressing gown to make use of the bathroom whilst no one else was up. With his teeth brushed and his bladder empty, he felt more enthusiastic about tackling the day, and bounded back into the hallway.

The house was only a small bungalow, so it worked out that the living room was opposite his room, and he was easily able to see that there, over the cold electric fireplace, were three plump stockings that had been empty the night before.

"Nice one mum," he said with a smile. That was a good start.

First, he fiddled with the thermostat and got the heating going a notch higher, then he selected the stocking adorned with a rather malicious looking penguin that his sister had found hilarious and therefore claimed as her own. Carefully, he crept into the bedroom next door, and approached the lump that was huddled under the duvet in the near darkness.

"Tills," he whispered, shaking his sister's shoulder. "It's Christmas, wake up."

Tilly gave a disgruntled moan that only a fourteen-year-old could truly master and reached out to yank her stocking from his grasp. She huddled it to her body as if it was a source of warmth, making all the packets of sweets lurking inside crinkle and crunch.

"Do you want tea?"

Another put-upon groan.

"Maybe later, yeah?" he suggested, but was met with a light snore. He chuckled and rolled his eyes as he tip-toed back out again and pulled the door to.

If Tilly wanted to sleep, then that was fine, but Matt was normally on his second cuppa of the day by now. He moved past both their rooms and into the kitchen to flick on the kettle. As it was merrily heating up, he went and fetched the other two stockings, laying them carefully on the counter as he reached up for a couple of mugs, teabags, milk and sugar.

He drummed his fingers absently as the hot water peaked. It would be fine. They would just have a nice quiet day, the three of them together.

Balancing the two over-stuffed stockings in the crook of his left arm, he grasped the two mugs of tea firmly in his right hand, then slowly traversed the study and around to his mum's room at the back of the bungalow. He managed to give a soft knock and waited for the answering call of "Come in" before he entered. His mum was already awake and sat up in her bed against the pillows, looking out of the window at the bright, wintery day, which was a good sign.

She'd done okay this year, keeping things together under difficult circumstances. She'd hardly missed any time off work and still made sure he and Tilly had gotten to school or hockey practice or whatever party was going on, with minimal grumblings from all of them.

But on the weekends, when they didn't have anywhere specific to be, he'd watched her struggle many a time to drum up the energy to even get out of bed. It had scared him, seeing her staring at the walls for hours on end, no more tears left to cry. He understood why, especially having done his own fair share of staring at nothing this morning, but he was relieved to see that she was galvanised for the day ahead.

As much as he loved Christmas, he was also now old enough to understand how much pressure it put on the people organising it, and he was worried his mum might have been thinking she'd have to organise the day by herself. That was why he was there, ready and eager with presents and tea.

Tea that he almost sloshed onto the carpet as he tripped over the door runner, and presents that slipped from his grasp as he prioritised the hot beverages over tacky toys and chocolate coins.

"Ah." He froze and looked down at the mess he'd made. At least only a few drops of tea had splashed his hand, not enough to scald. He just had to hope there was nothing breakable hidden inside the novelty woollen socks.

His mum just laughed though. "Oh dear." She swung her legs out of bed to get up and help. "Never mind."

"Sorry," Matt said sheepishly. "I come bearing tea."

He held out her favourite mug to take off his hands, and they both crouched down to scoop up the little gifts that had escaped their confines. Matt and Tilly had sorted their mum's stocking out, so he tried to hide their presents away without her seeing, at the same time attempting to get a good look at what he had waiting in his own one.

"Oi, no peeking," his mum berated with a flick on his nose. She gathered up her tea and the once-more bulging stocking, then made her way back under the warmth of the covers.

Her pyjamas hadn't always been that loose on her, Matt was sure. Then again, the dark circles under her eyes hadn't been as prominent, either. It was sad to think she'd changed so much, but he didn't say anything as he hopped under the duvet, too, and poked her with his cold feet.

She shrieked and glared at him. "You can sit on the floor if you're going to keep that up," she threatened. Matt crossed his legs to tuck his bare feet under his pyjama-clad legs, and promised to behave. "Any sign of life from the monster?" she asked.

"Nothing intelligible," he said.

He took a gulp of tea, then swapped their stockings, so they had the correct ones ready to open. They had bought a new matching set of three the previous year. His had a rather wonky Christmas tree stitched on the front, while his mum's had a snowman that had seemingly indulged in a bit too much eggnog, judging from its lopsided eyes.

Last year, they had been determined to start some new traditions, and there had been a fierce sense of valour to their efforts. But this year, reality had seeped in during the autumn months, and they had entered December knowing that this was it. Things would never really be the same again.

'Things' being his family, of course, and its untimely demise.

It was easier to think in abstracts, he found. The details were far too messy. 'Things' were bad for now, but 'things' would get better someday. 'Details' involved words like 'affair' and 'divorce,' and brought up memories that everyone—Matt included—would really rather not recall.

"I think she was up until the early hours of the morning arguing with people on Tumblr," Matt said, remembering his sister's early morning mood.

His mum raised her eyebrows and nodded sagely. "Well, I'm confident she sure showed them."

"Yes, all of them," Matt agreed, blowing on his tea. "The internet is now correct."

"Right." His mum picked absently at one of the threads hanging from the stocking snowman's scarf. Matt could guess what was coming, and he really wished it wasn't. "What do you think they're doing now?"

Tilly would probably have snapped that she didn't care what they were bloody doing, but Matt was a little more diplomatic than that—at least he hoped.

"I don't know mum." He sipped on his tea, not quite meeting her eye. "But it doesn't really matter, does it? We're going to have fun today, no matter what they do."

11

His mum wrapped the thread around her finger, causing the skin around it to go white. "And then you'll see him tomorrow?"

Matt shrugged. "That's the plan," he admitted.

Last year, everything had been in such turmoil that he'd been glad to hear his dad had taken his new family on a Caribbean cruise. It meant they didn't have to face each other. But this year they were expected to do the 'modern family' thing and split the holidays. Matt wasn't sure he was looking forward to it.

"You're going to see Aunt Karen, aren't you?" He changed the subject, giving her what he hoped was a cheery smile.

"Yes." She nodded firmly and unravelled the thread from around her finger. "In return for acting like a human climbing frame, I am apparently going to be rewarded with much food and booze."

Matt chuckled. His cousins were both under ten and rather fond of their Aunt Dawn, who had always spoiled them rotten, mostly with the intention of winding her little sister up. He was sure his mum would have a much better day than him and Tilly, but he didn't say that out loud. Instead he poked at his stocking.

"Is it present time yet?" he asked hopefully.

His mum nodded and placed her tea down so she could pick up her own one to test the weight. "I'm expecting a puppy and a diamond necklace, yeah?"

"Oh of course," said Matt with a wink, ignoring the squirm in his stomach. It was a lot harder for all three of them to buy presents this year, but he knew they'd done their best. His mum had gone back to work, and he and Tilly both had Saturday jobs, so they weren't exactly poor. But they all appreciated it would be a step down from the standards of the past several years.

He and Tilly had joined forces on a couple of homemade presents, and they had pounced online the second it turned midnight on Black Friday. He was confident they would have a lovely day and each get presents that made them feel loved. That was all he really wanted.

"Matilda Bartlett!" He banged on the interconnecting wall between the two bedrooms, ignoring his mum's outraged hiss about waking the neighbours. As far as Matt was concerned, if anyone wasn't awake by ten o'clock on Christmas morning, they bloody well deserved what they got.

An indignant shriek resonated through the wall, and Matt wiggled his eyebrows at his mum, who tried to look cross despite the twitch of her lips that betrayed her.

"Wah?" was the muffled reply.

"Get your arse in here before we have all the fun without you!"

It took several minutes and another round of tea to finally coax Tilly out of her pit, then they all gathered in their pyjamas around the Christmas tree in the living room before delving into their stockings and swapping the presents they'd bought for one another. There were a few from Nana Jenkins and mum's sister Karen, and even a generic £10 voucher for several stores from their godparents to both Matt and Tilly, but all in all it didn't take long.

Matt loved every single one of his gifts, from the shaving kit to the scarf, to the socks adorned with Father Christmas mooning his bum. Those, he gratefully slipped over his cold toes. He had a new poster of the latest Star Wars film to stick on his wall thanks to Tilly, and an awesome new clock made out of a pressed glass beer bottle of his favourite Japanese brew. His room would look a good deal more cheerful after all.

But as they all fiddled with the presents they'd announced to be their favourites, the day lapsed into an apprehensive silence. It was only eleven o'clock.

"Okay," Matt said, clapping his hands. "I shotgun first shower, since I'll take about three nanoseconds and you guys will need an entire dynasty between you."

Tilly walloped him good-naturedly with a throw cushion from the couch.

"Just because we're the pretty ones." She pouted and rubbed her eyes, shaking out her sandy blonde hair.

They both had their father's greyish-blue eyes, which Matt wasn't sure how he felt about anymore, and the same mouth that seemed more likely to purse on Matt and smirk on Tilly. Despite his mousy brown hair, they were easy to spot as siblings, with their lean build, medium height and broad shoulders. Tilly hated hers, but Matt felt it was the only aspect of his appearance that made him look masculine some days.

"You wish." He pinched Tilly's side as their mum sighed. "So, I'll go first, then I can start peeling veg or something?" He really had little idea what it took to pull a Christmas dinner together.

Their mum gave another tut and gathered her presents together. "Tilly can go next after you, and I'll set up the kitchen so we don't set off the smoke detectors and get the fire brigade round."

"That was one time!" Tilly protested.

Matt was happy, though. It seemed like a plan was in order.

That only guarantees us the next few hours though, he thought, stepping under the spluttering shower head that always tried its best. Normally they'd take a drive to visit Gran and Pops, or have some of their local friends around to break up the day. That didn't really seem possible this year.

Matt's dad's parents hadn't appeared all that bothered when Matt and Tilly had phoned up to ask if they wanted to see them, and their old neighbours weren't likely to drive over town just to drop in for a mince pie and a quick hello. Their Nana Jenkins would probably have loved to have seen them, but she was all the way up in the Midlands, so they'd agreed to drive up from Hampshire in the New Year to spend a weekend with her then instead.

There was the Doctor Who Christmas special later that evening, he supposed. Since they'd all received a couple of DVDs each, there was bound to be something else they could snuggle up in their onesies and watch, but that seemed a little...tame. Defeatist. He wasn't sure what else they could really do though.

They could figure it out later, rather than worrying about it just then.

Towelling off his hair, Matt vacated the bathroom and shouted that it was free before darting into his bedroom.

What today needed, he decided, was a truly hideous Christmas jumper to lighten the mood. It just so happened, he had a pretty impressive selection to choose from.

He wouldn't say his every day wardrobe was anything to particularly shout about. Anything more complicated than jeans and a t-shirt bamboozled him, and even then he tended to just stick to the generic labels rather than fun designs. He considered a polo shirt a bit flash, and only owned a pair of smart, black shoes because they had been his old school ones.

But Christmas jumpers were supposed to be terrible. It was literally impossible to get them wrong. Sadly, he'd grown out of a few the last year or so, but he still had several to choose from as he shoved on his jeans and the mooning Santa socks.

There was one that sported a tree decked in 3D tinsel, wrapped present boxes and a string of working lights that had been a real hit a couple of years ago. It was impossible to wash, though, and after several wears and numerous months shoved in the bottom of a drawer, its smell left a lot to be desired.

After much deliberation—and almost picking the one that said 'I love sprouts!' with some dubious looking green gas designed onto the back—he went for a classic-knit look one with the inscription 'Now I have a machine gun. Ho. Ho. Ho.' After all, nothing said 'Christmas' like Bruce Willis in a vest.

By the time midday rolled around, Matt was confidently peeling potatoes as Tilly applied extra glitter to her eyelids and shouted along (incorrectly he was sure) to some infectiously catchy K-Pop boyband from her room. The clicking on of his mum's hairdryer suggested it might be a while before he was rescued from solitary kitchen duty, but he didn't really mind; he was focused on the task and not worrying about anything else for a change.

That, however, was the precise moment the doorbell sounded.

Matt stilled, unsure what he should do. They absolutely were not expecting anyone, and his mind immediately flashed to ridiculous places involving Jehovah's Witnesses, an axe murderer pretending his car had broken down, or

15

the next-door neighbours complaining about the mispronounced Korean vibrating through the floorboards.

He was the only one not indisposed, however, so he wiped his hands on a tea towel, and edged towards the front door. It only had a small pane of blurred glass in the top half of the door, and he peered through to confirm that, yes, someone was on the other side. And they weren't going away. He glanced back over his shoulder, but it seemed like he was still on his own. So, he took a deep breath and unlatched the bolts, wondering who on earth it could be.

On the other side stood Aedan Gallagher, and Matt's heart all but stopped.

CHAPTER 2: ROOM AT THE INN

Occasionally, aspects of the universe crossed paths in ways that made Matt feel so out of place and off kilter, that it simply struck him dumb as he attempted to wrap his head around how two such unlikely events had come together. Like when he and his family had been on holiday in Tokyo and the elevator doors in the airport hotel had opened to reveal Matt's football coach, Dave Peterson, standing there with his own family. Despite seeing him once a week every week for several years during his childhood, reconciling suddenly being face to face whilst halfway around the world was too much for Matt to contemplate. When life held an infinite amount of possibilities, it was challenging to fathom the chances of such a coincidence taking place.

Some things just didn't belong with other things, and witnessing them come together created an inherent sense of wrongness that troubled Matt deeply. One day last year, during afternoon registration, he'd heard the 'trendy' lot—who normally only spent Mondays bragging about what parties they'd been too that weekend, and how much alcohol and sex they'd had at them—discussing one of Matt's favourite dystopian sci-fi book series that was being

17

adapted into a Netflix TV show. Matt already knew, of course. He spent hours and hours on the message boards and forum threads filled with other like-minded fans, dissecting the canon, posting crazy theories, and writing go-to technical manuals for others to reference. To hear the character names being mispronounced by people who, Matt knew for a fact, mixed up Star Wars and Star Trek had felt like a violation of his inner thoughts.

Life was made up of different spheres. Home and school, family and friends, online and IRL, reality and fiction. When they collided, it was hard to know where you stood in the world anymore.

Like when Aedan Gallagher showed up at Matt's family Christmas, completely unannounced and without precedent. That was the kind of event that confounded Matt to the point of muteness, as he wrestled with how such an incident could come to pass.

"Ta-da!" Aedan flung his arms out and wiggled his un-gloved fingers in showy jazz hands.

He had a flimsy blue carrier bag dangling from one arm, clad in the puffy sleeve of his parker jacket, the contents of which clinked as it swung. His neck and head were almost swallowed up by the faux-fur trim of his hood and a chunky-knit scarf with a diamond print pattern. The peak of his coiffured blond hair jutted out triumphantly into the cold air, and his normally pale cheeks were stained pink from the wind, making Matt wonder how long he'd been outside. As usual, he was sporting what he called his 'pirate eyeliner', and a hint of glitter just under his brows.

Matt realised he was staring when Aedan cleared his throat, brought his arms back in, and then shot them out again along with a pointed toe and an even louder "Ta-da!"

"Aedan." Matt spluttered, not wanting to be rude but also panicking more than he really should have been. Friends, no matter how close, shouldn't show up to your house on Christmas Day without even texting first. In fact, as far as Matt knew, none of his friends even had his new address.

Aedan had always been like that, though, just inserting himself into Matt's life whether he wanted him to or not.

When they'd first been placed in the same class together in Year Seven, Aedan had just decided that Matt was going to be his best friend, and sat beside him in every lesson. Matt had only recently moved into the area before the start of that term, and had been too shy to make any other friends, so initially he hadn't minded, simply because it meant not being alone.

However, he'd soon come to realise he quite liked loud and quirky Aedan, with his odd sandwich inventions and 80s pop music obsession, which was lucky because as it turned out, he was stuck with him from then on. It was also lucky for Aedan, since, through no fault of his own, it became quickly apparent that not many other people liked him all that much.

Matt didn't understand what 'pikey' or 'tinker' meant when he was eleven, but as he grew up and learned more about the gypsy camp site across town where Aedan lived, he began to understand how much those words hurt him. Pikeys stole things, and tinkers were dirty and had diseases, but Aedan was never like that. In fact, there were several Irish Traveller children in their school, and while some of them had behavioural problems, they weren't really as awful as they were made out to be. Matt always suspected they only acted out half the time because other students went around calling them names, and the teachers never expected them to achieve much at all.

Aedan wasn't really like that either—he never started fights or got caught smoking behind the bike sheds. He was more likely to get into trouble for falling asleep in French class, handing in the wrong homework or being ill for days on end without ever producing a doctor's note. One time, he'd announced he would no longer be wearing his school regulation tie, and substituted it for several different skinny hipster ones he'd salvaged from a charity shop down town. Matt had to admit they looked pretty awesome, but they had earned Aedan a detention for every day he'd refused to wear the proper attire. In the end, he had done nine days.

Aedan just wasn't afraid of people. When Matt quietly assumed he wasn't invited when other kids organised trips to the cinema or ice rink, Aedan dragged him along regardless, and gradually, they had begun to be accepted. Much like Matt, when other boys in their year realised Aedan wasn't going to get them into trouble and was actually pretty fun to be around, their circle of friends expanded. For that, Matt was grateful.

That didn't mean he'd even been comfortable having anyone over. He'd very rarely had Aedan or anyone else home to his old place, and never when any of his family had been around to snoop. Since the pain and upheaval of the divorce, he hadn't even considered it. Home was where he re-collected himself. It was his private space, and he didn't have any real experience of juggling that with his school life.

So, despite the fact he and Aedan messaged pretty much all the time (sometimes dozens of times a day,) Matt still was completely thrown at having Aedan land on his doorstep whilst he'd been in the middle of peeling spuds. Which was why he continued to have an issue with formulating any more words in the face of the wriggling jazz hands.

As if on cue, the jazz hands dropped, and Aedan bit his lip. "This was a terrible idea, wasn't it?" he said flatly. His brown eyes dropped, and he took a step back towards the quiet road on which Matt's mum's house stood.

The action woke Matt up again. Because, as unsettled as he was, his other instinctual reaction was that he liked Aedan very much, and really, it couldn't be that bad to have him meet his family, could it? What was the worst that could happen?

"No!" His hand jerked forwards. "No, don't be silly, I was just a bit surprised, that's all!" He waved Aedan over. "Do you want to come in? Is everything alright?"

Aedan lifted his eyebrows hopefully, then gave him a lopsided grin. "Yeah, fine babe," he said cheerfully, stepping back towards him. "It's just that Christmas was a bit of a bust around mine, so I thought I might see if you had room for one more."

"Why didn't you text?" Matt asked, then kicked himself. What an unwelcoming thing to say. "I mean, then I wouldn't have gawked at you on the doorstep."

Aedan didn't seem all that bothered, by the way he shrugged his shoulders. "I didn't really think. I just got a cab," he said.

He was smiling, but there was something off in his eyes that Matt didn't understand. What did he mean by 'a bust'? He had a large family. He couldn't have been lonely at his place, so why had he come to Matt?

Had something bad happened?

If that was the case, Matt had to swallow his anxiety. Aedan had been there for him over the past year or so, when he'd wanted to disappear as his whole world fell apart. Aedan had kept him coming out to see their friends and coaxed him through his exams. If there was a problem, Matt owed it to Aedan to help.

"Well, of course it's fine," he said and ushered him in, like it had been okay all along. "I mean, there's nothing much going on, but I'm sure you'll be more than welcome."

Aedan hesitated. "Are you sure I'm not intruding?" he asked.

He wrung his hands together. Matt guessed they were cold judging from the pink tips, and he felt awful for making him stand outside.

"No, absolutely not," he said emphatically. "I'm sorry, you just surprised me is all." He repeated himself from earlier. "I'd love for you to come in, as long as you don't mind a quiet, boring sort of day."

He'd meant to say it as a joke, but it had come out a little ruefully.

Aedan though skipped up and gave him half a sideways hug, before bounding into the hallway.

"Oh don't talk nonsense darling, look!" He held up the blue bag that clanked again. "I bought prosecco. I'm not that much of a terrible guest!" Leaning in close to Matt's ear, Aedan cupped his neck, giving him goose bumps. "I know how to make a decent bribery," he teased in a loud whisper, then gave him a wink.

Matt blinked and moved so Aedan could step inside. Aedan was never shy about invading personal space, but it normally didn't make his spine tingle. Strange.

Forgetting about it for the time being, he closed the door and offered to take Aedan's coat as he shrugged it from his shoulders. Matt hung it—and the obscenely long scarf—on the rack, then turned back around. As he did, he took in Aedan's attire, and slapped his hand over his eyes, giving a loud, mocking gasp.

"Bloody hell mate, I think you blinded me!" He grinned, then peeked out between his fingers.

Instead of taking offense, Aedan preened and gave a twirl. "I thought you'd appreciate it, although I must say, yours is a little tame this year. Where's the one with all the lights on?"

Aedan's Christmas jumper did indeed put Matt's Die Hard one to shame. It was entirely made of glittery red, green and black thread, and had gold sequins making up the words 'Don we now our GAY apparel!' stitched on the front.

It was so very Aedan that Matt had to grin, and he reached out casually to touch his sleeve. "Subtle," he said playfully. "The light-up one died a stinky death, so I'll just have to let you win this time."

"Marvellous," Aedan said. "Bravo to moi."

He bowed, accepting the victory, then yanked off his trainers to reveal socks with at least two holes developing at the toes. Matt made a mental note to make him take a pair of his new ones later. He couldn't stand the idea of cold feet, even on other people.

"Come on through, I'll find my mum," Matt said. He picked up the heavy bag of prosecco and led the way to the kitchen. "My sister will come out when she's ready, but that might not be for several hours judging by the average time it takes pick an outfit these days."

"A girl after my own heart," Aedan said solemnly.

Matt plonked the bottles down and set about pulling them free from the bag.

"Oh, nice." He eyed up the labels, although, in his experience, you couldn't really go wrong with prosecco. He opened his mouth to suggest a cup of tea first, only to turn around and discover that Aedan had already found the champagne flutes in the cupboard, as if drawn there by homing beacon. Bubbly it was then.

Chapter 2: Room at the Inn

The hairdryer was still going, so Matt decided not to disturb his mum for now. Instead he handed over the first bottle of sparkling wine for Aedan to tackle. He shimmied around the kitchen like he'd been there a dozen times, slim hips sashaying as he hummed something under his breath and whipped the foil off the bottle's cork with a flourish.

It hadn't been a shock in the slightest when Aedan had come out as gay back in Year Ten. Matt always felt anyone with eyes could tell that about him. He wasn't sure if that was homophobic to think that. He hoped not. There was always just so much glamour about him that it hadn't seemed possible he could be straight.

The fact of it was that when Aedan had been caught making out with one of the boys from the Catholic school down the road—the Deputy Head's son no less. Matt had just shrugged his shoulders and felt it had only really been a matter of time. It hadn't particularly affected their friendship in any major way. It was just another thing that made up the package that was Aedan Gallagher.

Matt busied himself by putting the other bottles into the already bulging fridge and wondered how his mum and sister were going to react to meeting his best friend after so many years.

"Ooh, nice socks babe," Aedan said gleefully, using a tea towel to open the prosecco. Matt looked at him for second before dropping his eyes to his feet and laughing at the Santas with their bums out.

"Christmas present," he said, wiggling his toes. "Does that give me extra jumper points?"

Aedan shook his head. "Nah, I still win the ugly jumper contest. I'm afraid."

The cork suddenly burst free with a loud POP! and the boys automatically cried out in jubilation.

"Matt?"

He hadn't even noticed the hairdryer had stopped blasting from the other room. Matt turned around to find his mum entering the kitchen, one novelty Christmas tree earring hanging from one lobe, the other still gripped between her fingers as she took in the sight of a stranger in her house.

Irrational guilt immediately swept through Matt, and he darted between them. Why, he wasn't entirely sure. Did he imagine they were going to attack each other like territorial dogs?

"Sorry," he spluttered. "Mum, this is my friend Aedan.

He was hoping he could hang out." That sounded less imposing than 'crash our Christmas', but he was really hoping she didn't see it like that. It wasn't like they were bursting at the seams with people after all.

"Aedan?" she repeated, her gaze flicking between him and Matt. Aedan had paused with a hopeful smile on his face, the opened prosecco and a half-full champagne flute in his two hands. "Oh," Matt's mum continued, her eyes widening. "Aedan Aedan? Your friend from school?"

"The one and only!" Aedan announced with a little curtsy. A hint of worry flashed across his face, like he already knew she wouldn't like him, or something. Matt wasn't sure.

His mum let out a delighted little "Oh!" noise, and dropped the second earring onto the counter so she could nip across the kitchen floor. "It's so nice to finally meet you! I'm Matt's mum, Dawn, I've heard so much about you!"

She opened her arms to give him a hug, but he had his hands full with the bubbly, so he sidestepped her at the last second. "Hi Dawn. Oops, careful!" He held up the glass and bottle by way of an explanation. Instead, he leaned over to place a noisy kiss on her cheek, with a confidence and familiarity that made Matt's heart skip a beat. She didn't seem fazed either, as she simply squeezed one of his shoulders, then stepped back to let him finish pouring the drink.

Matt had always been so sure that he didn't want his friends meeting his family, that it would be wrong and uncomfortable and they would somehow spill his darkest secrets about him to one another just by being in the same room. He wasn't really prepared for them to be at ease together.

"Matt, you should have said Aedan was coming over," his mum chastised as Aedan handed her the first full glass.

Chapter 2: Room at the Inn

"Honestly sweetheart, it's so nice to meet you. Matt talks about you all the time."

"Mum." His tone held a hint of warning he hoped she caught. She was going to make him sound weird if she kept saying that.

Aedan just gave a big grin though as he poured the next glass. "Oh no, it's all my fault. my Christmas was a non-starter, so I thought I'd surprise Matt. Sometimes I really ought to think before I act." He winked at Matt. "But he'd told me how nice you were, so I hoped you wouldn't mind."

Matt wasn't sure he'd ever talked much about his mum, had he? Was Aedan just being polite? Whatever it was, it worked; his mum placed her hand on her chest and beamed.

"That's so sweet of you, of course we don't mind having a guest."

"We've got enough food to include him, haven't we?" Matt asked, sure they did. He'd been dragged along to the supermarket yesterday, and was quite confident there hadn't been anything left by the time they had departed.

"Oh no," Aedan said hastily, waving a hand at Matt. "No, you don't have to feed me."

Matt's mum tutted before he could say any more. "We've got enough food going around to feed an army. I always buy too much. You'd be doing me a favour if you stayed for lunch—unless you already ate at home?"

Aedan shook his head, relief encouraging his shoulders to drop, but something not so pleasant tugged the corner of his mouth down ruefully, just for a second. Matt was sure he was the only one to notice.

"No, I didn't eat already thanks. If you're really sure, I'd love to stay for lunch."

Aedan didn't talk about his home or his family much; Matt had noticed that over the years. He'd watched that Gypsy Wedding TV show and gleaned the odd thing from the internet, but Aedan had always been hesitant to elaborate, saying it was all a bit dull and he was keen to move out as soon as he could. He had a couple of older brothers that always sounded to be in varying amounts of trouble with the law, and possibly a sister that Matt thought might have gotten married a little while ago.

Traveller men, particularly Irish travellers, were very macho from what Matt could tell. They worked with their hands and provided for their women, and probably didn't have much time for a pretty, gay boy like Aedan. Did that have anything to do with him abandoning his own family today in favour of Matt's?

Aedan didn't seem inclined to talk any further about why he'd ditched his own Christmas, though, and at that point Tilly emerged from her room in a waft of perfume to distract them. A lack of perky beats indicated she'd turned her music off and was ready to grace them with her presence. She was probably curious as to who Matt and their mum were talking to, but where he would be shy at realising there was a stranger lurking beyond his door, she bounded out with a flick of her hair and flutter of her false eyelashes. More than likely, she hoped they would get a reaction out of Matt for being a little too outrageous for just hanging around the house. Matt had worked out a while ago, though, that the best way to wind his baby sister up was to ignore anything she was obviously doing for attention.

Aedan, however, was another story. "Ooh, gorgeous lashes darling! Are they the Cheryl Cole ones?"

Tilly stopped short and assessed him. "Yes, they are." An approving smile crept onto her face. "Thanks...?"

"Aedan," he supplied, handing Matt his glass of prosecco.

Her eyebrows shot up and she snapped her head over to Matt. "Oh Aedan," she said in a delighted tone he didn't really like. Bloody hell, his family were going to make him sound like a stalker.

"Yeah, Aedan, this is my little sister Tilly." He smiled at her, silently begging her not to say anything inadvertently rude. "Aedan's going to spend the day with us."

He could see the obvious question of why? flit across her face, but something in their sibling bond apparently worked as she just nodded. "Cool," she said. "Can I have one of those?"

26

Chapter 2: Room at the Inn

Aedan laughed as Matt's mum considered the prosecco Tilly had indicated. "Alright," she said, then held up a finger. "But with orange juice."

"Sure." Tilly agreed eagerly, and ran to get the carton from the fridge.

"Right," said Aedan brightly. He finished by pouring his own glass and then held it up. "Merry Christmas, darlings!"

"Merry Christmas!" they chorused together.

Aedan didn't thank them again for inviting him in, but Matt could read the appreciation on his face. Suddenly the blurring of lines between friends, family, school and home didn't seem all that peculiar; Aedan was slotting in just fine as they launched into the epic task of getting Christmas dinner together.

Once she'd finally attached her second, abandoned earring, Matt's mum got him back peeling veg as Tilly flicked the oven on and unwrapped the chicken they were going to cook.

"I hope you don't mind?" Matt's mum looked up from reading the back of the stuffing packet. "A turkey is a bit big for just a few of us."

Aedan gave a dismissive flick of his wrist as he rummaged around in his backpack he'd brought in from the hall. "I think turkey's too dry," he admitted. He looked up, absently checking his hair was still in place with a skim of his fingers over his head. "I'd rather have chicken, or beef."

"Did you know," Tilly said excitedly, "that in Poland they have carp? Olesia says her family get a live one, and it lives in the bath tub until Christmas day!"

"And then what do they do they do with it?" Aedan asked, innocently batting his golden eyelashes. Matt saw his mum's face turn green and he threw up his hands quickly.

"They release it back into the lake in the Great Carp Freeing Ceremony," he cried. "Then they all go home and eat tofu."

Luckily that made everyone laugh, and his mum shook it off. She'd never been good with fish, something about

27

being "too slimy and staring back at you with dead eyes." Matt couldn't blame her.

"Ooh yummy, roast tofu," Aedan joked. He'd finally found what he'd been looking for in his bag; a portable Bluetooth speaker that he placed on the counter before he pulled his phone out of his back pocket. "Do you guys fancy some tunes?" he asked, flicking through his apps.

"Oh gosh," said his mum and frowned. "I never put music on any more. I can't even remember the last time I got a CD out."

Aedan looked horrified. "How do you even get through the day?" His tone was friendly, but Matt knew him well enough to realise that under the joke, he was being pretty serious. "I've got some fabulous festive ear-catchers to get us going. Just you wait."

Tilly scrunched up her nose. "Not if it's crap seventies Christmas songs I am so sick of those."

"Ahh," Aedan cooed as he wiggled his eyebrows at her. "How about Bon Jovi, Anna Kendrick, and a bit of Christina Aguilera?"

"Christmas music?" she queried. He nodded, and showed her his intended playlist. "Oh!" she exclaimed. "You've got that one from Home Alone, and The Darkness!"

Matt felt something warm wash over him as he watched his best friend impress his sister, and it only grew as they started singing loudly and jumped around the kitchen.

No, it didn't seem like Aedan was all that out of place there after all.

CHAPTER 3: FESTIVE CHEER

As it happened, none of them were particularly gifted in the kitchen department. They argued about the best way to tackle roasting the potatoes and managed to scald each other at least once with flecks of boiling oil. The oven wasn't big enough for all the food and they had to work out a schedule rotating things in the microwave and covering dishes with tea towels and tinfoil. Matt burned the peas. He wasn't ever sure that was something you could do, but he apparently managed it.

It was mostly okay, though, what with all the free-flowing prosecco and a refreshing mix of more up-to-date Christmas music from Aedan's playlist. There was one unpleasant moment, however, as Matt and his mum got into an argument over how thick they should do the gravy, and whether they should use the water from the broccoli. Matt thought that was gross, but his mum insisted the vitamins were good for them. That led to Matt shouting that was pretty stupid considering the amount of fat, salt and general calories were in the meal as a whole. His mum had stormed off with her glass of bubbly into the garden, which had pissed Matt off initially as he'd felt embarrassed at Aedan seeing them fight. Until he realised they were fighting over fucking *gravy* and he slunk out to apologise.

They used the broccoli water. What did it really matter after all?

As Matt went back to stirring the pan, his mum and sister migrated to the study to extend the table and then lay it with the special Christmas linen they only used once a year. He jumped as he felt an arm slip around him, and Aedan gave him a half-hug from behind.

"You're a knob," he teased, and Matt blushed.

"Yeah, well," he grumbled. "What's Christmas without a few pointless arguments?"

Aedan patted his chest and gave him a quick peck on the cheek. "Precisely. Thanks for letting me be a part of it. You're so cute when you're mad." He slapped Matt's backside, making him yelp in a most undignified fashion.

After a shocked pause, Matt burst out laughing, and Aedan joined him. He was pleasantly surprised at how un-awkward he felt. It was probably the prosecco's fault.

Aedan was often quite tactile. He'd reigned it in after coming out, probably wary of how Matt would take it. After a few weeks of awkwardness Matt had become bored of that, and started initiating back slaps and head rubs himself. They had soon gotten back to normal.

In fact, until now, Matt realised he'd been pretty hands-off today. He wondered if there was a reason behind that? Perhaps he was just shy in front of Matt's family? He'd probably be a bit more like his usual self now, although Matt wasn't sure he was exactly after another arse slap.

Their Christmas dinner probably wasn't going to go down in history as anything spectacular, but once everything was doused in a puddle of (perfectly fine) gravy it was all rather yummy. Crackers were pulled, terrible jokes told and tacky toys pinged across the table. The four of them ate until their bellies were sore, and even then, Matt found room for an extra Yorkshire pudding.

When his mum produced a Christmas pudding for dessert, they all groaned, but then Aedan excitedly asked if there was any brandy in the house. A quick check of the cupboards confirmed there was.

"Alright, give me a second!" Aedan ushered them all to sit down whilst he poured a good glug of spirit into the smallest pan and began to heat it on the hob.

Matt frowned nervously as he took another sip of bubbly. "You're not doing what I think you're doing, are you?"

"Hush, you," Aedan called back from the kitchen. "You're going to love this, I promise."

Matt looked at his mum, who bit her lip.

"Oh, don't be so boring." Tilly cheerfully lifted her own glass. She and their mum had been in a silent sort of battle as to how much prosecco was ending up in the Buck's Fizz ratio; Matt suspected Tilly was winning thanks to the extra top-ups Aedan kept giving her.

"Okay boys and girls," Aedan said. He walked carefully back to the table with a ladle full of hot brandy, then fished out a lighter from his back pocket. "Are you ready?"

"Oh God," said Matt, peeking out from behind his fingers.

"Yes, yes!" Tilly bounced in her chair.

Luckily the Christmas pudding was on a plate with quite a high rim, as Aedan liberally sloshed the brandy all over it, then clicked his lighter on against the top.

The pudding lit with a *whomph!* Aedan and Tilly cheered as Matt and his mum gasped in shock. But then Matt laughed and gave Aedan a round of applause.

"Alright," he admitted reluctantly as the blue flames danced. "That was pretty cool."

They played Twenty Questions as they waited for the pudding to become edible, then when they really couldn't fit anything more inside their stomachs, they all chipped in to load the dishwasher and clean the up kitchen.

Matt's mum had obviously been inspired by their after-dinner game and went rummaging around in her room until she returned triumphantly with Trivial Pursuit, Taboo and Articulate!, which meant the next few hours passed in a happy blur of competitive yelling and much cheating on everybody's part. After a particularly brutal round of Charades, Tilly and Matt's mum announced they were going to go for a walk to clear the cobwebs and help digest their dinner from earlier. Mostly, Matt suspected, so they could crack out the cheese and biscuits when they got back.

Aedan said he had something he needed to do, if Matt didn't mind him borrowing his computer. Matt didn't, of course, and decided to stay and keep their guest company out of politeness. But he also liked the idea of having Aedan to himself for an hour or so after all that activity.

Matt lounged sleepily on his bed with a cup of tea and one of his new books, glancing up regularly to watch Aedan concentrating on the PC screen.

"You know your anti-virus software is shit, babe." Aedan muttered.

He barked out a laugh. "Yeah, probably," he teased. Knowing Aedan, he was most likely already upgrading it whether he asked him to or not.

"So," Aedan said as he carried on doing whatever it was he was up to. "You and Tilly are spending the day with your dad tomorrow?"

Matt tapped his fingers against his stomach. "Yeah," he said glumly. "First time we've done the split Christmas thing, we're not coming back until the 27th. I hope mum'll be okay."

"Does she not want you to go?" Aedan asked. He turned away from the computer to regard Matt with a small frown.

Matt let out a mirthless laugh. "Nobody wants us to go," he said. He stared at the ceiling, not sure he liked talking about this. But if he was going to bring it up with anyone, it was most likely to be Aedan anyway. He'd kept it pretty quiet at school in general, but he'd confessed the most pertinent details to his best friend, and his teachers had been informed as his parents' addresses had both changed. Word got around eventually.

"Not even your dad?" Aedan probed.

Matt considered that. "He often does things for the sake of appearances, just because he should. So, he might want us there, but not necessarily to see us, if that makes sense?"

"I guess, maybe?" Aedan frowned further. "So why go at all?" he asked.

Matt sighed. Did he want to explain?

"We just have to," he said with a shrug. "Shared custody is part of the divorce agreement or whatever you call it. We're both under eighteen, so it's in our best interest to play nice."

Aedan scoffed and went back to tapping on the keyboard. "You'll be eighteen in March though, so will that change things?"

No. Matt knew it wouldn't. There were too many things at stake. "We'll see. How about you?" he asked, changing the subject. "Are you going to go home tomorrow? You're more than welcome to crash here tonight," he tagged on quickly. "Mum's in no fit state to drive, and there can't be any taxi companies open today."

"I got one earlier," Aedan pointed out. "Or did you think I turned up on your doorstep looking that good after an hour-long trek?"

He winked and Matt's stomached flipped. Aedan did look good, though he guessed it was a bit of unpleasant envy on his part making him feel that way. He was just so dazzling though, and Matt was so plain, it was hard at times not to feel the difference. He huffed and smacked Aedan's thigh to cover any awkwardness.

"You got a taxi?"

Aedan smirked. "Not everyone celebrates Christmas, babe," he said lightly. "The corner shop down the end of your road was open, too. Where did you think I got the booze from?"

He hadn't thought, but the corner shop was run by a Pakistani family, so he guessed that made sense.

"So, you want to go home tonight?" he clarified. As he said it though he realised he didn't want Aedan to leave. He didn't want to pop this strange little pocket of reality they'd created by crashing worlds together.

Aedan chewed his lip. He did that a lot, making his lips wet and plump almost constantly. "No. I mean, if that's okay? I'd really like to stay."

Matt didn't understand his cautious tone. "Sure, of course, mate. We've even got the sofa bed in the lounge, so you won't have to slum it."

Aedan continued to look pensive though as he pushed and clicked the computer mouse around. "Thanks," he said quietly.

"Unless, you want to head off," Matt said, a bit lost. "Don't feel you have to stay."

"No, no." Aedan turned quickly, his eyes wide. "That's not——" He sat back in the chair, then drummed his feet on the floor. "No, I just…" His face brightened with a big smile. "Well, actually I thought maybe I could spend tomorrow with you? At your dad's?"

"Ha!" Matt barked, before he even had a chance to think. "Yeah, my step-mum would *looove* that."

He laughed again at the ceiling, but by the time he turned back to Aedan, he realised he'd made a mistake.

"Okay," he said. His eyes dropped, colour rising on his cheeks.

"No, hang on," said Matt, sitting up a little too fast. He appreciated how much prosecco he'd probably already had in that moment.

But Aedan was already rising to his feet, brushing his hands on the tops of his jeans. "Actually, you know what, I think maybe I should go. This is your Christmas after all."

Matt shook his head, as if that might stop it spinning as Aedan moved around the bed. "No wait, dude, that's not what I meant!" he laughed, but Aedan's expression was tense and fixed. "Aedan, stop, what are you doing?"

He managed to scramble off his bed just in time and place himself between his friend and the door that they'd left ajar. Aedan pulled up short as his exit was blocked, his eyes not meeting Matt's. "I shouldn't have come over. It was so out of order," he said. His tone was flippant but his downcast eyes were glassy. He moved to try and dart around Matt.

A flare of irritation stabbed through Matt. That wasn't how he felt or what he meant in the slightest, and Aedan should bloody well know enough to understand that.

"Hey," he snapped a touch aggressively, and grabbed the top of his arm.

Aedan flinched so violently he bounced off the door and slammed it shut with his side, his breaths suddenly heavy as he held himself rigidly and stared at the carpet.

Matt froze.

"Aedan?" he asked.

For what seemed like an age, they both just stood there, Matt staring at Aedan, and Aedan not taking his gaze away from the floor for even a second.

Matt's mind was racing. *What was wrong? What was going on?* He said the first and most prominent thing that came to his confused, slightly sozzled mind. "I don't want you to leave," he uttered softly, reaching out carefully to touch his fingertips to the edge of Aedan's shoulder, relieved when it was allowed without protest. He reminded Matt of his old dog Buster when he he'd been a puppy and backed himself into a corner in a panic over the vacuum cleaner.

"Sorry," Aedan whispered.

"You don't have to apologise for anything," Matt assured him immediately. "I said that about my step-mum because she's a cow. I was just joking. Please don't go."

Aedan closed his eyes, his breathing still deep and noisy, like he wasn't really inhaling enough oxygen despite his best efforts. "Sorry."

Matt swallowed, a trickle of fear tickling down his spine. How had they got to this in a matter of minutes, after having had such a lovely day? "Aedan," he pressed gently again. "Please tell me what's wrong. Did I hurt you?"

"No," he cried, snapping his head up. They locked eyes, and Matt wasn't sure if that was better or worse. Aedan's brown irises, normally full of warmth, were practically vibrating and filled with tears. "You didn't hurt me."

Matt licked his lips, anxiety making him tremble. "It felt like I did." he said.

Aedan swallowed.

Carefully, he stepped away from Matt, but further into the room rather towards the door. Without saying anything, he hooked his fingers under the hem of his sparkly jumper. He waited a beat, taking in a breath as his brow creased, then pulled it and the t-shirt underneath up and over his head in one fluid motion. He balled the material into his right hand, then let his arms hang limp by his side, his jaw clamped and his gaze once again stuck to the floor.

Matt's jaw went slack. Along the left side of Aedan's body—starting at his shoulder and going down his arm, across his chest and back, above his hip and the skin that vanished below his jeans—were a series of livid purple bruises, glistening they were so fresh, and a number of scrapes and scratches to go along with them.

"Fuck," Matt breathed with feeling. Then his brain kicked in. "Aedan!" he hissed, taking a step closer, his hand darting forwards, then dropping abortively. "Why didn't you say anything? These need ice on them, and pain killers. Shit, you probably need an x-ray for broken ribs!" His mum had done a first aid course recently, and he and Tilly had been drilled in proper procedure as a result.

He looked up to see a wry smile tug inexplicably at Aedan's lips, and their eyes met. "I didn't want to do that. I wanted to have a nice Christmas, and I did."

Matt guessed that explained why he had been avoiding physical contact all day when it was so unlike him, but he really wasn't happy that Aedan would hide something like that from him. "Is…is this why you left your house? Why you came here?"

Aedan twisted his t-shirt and jumper in his hands, dropping his gaze again. "My uncle came down from Liverpool, just for a couple of days. Normally I'm a little faster…but…"

Matt's stomach turned, and he had to swallow down his nauseated reaction. "He did this to you?"

Aedan tilted his head in a kind of affirmation. "Fairy bashing was always one of his favourite hobbies. It's been a while since he caught me though, so…"

Anger eclipsed Matt's vision for a second, and he balled his fists. "You need to press charges," he growled.

Aedan gave a hollow laugh and hugged himself. "It doesn't work like that, babe," he said sadly, scuffing his toe against the carpet. "Anyway, it's fine. Tony—that's my sister's fella—he pulled him off before he could do any real damage. He'd probably look after me. He's a good sort, but I just thought…" He chewed his lip briefly. "It's better for everyone if I just make myself scarce until him and his family go back up north." He rose, his eyes shining. "Not that I didn't want to see you. I wasn't just using you guys as a place to hide."

Matt let out a disbelieving noise and tugged at his hair. "You can bloody hide here as long as you want. And I still say you should call the police! That fucker can't get away with hurting you like that!" His insides contorted. He could picture Aedan on the floor, curled up, trying to protect himself as some brute kicked him over and over... He clenched his jaw as his eyes burned. There were two more worlds that had no right to intermingle: sweet, thoughtful Aedan, and the business end of someone's Doc Martins.

Aedan's face softened. "Thank you," he said, giving Matt's elbow the briefest of touches. "That's really nice to hear. I mean it. But honestly, I just like being here. You've done enough."

Impulse took over Matt, and he threw his arms around Aedan's body, careful to avoid putting too much pressure on any of the damaged skin. He felt extraordinarily protective, with the mad urge to not let anything else to happen to Aedan if he could help it.

"Right, fine, yeah," he said gruffly. "Look you can stay with us as long as you like. I'm sure Mum'll be totally fine with it. You can come with me and Tilly tomorrow if you really want to the dragon's lair, or you can go with Mum to Aunt Karen's—she's married to this nice bloke and our little cousins are a bit mental, but if you don't mind plaiting hair or debating which My Little Pony is more badass—"

It was only as Aedan pushed away slightly that Matt realised he was still hugging him, and that Aedan was half naked. Embarrassment surged through him, but it was alleviated a tad by Aedan's watery smile. "I'll stick with you, if that's okay?"

Matt let go of him and shoved his hands in his pockets, looking up through his eyelashes. Bloody hell, he was such a loser. "Uh, yeah, I'd like that too. You might make everything a little less awful," he added with a nervous laugh. "If Sheila gets the hump, that's her problem, isn't it?"

Aedan began pulling his t-shirt apart from the jumper. "Is that your step-mum?"

37

Matt shrugged. "Yeah, don't worry about her though. We'll present a united front, won't we?" He gave a lopsided grin, but all he could really think was how stupid he'd been to think Sheila was anything to worry about compared to what Aedan had been through.

Was this the first time? Probably not, from the way he'd talked so casually about it. If this was his idea of 'stopping before it got too bad,' he hated to think what else he might have had to deal with in the past. Had tiny little Aedan had to face that monster? When had this wanker worked out Aedan was a 'nance' and taken his fist or his boot to him? Had all that time off school really been because he was sick, or had he been too bashed up to been seen in public without raising questions?

The thoughts whirled around his mind, crashing into one another and making Matt feel stupid for not noticing anything earlier. He balled up his fists and let out a frustrated growl. Why hadn't Aedan said something, for fuck's sake?

He couldn't do anything about that now. It was in the past. The present, and the future though, that was within his power to change. There were a number of things he could do to make the current situation better.

"Wait a minute," he said as Aedan went to pull his t-shirt back on. "I think we've got some Arnicare gel. It'll help with the bruises. Just wait there a sec."

Aedan nodded, gratitude apparent in his expression, and Matt nipped from his room and into the bathroom, opening the cupboard under the sink to raid the medical box. They had all sorts of bits and bobs there, but he was sure they had Arnicare for when Tilly got thwacked with a hockey stick during her matches. Those things really packed a punch.

Sure enough, he quickly came across the tube and shoved everything back into the cupboard. He stood and realised his hand was trembling. Not badly, but enough that he felt the need to shake both his hands out from the wrists, and he jumped up and down a couple of times to dispel the extra energy he could feel in the rest of his body. He hated the idea of Aedan being hurt with such vehemence it made him want to smash something. Who the fuck thought they had the right to do that?

It didn't make sense why Aedan wouldn't want to press charges. Surely that was the logical thing to do. But he'd seemed so insistent that Matt didn't want to push it. All he could do instead was look after him now, and that started with the anti-bruising gel.

As he went into the hallway again, the front door opened. He paused to greet his mum and sister as they entered in a wave of freezing cold air.

"Blimey!" his mum cried cheerfully. They both stamped their feet and hugged Matt like they'd been on Scott's expedition to the Antarctic. "You should have joined us! We're all fired up for round two now."

She grinned as she unwound her scarf, but his face must have betrayed something. She slowed down a bit, giving Tilly time to struggle out of her coat first, then dart into her room babbling about her onesie and hot water bottle.

"Everything okay?" she asked, folding her scarf into her hands.

Matt nodded. "Yeah, yeah," he said. "I just wanted to check if it was alright for Aedan to stay over tonight? It's a bit late for him to start trekking home."

His mum chuckled and hung up her coat. "Oh of course. Is that all?" She waved her hand and headed into the kitchen to boil the kettle. "I was expecting him to stay. I chucked the spare bedding into the tumble dryer a little while ago to heat it up."

Matt sagged a little in relief. "That was nice of you," he said genuinely. But then the rest of his request bubbled up in his throat, and he felt a prickly rash of nerves across his skin. He hated asking for anything, it was so bloody stupid. "Uh, though, I was—would it be okay—I mean—"

His mum stood a bit straighter. "Matt?" she asked, her brow creasing.

It was best to just blurt it out, before her mind ran away with her. "Aedan can't go home for a couple of days. Can he come with us to Dad's? He says he wants to brave it." He dug his fingernails into his palms and watched as she considered it.

"Are you sure that's a good idea?" she asked slowly.

Matt had expected that. It was his own initial response after all. "For who?"

"Your dad won't like it," she said apologetically, like it was her fault.

Matt knew that, but he thought of those bruises again. He still held the Arnicare, the metallic tube cold against his palm, and he gripped it a little tighter.

"Screw him. Aedan needs a friend right now. We…had a talk." He raised his eyebrows, pleading that his mum wouldn't ask him to explain any further. Now he thought he understood why Aedan hadn't said anything earlier. He didn't want Matt's mum looking at him with pity, like he was something less because a shitty thing happened to him. "I'll look after him. I just wanted to make sure you were okay to drive us all over tomorrow and pick us up the day after."

Her expression softened. "You know that's not an issue." She pulled him into a hug. "If that's what you boys want, I'll be happy to help however I can."

Matt's whole body gave a little shudder. "Thanks mum," he mumbled into her jumper.

"Anytime sweetheart."

"Oh, is that tea?" Tilly came into the kitchen in her purple onesie, ignoring as Matt and their mum pulled apart. "I want tea. Can I have tea? Ooh, unless there's more bubbles. Bubbles are good."

"I think tea sounds good," his mum replied firmly. "And some food. No more bubbles for you, young lady."

"Urgh, Mum," Tilly pouted.

Matt chuckled as he left them to it and returned to his bedroom.

Aedan looked up as he entered. He'd perched on the end of Matt's bed, his jumper and t-shirt still balled up between his knees. He looked smaller like that. Aedan always been taller than Matt, ever since they had first met as gangly eleven-year-olds, but at that moment, he seemed tiny.

Matt quietly clicked the door shut and came to sit beside him, offering up the Arnicare gel. "Mum says it's totally fine to stay tonight and come with us tomorrow, as long as you're really sure."

"I'm really sure," Aedan affirmed, taking the tube from him.

Their fingers brushed and Matt felt the sensation fizzle all the way up his arm. He blinked, uncertain of what to make of it. It was probably just the weirdness of the situation. Aedan was hurt, and he didn't like it. It made Matt ache with anger and regret and frustration, and Aedan was sitting there all vulnerable whilst Matt helped him. It was natural to feel a heightened sense of…something.

He watched as Aedan carefully unscrewed the cap and squeezed out some of the menthol gel, gently rubbing it into his shoulder. At first he grimaced, but then he exhaled, relaxing at its cooling effect. He moved to apply some to his back, but he couldn't quite reach.

"Hey." Matt held his hand out before he'd considered what he was doing. "Do you want me to do that?"

For a moment, they stared at each other. Matt took a mental step back, and realised he'd essentially offered to massage his gay best friend. But, Aedan knew he wasn't gay, right? He was just being nice and practical. This was essentially a medical procedure, nothing weird about it.

Aedan must have agreed, because he smiled and handed the tube back. "Yeah," he said softly. "I'd appreciate that."

The gel was cold, but that was the whole point of it, so Matt didn't try and warm it as he moved behind Aedan

"Brace yourself," he said. His cheeks burned as he realised what he had said. He had watched enough porn to realise what else that could possibly mean.

Aedan didn't react in any way, so Matt got over his own dirty mind and began carefully stroking his slippery fingers along Aedan's tender skin. He paused at an especially ugly bruise as Aedan hissed in a breath and flinched.

"It's fine," Aedan assured, shaking his head. "Keep going. I'm okay."

Matt ground his teeth. "Are you really sure they're not broken?" he asked quietly.

41

Aedan hung his head. "No," he admitted. "But all you can really do with cracked ribs is bind them. I Googled it. If they're still bad in a few days, I'll go to A&E, I promise, but…not now. I just want to have a nice day."

A pleading note tinged his voice, and the protective part of Matt wanted to do whatever he asked.

Sometime after Aedan had staged his little stunt with the non-school ties back in Year Nine, Matt had learned the truth of the debacle. That some of the shits from Year Eleven had stolen his proper tie whilst he'd been in the shower after P.E., and he hadn't been able to get himself a new one for almost two weeks. Rather than go to his teachers or admit the truth and ask for help, Aedan had acted like it had been his idea the whole time, that it had just been a silly bid for attention. That had puzzled Matt at the time, annoyed him in fact, but he'd never challenged Aedan on it, figuring it was over with and not worth rehashing.

He was glad he didn't. Months later, prompted by nothing in particular, Matt realised why Aedan might have left his mouth shut. It meant he'd kept his power. He hadn't let those arseholes win by humiliating him. He had humiliated himself and become a minor urban legend for a while—the weird gypsy boy who'd thrown a fashion fit, rather than the little queer who'd been held at the mercy of tormentors.

Matt had always felt, or maybe hoped, that had he known the truth at the time, he would have joined in and worn some of his dad's novelty ties as well. He could have stood by Aedan, in comradery.

This wasn't quite the same, especially as he had real concerns about Aedan's recovery if he didn't see a doctor, but he thought he could perhaps make good on that retroactively made promise now. If he could stand by Aedan and support him, then maybe together they could get through this.

"Okay," he said. He realised his hand had stilled whilst he'd been thinking, wrapped around the side of Aedan's ribcage and he could feel him breathing slowly in and out, every breath measured. For a second, Matt was lost in the moment.

This went beyond anything their friendship had presented them with so far in the past seven years. They were connected—physically and emotionally—by Aedan's secret and the care Matt was now giving him. It was a bit overwhelming, and Matt wasn't quite sure what to make of it.

Aedan turned his head slightly so he met Matt's eye. "Everything alright?"

Matt blinked and shook his head. "Yeah," he said and cleared his throat. "Just thinking about how I'd like to kick the shit out of your uncle." He wiped his sticky hand on his jeans, and moved back around.

Aedan sniggered. "Yeah, he's about six foot eight," he said convivially. "But, thanks. I appreciate the thought of violence on my behalf."

Matt handed the Arnicare back to him, and lightly bumped his good shoulder with his own. "Any time."

He watched as Aedan gently applied the gel to the rest of his bruises. He paused as he got to the top of his jeans, then shot a glance in Matt's direction.

Matt realised, belatedly, that Aedan probably wanted to take them off so he could reach the rest of his injuries. "Um," he stammered. He jumped to his feet, averting his gaze as he felt the back of his neck warm. "How about I get you some pain-killers? The good ones my mum saves for her migraines."

He wasn't sure it was ideal to mix those with alcohol, but if Aedan didn't drink any more, he figured he'd be fine.

Aedan nodded. "Okay."

Before he could move to the door, Aedan reached up and snagged Matt's hand with his own. Matt looked down at their entwined fingers in surprise.

"Thank you," Aedan rasped with a twinge of a smile.

Matt smiled back, his heart swelling. No matter how strange or daunting the situation was, he was very glad he could help. "You're welcome."

CHAPTER 4: SEASON'S GREETINGS

Matt had slept reasonably well until sometime around four in the morning, and then he had woken up practically every half hour, anxiously chewing over the day's impending visit.

He hadn't spent much time with his dad since the divorce and subsequent move. Not that he'd seen him a whole lot before that either, but some sort of relationship had been better than the almost non-existent one that now hovered awkwardly between them.

Brian Bartlett worked for a big financial office in London during the week, and had inherited step-kids when he had married his new wife, Sheila, so his evenings and weekends were swallowed up doing stuff with them. The few times he had arranged to meet up with Matt and Tilly to do something (normally an activity where minimal conversation was required, like a football match or trip to the cinema) their plans always seemed to change last minute. Either his dad wanted to invite the twins along—a pair of seven-year-old boys with the attention span of ADHD puppies named Ryan and Taylor—or even worse, Sheila and her daughter Debbie as well. Sometimes he cancelled altogether with some vague excuse about life being too busy, but then got irritable when Matt and Tilly did the same thing.

Matt knew they should try harder, but it was difficult when they were always expected to go over to the massive house his dad and Sheila now shared as one big, happy family, with new photos on the walls from all the holidays and day trips out they'd already been on. Sheila had a lot of pictures of her three children from when they were growing up as well, but there was just one single school photo present of Matt and Tilly from about five years ago, and it looked as odd amongst the rest of the pictures as Matt felt around the real live subjects.

Today would be the longest they had all spent together, and he was worrying how it was going to go.

That had been the reasoning behind his initial out-of-hand rejection at the idea of Aedan coming along. He knew it was going to be a delicate day, and adding someone else to the mix could only make it more volatile.

But he figured, as he lay there half watching dawn break through the curtains in his room, that he didn't particularly care about Sheila's reaction, or even his dad's. A hot surge of frustration came over him as he thought of all the many times they hadn't considered his or Tilly's or his mum's feelings. Quite the opposite on many occasions. This day was going to be difficult no matter what, so he might as well have Aedan's company and keep him away from his uncle's fists whilst he was at it.

That was it; he just had to remember that whatever nonsense anyone tried to pull today, Aedan's physical safety was more important than any of that.

He thought of his friend on the sofa bed across the hall in the living room, wondering if he was lying awake too, and if so what was going through his head? As much shit as Matt had gone through at home over the past couple of years, he had never felt unsafe there. That must have been so awful. At least Aedan had his brother-in-law who had intervened to keep him and his uncle apart long enough to give Aedan time to pack a quick bag of essentials that would see him through the next couple of days.

Matt had gleaned that none of the family had apparently even considered calling the police on their uncle, treating it as just one of those things. That 'boys will be boys' culture. Tilly had a great deal to say about that after discovering feminism and embracing it whole heartedly. Matt had to admit he agreed with a lot of what she had to say, especially after seeing how 'toxic masculinity,' as she called it, made so much of Aedan's everyday life that much harder in a multitude of little ways.

Aedan was so obviously gay that there was no way anyone who was even half aware could miss it. It was in the way he stood, how he used his hands and the timbre of his voice. He would probably never be mistaken for straight, and more to the point, had little desire to do so. He was who he was. He was the kind of guy that would see glitter added to everything if he could, and nothing anyone said would ever make him shy away from that.

How did that fit in with a community whose men tended to gravitate towards manual labour jobs, pony-trap racing and drinking ale down the local pub?

Aedan had talked a lot about moving away, Matt remembered, so maybe that was how he was managing it: with a long-term goal to get out and stay out.

He wasn't applying to university like most of the other Year Thirteens, but he had been teaching himself popular JavaScript frameworks from books in the library to bulk up his CV, in the hopes of getting a job in IT. He'd talked about the bright lights of London a lot, which made Matt a little nervous, as he wasn't sure where he would end up yet. He had applied to a couple of universities in London himself—in fact they were his top choices—but also ones in Warwick, Manchester and even Edinburgh. He was sure their friendship would survive wherever they ended up thanks to the joys of the modern technology, but after last night he felt something had shifted between them. Maybe it would be nice if they were still in the same town or city, so they could still hang out regularly.

He wished he hadn't been so cagy about having him over to his house before. It had always seemed too much of a risk to open up his home life to anyone, but having now jumped in with both feet, he realised he'd had nothing to fear at all, not with Aedan in any case. Now though, a seed of panic threatened to wriggle in. He could envisage Aedan coming over all the time, especially if he wasn't welcome at his own home. But what if that was only going to last until September, or sooner if Aedan got a job in the city? What if he'd wasted so many years, over nothing really at all?

He sighed. That was definitely something to worry about another time. Today, he had to face his dad and step family, and he might as well take advantage of being awake early and nab the shower first to get guaranteed hot water.

An hour or so later, he stood in the kitchen, having washed, dressed and packed for the day, munching toast with his second cup of tea, his new novel in hand as the rest of the household began to stir. His mum was the first to appear, making a brew for herself and then taking it into the bathroom to accompany her 'beautification'. Matt thought though that beneath her flippant words she was just as tense as he felt, despite not having to even face his dad or his new family. Matt would insist she stay in the car, no matter what.

Next to stumble through was Aedan in his Christmas onesie that made him look like a parcel waiting to be unwrapped. Matt smirked at the gregarious patchwork quilt effect on the pattern, and handed Aedan a cup of tea of his own. "You take sugar, don't you?"

"Yeah, thanks babe," he said, giving it a tentative sip. "What time do you think we'll be heading out?"

Matt looked at his watch. "Well, Tilly will take at least an hour, probably longer, so we should probably go wake her."

"Glass of cold water to the face?" Aedan suggested, batting his eyes over the rim of his mug.

Matt didn't take it quite that far in the end, but he did more or less have to drag her from her room and shove her towards the bathroom by force, ignoring her squeals and grumbles of protest.

"Serves you right to be hungover," he chided through the closed door, listening to make sure he heard the shower start up. "You shouldn't have snuck all that extra alcohol."

He arched an accusing eyebrow at Aedan as he said it, but his friend just crossed his heart and pressed his hands together to show what an angel he really was.

"Yeah, yeah," Matt told him, pretending to be annoyed.

The truth was, Tilly was probably old enough to experience her first real hangover, and it was better if her family was there to coax her through it.

Aedan's skincare routine meant he took almost as long as Tilly to get ready. Matt was amazed at how many moisturisers and serums one person could put on their face, and that was before he started on the makeup. When he spotted Matt watching him, Aedan patted next to him, where he was sat on the now-made sofa bed, and proceeded to explain some of what he was doing for Matt's benefit. He wouldn't have said he really cared—Matt rarely even remembered to wash his face if he didn't have a shower—but he thought it was cute how into it Aedan was.

He allowed Aedan to put a little moisturiser on his cheeks, but he drew the line at BB cream, which looked suspiciously like his mum's foundation.

"It's good for you," Aedan squeaked indignantly, but Matt shooed him on.

He left off the glitter today, which Matt thought was probably sensible, but he still took his time over the black outline he carefully built up around his eyes. Matt thought it must have hurt – he was practically sticking the pencil inside his eye at times—but Aedan completed the task with practiced ease, giving the effect that he woke up with Kohl smudged under his lashes.

Matt, true to his word, forced a clean, hole-less pair of socks on him, then left him to fuss over what he was going to wear. The nerves crept back into his belly, and he attempted to placate them with a third cup of tea whilst he waited for everyone else to finish up.

By the time they were all packed up piling into Matt's mum's car, the mood had grown sombre. Tilly buckled in up front, Matt joined Aedan in the back seat, and his mum keyed in the post code to his dad's new address into the Sat Nav, all without much of a word being spoken.

"Is it far?" Aedan asked quietly as they pulled off the driveway.

Matt hadn't done the journey that many times, if he was honest. "Depends on the traffic. Maybe half an hour?"

His dad and Sheila had bought a house close to the station for their commute into London, and as a fresh start for their newly combined family. Sheila's children lived with them all the time, as her ex-husband had moved out to New Zealand before their divorce had even been finalised, or so Matt had heard on the grapevine. His mum's estate agent had been more sympathetic to her plight than was strictly professional, and relayed back all the gossip she could from dealing with his dad for the sale of their old house.

Matt didn't even know the name of Sheila's ex, but he thought about him from time to time. He couldn't imagine what it must be like, committing to spend your whole life with someone, to build a life and a family with that person, only to have it all fall apart. Would it be better to throw your hands up and leave it all behind like that, or do what his mum was doing and still maintain some of that life you had worked so hard to create, at the price of being constantly reminded of what you had also lost?

He watched her as they quietly drove through the streets, the traffic back to normal on the roads as other people were also travelling to spend the day with other family members, or perhaps even braving it back to work. She wasn't giving much away in her expression, but after the year and a half she'd had, Matt was willing to bet she'd burst into tears as soon as he and his sister were out of the rear-view mirror.

That was it, he guessed; why today was ultimately filled with such dread. Christmas was a season of family and belonging, and his dad had made them feel replaced.

He wasn't so stupid as to think people never broke up, that they didn't grow apart or rush into marriage for one reason or another. If his dad had been unhappy, which he obviously had been, then he didn't begrudge him doing something about that. Life was too short to be miserable, Matt firmly believed that. He just wished he'd done it in a way that was less likely to leave the path behind him strewn with casualties.

Matt had avoided coming face to face with that rejection for over a year, but he was going to have to deal with it now. Literally. They had just turned into the long drive that would lead them to the house.

He must have tensed, because the next thing he felt was Aedan's hand slipping over his own and giving it a squeeze. "It's going to be alright," he whispered.

Matt wished he didn't need that reassurance, but it washed through him like a warm wave on the beach, and he nodded back his thanks, almost sad as Aedan took his hand back.

"You can stop here Mum," he said as they rounded the corner to the house. "We'll be fine from here."

"Are you sure?" she asked dubiously. But she was already slowing down by the curb.

"Yeah," Matt assured, with a smile he hoped didn't look too forced. "That way you've got enough space to turn around."

He was the first to get out, followed by Aedan. As they slammed their doors, Tilly leaned over and gave their mum a hug goodbye, then slouched out of the car. Matt went over to the window as his mum lowered it to give his own hug. "See you tomorrow," she said, her voice only catching a fraction at the end.

Matt squeezed her extra tight, then let her go. "Have an awesome time at Aunt Karen's. Give the girls big kisses from us."

"Will do," she agreed with a firm nod.

Aedan appeared at his elbow as Matt stepped back. "Thanks so much for having me Dawn," he said, and bent down to half-hug her as well.

"It was my pleasure—oh, what's this?"

Aedan beamed at her as he handed over a mix-CD with a printed out cover that read *Badass Lady Bosses*, which could only be an Aedan creation. *Had he made that before he'd come over?* Matt wondered. Then he remembered the time he'd spent on his computer yesterday, and figured he must have put it together when Matt wasn't watching. He couldn't help but smile at his friend for such a thoughtful gesture.

"That's just something to add a little glitter on the garland," Aedan said, rocking on his heels, clearly quite pleased with himself.

"A little…?" Matt's mum repeated with a frown as she turned the disk over to read the track listing.

"Glitter on the garland," Aedan said with conviction. He lifted his hand and flicked it from the wrist. "It's something my aunt used to say. She was also a firm believer that everything deserves as much sparkle as you can get on it, especially at Christmas."

Matt's mum looked back up at him with a fragile but open happiness. "Well, you certainly gave us that sweetheart. You're welcome to visit at any time you know—you can come back and stay tomorrow if you want?"

Aedan glanced at Matt, who nodded in confirmation. "Thank you," said Aedan again, with sincerely. "You're too sweet. I'll let you know."

They stood and waved as the car darted through a three-point turn, and didn't move until it had vanished around the corner. Matt sighed. "She's going to be rapping Nicki Minaj by the time we get back, isn't she?"

"Yep," replied Aedan a little too smugly.

They turned and began to trudge along the pavement towards their dad's house up ahead. All the homes either side of the road were at least three stories high with huge front gardens lined by towering evergreen trees and sweeping driveways that contained two—if not three—cars that Matt guessed each cost about five times what his mum's old Ford was worth. It made his skin crawl just walking past a neighbourhood like this, like people were going to lean out of the windows and start yelling at the three of them that they were trespassing and should sod off before they brought the house prices down.

Of course no one did, but the urge to keep on running and not stop persisted.

The day was gloomier than it had been yesterday, with a pregnant looking grey sky rather than the previous brilliant blue.

"Do you think it might snow?" he voiced out loud, more for something to say than anything.

"God I hope not," Tilly moaned. "I don't want to be stuck here a minute longer than we have to be."

"So, your dad left your mum for this woman, right?" Aedan asked as they got closer to their destination.

"They were having an affair," Matt explained flatly, eager to get the details over with as soon as possible. "She works in one of the other offices at his company. They got together at an away weekend."

"We're not supposed to know that," Tilly said with a mixture of anger and pride. "Dad uses the same password for everything though. Or at least he used to."

"They were sneaking around for two years," Matt continued as they reached the drive and turned in. "Then her husband found out and it was divorces all around. Mum was the last to find out. She felt pretty stupid."

He swallowed the lump that had formed in his throat. The truth was, he'd felt exactly the same, but he reckoned it had to have hurt his mum ten times as much as it had him. His dad had lied *so much* to them all about having to work extra hours and why he was on his mobile phone all the time. It sucked pretty badly to realise someone thought so little of you to treat you in such a disposable manner.

"It wasn't her fault though," Aedan insisted as they approached the door.

Matt shared a look with Tilly. "Yeah," he admitted. "But it doesn't always feel that way."

He took a deep breath, reached up, and pressed firmly on the doorbell.

The gentle *ding-dong* resonated through the inside of the house, and the three of them clutched at their bags as they waited for a sign of activity on the other side of the door.

"Oh good, there's no one in," said Tilly after thirty seconds. "Let's go home."

She made to spin on her feet, but Matt grabbed her shoulder and held her firm. Just then a shape moved beyond the frosted glass, and the door swung inwards.

The new Mrs Sheila Bartlett stood before them. She was slim in a way that said she worked out a lot, but the lines around her eyes betrayed the fact she was still about the same age as Matt's mum. Her dark brown hair was curled in vintage waves, bouncing on her shoulders as she stopped to greet her guests. Her lips and nails were cherry red, and she wore a 1940s A-line dress complete with frilly petticoat, and polka dot heels.

"Uh oh," Aedan uttered in horror, pressing a finger to his glossy lips. "Did we time travel?"

Matt kicked his shoe.

"Hi Sheila," he said brightly. "Merry Christmas!"

"Matthew, Matilda." Her smile didn't slip a millimetre, but it didn't reach her eyes either. "You've brought a friend?" She took in Aedan's gravity defying quiff and lined eyes. Aedan didn't shy away from her gaze though, instead he popped a hip and beamed up at her.

Matt cleared his throat. "Yes, sorry, it was all a bit last minute. Sheila, this is my friend Aedan Gallagher from school. Aedan, this is my step-mum Sheila."

"Pleased to meet you," Aedan said, thrusting his hand forwards in a way Matt interpreted as a challenge.

"Oh," said Sheila. She hesitated as she eyed him up, as if assessing whether or not he was in fact there sent to assassinate her. "And, you're joining us for the day?" She touched her hand to his, and winced as he pumped it once.

"Only if that's okay." He waved his hand back and forth like he was shooing a fly away. "I'd hate to be an imposition. I promise, I'll be so quiet you won't even know I'm here."

"Right." She seemed frozen in place for a second too long, before she regained her wits and stepped backwards. "Well, let's get you out of this chill, hey?"

The three of them walked obediently inside, one after the other, and Matt watched Sheila warily as she closed the door with a little more force than was probably necessary.

"*Brian*!" she hollered up the stairs, her hands clasped in front of her chest. "*Your children are here*!"

Matt winced behind her back. It would always be 'your children' and 'my children' he guessed, but it still stung a bit.

His dad trotted down the steps in a shirt and honest-to-God bowtie, beaming down until he caught sight of Aedan, and widened his blue-grey eyes at Matt and Tilly. "I only remember having *two* children," he joked, but there was an underlying accusation there that Matt didn't fail to notice.

"Hi Dad," he said sheepishly, opening his arms to be hugged briefly. "I'm sorry we didn't let you know sooner, but this is my friend Aedan, and he's staying with me for Christmas. He's had some, uh, issues at home."

"Aedan Gallagher?" his dad confirmed, his eyebrows rising.

"Actually, it's pronounced *Galla-her*," Aedan corrected, offering out his hand once more. "I'm actually Irish, unlike those Oasis boys."

Matt expected his dad to point out that he didn't *sound* Irish, but he just narrowed his eyes instead.

"Right," he replied, and shook his hand a couple of times. "Yes, I remember Matt talking about you, from school."

Matt frowned at that. Really? He didn't think his dad had picked up on anything he'd chattered on about over dinner, let alone enough to remember Aedan's full name or have a decided opinion of him. But he'd fixed his parent/teacher night grin on his face, and that made Matt instantly wary.

"How about I take your coats and we can head into the living room for some *crudités*?" Sheila asked. She was at least trying to be pleasant, Matt appreciated. "The twins are lurking about near the tree I think, and Deborah will be down shortly."

Matt's dad clasped his shoulder, making him jump. "How about you help me with some drinks, chap?" he asked. Matt's stomach sunk.

The ground floor of his dad's house had a drawing room with a baby grand piano, the living room where Tilly and Aedan were now being led, a dining room with the long table already laid for lunch later, and past the foot of the stairs took him and his dad to the enormous open plan kitchen. Matt was pretty certain that the circumference of the island counter in the middle was the same size as his mum's whole kitchen. He stopped walking as his dad turned to face him, and he folded his arms protectively over his chest.

"Matthew, I'm very disappointed in you," his dad said.

Matt's eyebrows slowly crept upwards. "Sorry?" he said.

"You know how hard your step-mother has worked to make this a special day, for all of us, as a family," he said, shaking his head. He wore oval glasses on his pudgier-than-usual face, and they glinted in the beams from the LED downlights installed in the ceiling. "And now you go and bring *that* boy here. Don't think I don't remember him."

Matt was genuinely a bit bewildered by this line of conversation. "I'm sorry dad," he said, hating the way his shoulders slumped. "But he's my best friend and he's had some trouble and I didn't know how else to help."

"Of course he's in trouble," his dad replied, exasperated. "He's from that, that-" He flailed around for the right word. "*Gypsy* camp. They're always in trouble! You're putting us in a very uncomfortable positon here Matthew. I'm stunned at you to be so selfish."

"Selfish?" Matt spluttered. He thought in particular of the largest bruise on Aedan's side, the one that was already turning green and yellow outside of the purple. But he didn't want his dad knowing what he'd been through, or his step-family. It was too personal. They didn't deserve to see that aspect of Aedan's life when they knew precious little else about him. "It's not like that," he said instead. "*He's* not like that. He's just my guest, okay? He doesn't expect presents or anything, and he can share my dinner if there really isn't enough."

His dad took a step back and regarded him oddly. "Matthew," he said softly, a warning tone clear. "Are you two *together*?"

"What?"

"Are you together? He's gay, isn't he?"

"What!" Matt cried, his skin turning cold. "What, Dad, no, that's ridiculous, he's just my friend!"

Almost immediately, he felt shame rinse all the way through his body, starting at the tips of his ears and flooding down to his toes. Why on Earth had he said that?

He didn't care that Aedan was gay. Why would he get so upset at the thought of them as a couple? He swallowed around the thick lump that had blossomed in his throat.

His dad nodded though, not pleased, but apparently placated enough. "Well, whatever the case, you should have given us fair warning. It should have been our decision whether or not to allow him into our home." He pinched the bridge of his nose where his glasses sat, and sighed. "I suppose he's here now, so we'll have to work around it. I want you to take responsibility for him though, is that understood?"

Matt felt awful. He wanted to demand to know what his dad meant by that—did he think Aedan was going to pilfer the good silver, or perhaps trick Sheila into getting her driveway re-tarmacked? But instead he just nodded miserably.

"Right, fine," his dad said, clapping his hands and giving his shoulders a little shake. "Let's get these drinks sorted, and re-join the others."

Matt waited silently as he held out a tray and his dad filled several tumblers with sparkling elderflower water for them to take through. He'd have much rather had a strong cup of tea.

Aedan and Tilly were standing awkwardly between the mantelpiece and the seven-foot-high Christmas tree when they entered—abandoned by Sheila for the moment—watching as two identical boys tore up and down the living room, pretending to be fighter planes from the sounds of it. That seemed like a very bad idea, considering every surface of the room was intricately garnished with delicate looking decorations, from glass reindeers to wobbly wooden nutcrackers, prickly holy creations, spindly wicker elves and about a thousand tiny little fairy lights strung up to connect everything like an especially beautiful spider's web.

"*Matt!*" they both screeched at the sight of him, making a beeline for his legs.

"Err," Matt croaked awkwardly, holding out the tray of drinks urgently, only just managing to pass it off to his dad in time before the boys collided with his lower half.

"You're here!"

Chapter 4: Season's Greetings

"You came back!"

"Will you play computers with us later?"

"Did you bring us any presents?"

"Whoa, whoa," Matt said, holding up his hands, aware of Aedan and Tilly laughing at him behind their hands. Luckily his dad had busied himself putting the tray down on the table. Matt looked down at the eager faces before him. Both boys were in white shirts, matching ties decorated with robins, and mini suspender belts. He felt that was a bold move to expect them to keep that all on for the whole day, but he guessed Sheila enjoyed a challenge. "Yes, you have presents," he answered them both, still completely unaware of how to tell them apart. "And maybe we can play computer games later, we'll see how things go, yeah?"

Ryan and Taylor cheered, then turned on one another with sudden growls, wrestling each other to the ground in a ball of flailing limbs. Matt hopped out of the way over to where Aedan was sniggering.

"You have a fan club?" he observed.

"Apparently," he agreed. He hadn't thought the twins even remembered he existed, but it seemed they did.

He took a second to smile at Aedan, trying to telepathically apologise for not defending him enough to his dad. Shit, he would be absolutely mortified if Aedan had heard the way he'd spoken, and he was grateful to the universe that he would never know.

Sheila re-entered, having added a pinafore apron to her ensemble. "How are we all doing?" she asked cheerfully, completely ignoring the tousling children at her feet. "All settled in?" She frowned and turned to Matt's dad. "Still no Deborah?"

He chuckled. "You know what girls are like with their makeup." He winked at Tilly, who stared blankly back at him, as if he'd spoken Russian.

A scrabbling sound at the French doors at the end of the room drew Matt's attention, and he turned around to look through the windows that led into the conservatory, showing the impressive view of the garden beyond. There in the conservatory, on his hind legs looking ever so

57

hopeful, was a scruffy little Border terrier, his tail wagging so furiously it was in danger of flying off.

"BUSTER!" Matt yelled, charging around Sheila and his dad and over to the doors. The little dog began jumping so high he was half way up the glass pane, yelping and whining in excitement. "Hey boy! Hey!" Matt cried, and went to grab the handle.

"*No!*" Sheila screeched from behind, and Matt jerked back as if the door was suddenly electrocuted. He bunched his fists and glanced anxiously at his step-mum.

"Sorry, mate," his dad chuckled, rubbing Sheila's back as he apologised on her behalf. "Didn't mean to scare you. I'm afraid Buster has to stay out at the moment, because of all the decorations. He's missed you though! How about we go through the kitchen to see him?"

He looked hopefully at Tilly, who frowned at Matt, and then down at Buster. Matt turned back to their old family pet, only to find him cowering on the floor, his ears back and his eyes trained on Matt. "He's not allowed in the house at all?" he asked, an unpleasant sensation creeping along his skin.

His dad shrugged. "Just for now. Come on, let's go see him, I bet he's cross at you for not visiting more often!"

Matt scowled for a moment, then decided that was a battle for another time. Did they mean to say he had been shut out for weeks, when had they put their millions of ridiculous decorations up? He wasn't happy about that at all. But right then, all he wanted to do was pet his dog. "Sure," he said, attempting joviality. "Aedan, do you want to meet Buster?"

"I'd love to," he said, and linked arms with Tilly so they could parade out of the living room after Matt's dad.

Matt's jaw was still clenched as they made their way through the house, but as they opened up the second set of doors, and Buster realised they had come to him from a different direction, all his anger melted away.

"Oh buddy, have I missed you," he said.

He sunk to his knees as the terrier sprinted across the tiles and hurled himself into Matt's lap, jumping up his chest and licking his face all over. The kitchen door had a vicious snap-back on it, making it slam so everyone except

Matt's dad jumped out of their skin, but Matt was soon distracted again by an excitable little dog.

"Oh Buster, get down," his dad chastised. He tried to wave him away, but Matt clung to him even tighter.

"He's fine," he protested.

They had only had Buster a year before the big split had happened, but Matt had very much come to think of him as *his* dog in that time. Whenever he could get away with it, he'd had Buster sleeping on the end of his bed, and he'd been an absolute champion at comforting Matt when he'd been listing to his parents scream at one another, the only one to ever see him cry over the divorce.

Aedan came and sat on one side of him, and Tilly on the other, both of them reaching over to stroke his fur as he started to calm down. "He's adorable," Aedan said, and Matt leaned into him absently.

"Yeah, he is," he agreed happily, allowing his nose to be licked.

"Hang on," his dad said, wagging his finger. "Let me go get the camera. We need some photos of the reunion!"

He vanished back into the house, and Matt found himself glaring at his retreating back. It wasn't exactly warm out in the conservatory he'd noticed.

"Why doesn't he live with you guys?" Aedan asked, also narrowing his eyes at where Matt's dad had gone. "Seems like your step-mum doesn't like him very much."

Tilly scoffed. "Because they got *everything*," she said quietly, not taking her eyes off Buster as he wriggled against her hand. "They just wanted to win."

Matt nodded sadly. "I think," he said softly, aware his dad would be back any second. "He thought if they kept him, it would make us come visit more often. They said he would be too hard for my mum to manage by herself, but, I think that was the real reason."

Aedan's hand had drifted down from the dog, and now rested warm and solid on Matt's knee. "And obviously, you didn't want that? To come here?"

Matt swallowed. "Every time we visited him, we just had to leave him behind again. He was so confused, his little face…" Matt had fucking hated that, being held to ransom. In the end, it was easier not to come.

But now he held Buster close, rubbing his cheek against his fur, and hoped his little friend understood just how much he had been missed.

CHAPTER 5: ALL WRAPPED UP

Matt and Tilly sat obediently on the tiled floor for several staged photos with Buster whilst Aedan watched on. Matt didn't like him being excluded, but after his conversation with his dad in the kitchen, he didn't think it was a good idea to push his luck.

His dad had a fancy camera, one with a proper lens and everything. Matt didn't know anything about cameras, but his dad was evidently really getting into it, and even responded keenly when Aedan asked him about some of the settings.

Then, however, they were ushered back into the living room, forced to leave Buster behind so he had to sit and look forlornly through the French windows again. Matt had to accept that was how it was for the time being as his next challenge arrived in the form of his step-sister, Debbie.

She was a couple of years older than Matt, and physically a dead ringer for her mum with the same heart-shaped face and dark hair, also styled like she'd just dropped in from Stepford. Her black dress had a subtle sparkly thread running through it to compliment the crystals draped around her neck and the diamanté buckle on the side of her high heels.

One look at Matt, Tilly and Aedan, and her face clouded over like thunder. "I thought we were doing formal wear?" she demanded as her mum fussed over the twins, who had unsurprisingly already divested themselves of a tie, a belt and a shoe between the pair of them.

Sheila sighed and looked at the three visitors, before addressing Matt's dad. "I did say," she told him petulantly.

Matt tried not to feel awkward and stepped closer to Tilly and Aedan, as if that could protect them and their collection of ugly Christmas jumpers. He'd gone with his Die Hard one again, because Aedan had reckoned that despite not being sparkly it was still really cool, and Tilly's had a motif of kittens in Santa hats. Aedan had been delighted with an excuse to wear one too, having bought himself three in the run-up to Christmas, but then fretted he wouldn't have enough excuses to wear them all. This one wasn't sparkly, but featured a pair of unicorns rising up to greet one another, surrounded by an assortment of different sized snowflakes.

"No," Matt replied hurriedly to his step-mum, willing to take the blame. "I'm sorry, dad did mention it, but I forgot, and Aedan didn't have anything like that to wear, so we just went with jumpers. I hope that's okay."

That was a big fat lie. The three of them had known full well what they'd been asked to do, and Aedan could have borrowed a shirt of Matt's if necessary. They'd all just unanimously agreed on a spot of rebellion for kicks. Matt's argument was that the day was going to be unpleasant enough, and he'd rather be comfortable than strangled by a shirt and tie.

Sheila pursed her lips into a thin line. "It's fine," she said, in the air of a long-suffering martyr. "We can just do separate portraits. Brian darling, shall we set up the camera whilst everyone is still looking their best."

Matt didn't miss the way one of the twins pointedly tugged at his collar and glared at his mum. It appeared they weren't the only ones unimpressed by this farce.

As he sat on the couch with Tills and Aedan and watched his dad faff with the tripod in front of the

Christmas tree, he thought he should have been more upset that they'd been kicked out of the family portrait, but he didn't actually want to stand next to Debbie or Sheila, and concluded their little protest had been highly successful.

"Where are your presents?" Debbie snapped in Matt's direction. She had failed to say hello yet, or even wish them a Merry Christmas he noted with a touch of amusement. "You should put them under the tree, for the photos."

"Oh sweetie, surely Matt and Tilly should wait until their own turn," Aedan replied without missing a beat. "Their paper is only from Sainsbury's after all, and Matt can barely get the sticky tape in the right place." He rubbed Matt's hair affectionately, and Matt batted him off with a grin. "I'm sure they wouldn't want to mess up all the gorgeous six-inch ribbon curls you guys obviously slaved over." He beamed up at her, and Debbie frowned, unsure as to whether or not she was being messed with.

"I don't think we've been introduced," she said slowly, and held her hand out from where she loomed above the three of them on the couch. "Deborah Wilks," she added.

Matt had half wondered if she would take his dad's surname or not, she was so into this whole happy family charade. He felt the tiniest sliver of triumph that she hadn't.

"Aedan Gallagher," he replied, shaking her hand with confidence. "Sorry to gate crash your day. Matt's being awfully kind and looking after a stray waif."

Debbie glanced at Matt, as if it had never occurred to her that he could be kind. "Oh, okay," she said, then shrugged. "Well, it's up to you. It would probably look good if there were a few more presents under the tree, and if they're badly wrapped we can always tuck them under some of the others."

"Gee, thanks," Tilly drawled. Debbie didn't really have a choice on how she could interpret that, so she just rolled her eyes and went to go join her mother by the crudités.

Matt suspected it would have been easier if his dad had asked him or Tilly, or even Aedan who knew a thing or two, to help take the photos. But he insisted on using the automatic timer, so the flash kept going off at what felt like random moments, and it took twenty minutes to get a picture where everyone was simply smiling and looking at the camera, rather than talking, fidgeting, pushing for space (the twins) or, on one occasion, sneezing.

Matt would have been bored stiff by the end of it, except Aedan kept up a running commentary under his breath, like they were watching a nature documentary. "*And here we see the mother suburbanite,*" he whispered into Matt's ear in a David Attenborough voice. "*A prickly creature by nature, contemplating which of her young she would be least inclined to devour, in order to see her through the winter months.*"

He had to bite on his tongue to stop himself from laughing, which only made Aedan do it more, of course. He swore Sheila caught on to what they were up to, shooting them several dirty looks in between posing for the last few snapshots.

Finally, it was time to swap over, and Matt woke Tilly from where she'd fallen asleep against the side of the sofa. "Alright you guys," said their dad, rubbing his hands together. "Let's show them how it's done, hey?"

Matt hated having his photo taken at the best of times, but after he and Tilly had stood with their dad's arms around them for the first couple of shots, he had already had enough. He felt hot with everyone watching them; the twins were restless wanting to go play again, and Debbie kept smirking at them, no doubt finding it amusing with how miserable they looked.

After they had suffered through a half a dozen more, Matt spoke without thinking. "Can Aedan be in one?" he blurted out.

His dad blinked. "Well, he's not family," he said, and something dark boiled inside Matt.

"Yes," he said, valiantly not snapping the word out. "But if he's not in any photos, then it'll be like he wasn't here at all." He knew that was probably his step-mum's intention, but he was too irritable to care whether or not calling her and his dad on it was a good idea. "Come on, one photo won't hurt, will it?"

"It's just we pay to get them developed professionally," Sheila began, but Matt was surprised when his dad cut in, probably to save face.

"Sure, of course – you're right, we should get a couple, if that's what you want?"

Matt turned to Aedan, whose face had lit up, and Matt raised his eyebrows. "Definitely," Aedan cried, rocketing to his feet. "Can I just go get a prop?"

"A prop?" Matt's dad stammered, but Aedan was already racing from the room, shouting that he'd be right back.

Tilly caught Matt's eye, but he just shrugged in response, not sure what his friend was doing until he heard the signature slam of the kitchen door, and when he came walking carefully back into the lounge, Matt realised he should have guessed.

"What are you—!" Sheila began, but Aedan didn't pause.

"This little poppet won't be any trouble at all, will you precious?" He stoked Buster's head fondly. "We'll keep him in our arms the whole time, won't we Matt?"

His heart skipped a beat as his best friend handed him his best four-legged friend, and he leaned in to allow Buster to lick his nose. "We promise Sheila, he won't be any bother and then he can go right back outside."

She flashed her eyes at Matt's dad, then whipped around and stormed off. Matt felt a surge of guilt, but then Buster's tail wagged against his arm, and he figured that if she wasn't so uptight about having him in the house in the first place, it would never have been a big deal. It wasn't as if Buster was a puppy any more. He didn't chew on things or race around like a maniac.

Debbie huffed and followed her mum with an impressive flounce, which then gave the twins licence to race upstairs for a bit of long-awaited freedom. Matt's happiness drained as his dad glared at him. "Was that really necessary?" he demanded.

Matt hugged Buster protectively. "He's not hurting anyone though," he protested in a childish sounding whine. "Why can't we just have a photo?"

"It's not that," his dad argued in exasperation. He glanced at Aedan, but then continued to address Matt. "It's the fact that you completely discounted mine and Sheila's wishes, *again*. This is our house young man."

"Yeah, obviously," Matt snapped back. "But Buster's my dog, and it was really nice of Aedan to think I'd like a picture with him to take home to Mum's, seeing as I can't actually have Buster."

Two pink spots rose on his dad's cheeks, and he worried he'd pushed him too far. But he inhaled deeply as he closed his eyes, then exhaled and looked at him again. "We'll talk about this later, alright?" he said in a voice that was perfectly cool and composed.

He turned on his heel and walked calmly out, just as one of Cliff Richard's Christmas songs came blaring abruptly and a little too loudly from the direction of the kitchen.

"Oops," said Matt faintly.

"I'm so sorry," added Aedan weakly. "I didn't think they'd get their knickers in that much of a twist."

Tilly scoffed. "Are you kidding? That was bloody brilliant. Can we take a decent photo now?"

Matt laughed, and Aedan's face lit up again. "Oh," he said, yanking his phone from his back pocket. "Okay, but let's get some we can keep, yeah?" He balanced his phone on top of the proper camera, and set it up to take five shots at five second intervals. "A different pose for each one," he instructed, running back over and slinging his arm casually around Matt's waist. The light blinked rapidly. "GO!"

They stuck out their tongues, did the macho man, gave Hello Kitty victory Vs, and held Buster up like Baby Simba, before smiling nicely for the last one. Aedan retrieved his phone so they could all scroll through them together, and Matt felt a lump rise in his throat, this one from happiness for a change.

"Perfect," he proclaimed.

They were. He wasn't sure he and Aedan had ever had any photos taken of them together before—certainly none that Matt possessed. It was nice to see them both side by side, with his baby sister and a happy, wriggling Buster.

His mum was missing, of course, but the images really did ring of 'family' for him, unlike the stilted ones his dad and Sheila had just taken.

It was funny how quickly he had accepted Aedan into that category, having firmly thought he could only be a 'friend' until yesterday. He had presumed that blurring the lines would be a little more unnerving, but Aedan just made it feel easy.

As promised, they made a big show of taking Buster back outside to the conservatory, and Matt found a portable heater to flick on so he was happier to leave him there until he could next get back out to cuddle him. Seeing as Sheila hadn't explicitly said she was mad at them from bringing the dog in, Matt acted as if nothing was wrong as the three of them re-entered the kitchen, and Tilly and Aedan were happy to follow his lead.

"Is there anything we can do to help?" he asked over the din of Cliff Richard. Sheila obviously had a whole album of the stuff, and wasn't afraid to play it through.

"No thank you," she said stiffly. She pulled her Cath Kidston oven mitts off, and gave him a champion bullshit smile. "I just remembered I hadn't checked the turkey. It's smelling good, isn't it?"

They all made murmurs of agreement despite their conversation yesterday about none of them really liking it. Debbie didn't seem to be fooled though from the way she was scowling at them, peach bellini in hand that no one else had apparently been offered.

Matt's dad rubbed Sheila's shoulders and gave the back of her neck a kiss which made Matt's empty stomach roll. "Seeing as everything looks to be in order, how about we open some presents"

As if waiting for the magic word, Ryan and Taylor, burst forth into the kitchen, arms waving above their heads as they bellowed, "*Presents! Presents!*"

Matt's dad chuckled. "That's the spirit lads," he encouraged. He watched as they mauled each other on the way back into the living room, and Matt wondered, not for the first time, why nobody bothered to try and discipline them.

They all found a space to sit; Matt's dad, Sheila and Debbie took up dignified perches on the sofas and chairs, whereas Matt, Tilly, Aedan and the twins sprawled out over the floor. Matt pulled his rucksack over and removed the presents he and Tilly had bought, which, as Aedan had quite rightly pointed out, looked as if they had been wrapped by Buster they were so shabby in comparison to his step-family's work. Matt didn't care particularly though; they'd tried to put in effort into the gifts underneath the wrapping, but they didn't really know the people they'd been buying for, and had only a small budget to spend, so he couldn't say he was excited about their reactions like he had been at home the previous day.

Aedan sat behind him so he could peer over his shoulder, obviously putting some distance between himself and what passed for 'the family.' Matt half-turned so he could still see him, to show he hadn't forgotten about him. It made his lower back touch Aedan's knees. The whole point was to get through this together, and he wanted to keep him included as much as possible.

Tilly was also sat by his side, and he gave her a hug before they began opening their pile of offerings.

Matt's first, generous, impression was that it seemed his dad had tried hard. There were a couple of body wash sets and scents for them both, and a makeup kit for Tilly. None were the brands they used, but they were all good quality and probably cost a fair amount. So that was nice. Then he got an Xbox game, despite the fact that his console had packed in a couple of years ago, and he only ever played on his PC now. Tilly must have stared blankly at the Psy album she'd received for a good three minutes before their dad noticed.

"That's K-Pop, right?" he asked cheerily, making everyone turn to look at her. "I asked the sales girl, it's the one with 'Whoop em gan gan style' on it."

He was obviously pretty pleased with himself, and Matt nudged her knee with his. She was clearly quite insulted, probably because it showed how little their dad paid attention to them if he'd bought such outdated gifts, but now was probably not the time to hash it out.

"I tend to listen to more of the boy and girl bands," she said dubiously, but made herself perk up. "This is fun though! I'm sure there's some good stuff on here."

"Brilliant," said their dad.

Matt thought he could probably tell he hadn't quite hit the mark. It was sort of the equivalent of buying a hardcore metal fan Nickelback, or an opera fanatic Susan Boyle.

They all carried on, Sheila intermittently shouting at them to scoop up their rubbish and tidy it into the black bin liners she'd already provided. Matt unwrapped some fancy chocolates, which he immediately opened gratefully and began to share around. He was so hungry his stomach was cramping, but only Aedan and Tilly seemed interested in having any. Matt wondered if they were so nice because they meant to be savoured. And if that was the case, had he just committed another social faux pas? He shrugged mentally; they tasted bloody good, that was for sure.

On the final rubbish sweep, once all the gifts had been opened, Matt managed to snag a certain Korean CD from where it had somehow ended up amongst the paper, saving it before it got lost forever to the waste heap of unwanted presents. He subtly slid it back onto his sister's pile and arched a single brow at her. She could chuck it away at home if she liked, but it was at least going to stick around for now. They didn't need to antagonise anyone any further.

As the twins went crazy over the quad bikes they now knew were waiting for them in the garage, and Debbie set about booting up her new MacBook, Matt leant against the foot of the armchair next to where Aedan had propped himself up.

"That wasn't so bad," he murmured to him.

As he made himself comfy, he thumbed through a couple of books he'd actually really wanted, then suppressed a sigh as he noticed the price tag still left on one of them.

None of these little things were a problem by themselves, but adding them up together spoke of a carelessness and thoughtlessness that reinforced his deep-rooted belief that he and Tilly had been replaced. The knowledge sunk down in his gut like cold water. Would it be better to get nothing than to be reminded that you were an afterthought?

Aedan scooted closer, so they were side by side, and his body warmed Matt's immediately. Matt realised that Aedan hadn't got him a present (not unless he counted the prosecco he'd shared with his family) and yet he always made him feel wanted and important. He'd chosen Matt, out of everyone he knew, to come spend his Christmas Day with. In that moment, that felt better than getting all the presents currently piled up next to him, and then some.

Aedan made a show of checking his watch, then leaned in to whisper in his ear, tickling Matt's neck with his breath and making his entire body shudder. "Hmm, yeah," he said seriously. "And we've only got another, oh, nine hours to go. Easy."

Matt blinked, swallowed, and then remembered to laugh. Aedan grinned, then casually leaned over Matt's lap to pick up the Xbox game to look at it.

Matt was suddenly incredibly aware of his groin in proximity to Aedan, which sent all kinds of confusing messages flying through his brain. It was just hormones, he reasoned, on top of being over emotional. He was feeling rejected by his dad, but wanted by Aedan and their bodies were just really close together right now. It was natural, this squirmy sensation of pleasure; instinctual, or whatever.

Right?

Right, it had to be. Matt wasn't *gay*. Aedan was just being a good friend on a shitty day, and that was that. Anything else would be ridiculous.

Matt pulled a cushion from off the sofa behind them to hug and silently watched Aedan inspect his presents until they were they only two left in the living room.

But that wasn't weird, since they hung out all the time, both at school and in town. Just because he'd seen *both* of Matt's new homes in the past two days—and probably knew twice as much about him now in that time than he did before—didn't mean it wasn't fine. Because he was Matt's best friend, and he trusted him.

He mentally sighed, exasperated. What was really the problem here? Did he like Aedan? Yes. Was he happy to be spending time with him? Yes. Did he want him to go away? No.

He just needed to stop overthinking things, and calm the hell down.

CHAPTER 6: CHRISTMAS CRACKERS

If Matt had thought arguing over how they should do the gravy with his mum yesterday had been absurd, he quickly realised that was nothing compared to the levels Sheila and Debbie were able, and were willing, to reach. The parsnips had to be cut exactly two inches long each, and any extras were to be discarded. The bacon strips had to be rolled anti-clockwise around the cocktail sausages, no more than three times, and pierced with a cocktail stick at a forty-five-degree angle. Hands had to be washed after every single stuffing ball was complete. No one was allowed within three feet of the oven without either woman's explicit permission.

"I'm exhausted just watching this," Tilly mumbled as she munched on a bowl of macadamia nuts.

Matt had managed to navigate around his step-mum and step-sister long enough to make cups of tea for the three of them, and now they were sat at the island counter well away from the carnage. Cliff Richard had gotten louder, if possible, and Matt was convinced he was on his second whirl around the CD player.

He had to say, after awkwardly watching for fifteen to twenty minutes, Sheila's problem was that she was just so obsessed with this idea of *Perfect* (with a capital P, he could hear it in her voice.) Christmas had to be *Perfect*, and nothing less would do. But Matt couldn't help but feel from his own personal experience, that nothing was ever perfect, let alone a day so typically fraught with emotion and potential for unpredictability.

He felt like giving her a hug, or, more likely, having a good shout at her and asking what was really the worst thing that could happen if they didn't have precisely two Yorkshires, four roasties and three trees of broccoli each? Or if the top of the turkey was a little crunchy? Or, most pertinently to him, why it was really such a palaver to add an extra space at the table? Were they really going to look back on this day in ten years' time and go "Oh, yes, lovely Christmas, but I only got thirty-one peas, and seventeen of them were colder than the rest"?

He didn't say anything of course, as that would have gotten him in even more trouble. He wasn't allowed to help either, as Sheila kept shrilly repeating that men were "No good in the kitchen," which pissed him and Aedan but mostly Tilly off, as she argued vehemently and regularly against the gendering of pretty much anything. Sheila insisted Matt's dad go put his feet up, and had snatched the first utensil Matt had touched from his hand, insisting she had it all under control.

After their tea cups were empty, Matt suggested they leave the two ladies to it; it was safer for everyone involved. They slipped away and made themselves comfy in the marginally warmer conservatory, and Matt found a chew toy that he and Buster could play tug with.

"Are you glad you let yourself in for this?" he asked Aedan, only half joking.

He was still reeling somewhat from his strange reaction to Aedan earlier. *Was this because of the Arnicare gel yesterday?* he thought. It had been a very intimate moment for them, but it hadn't felt bad at the time, at least not to Matt. Looking after Aedan felt nice. Natural, in fact. He was still absolutely livid that someone had hurt him, and it had felt good to help; he'd wanted to do something, anything to make it better.

Perhaps that was it. He was still churning up his anger over his uncle's homophobia. *Everyone's* homophobia. His dad hadn't been all that nice about it after all. So, he was misinterpreting his protective urges as…what? Affection? He rubbed his eyes in frustration. He was too tired to try and decipher anything like that now on top of anything else, especially as he winced at a muffled crash from the kitchen and another stressed shriek.

What he *really* couldn't wrap his head around at that moment was that his dad would leave his mum for someone so uptight and miserable. Couldn't she find joy in anything? Why was everything so difficult? Had Mum really been so boring, or not ambitious enough, or whatever it was that drove Dad into the arms of someone who only seemed to find pleasure in chasing unattainable standards.

He knew she wasn't exactly a warm person from the couple of times they'd met before; at the wedding, she had been distant and once again completely focused on getting everything *Perfect.* The couple of times she had accompanied Matt's dad on one of their short-lived weekend activities, she had spent the entire time answering work emails. But after the morning they'd all had together Matt felt he'd got an even clearer picture of her personality, and it wasn't all that flattering.

Aedan shrugged in response to his earlier question, busy doing something with his phone. "Ah, it's fine, it's sort of funny really."

Matt scowled and looked up, disbelieving. But Aedan was still tapping on his phone screen. "Well, I'm glad my awful family could be so amusing," he grumbled, unable to keep the hurt from his tone. Funny? Really?

He felt a nudge in his side, and looked down to see Aedan's big toe poking him. "Hey," he said softly as Matt looked up. "I didn't mean it like that."

Matt knew that, and he knew Aedan had been through something far shittier yesterday morning, but that didn't mean he had the monopoly on crappy families. Matt was entitled to feel rubbish that his dad had left his mum for a knob and he and Tilly were being treated like second best when they had come first. If Aedan knew what his dad had

74

said about him in the very kitchen earlier, would he still defend him so easily?

Would he want to if he'd heard Matt's response?

Matt pulled Buster to him and hugged him in his lap. "Yeah, sorry, I know," he mumbled, feeling cold with guilt.

Why did Aedan seem so complicated all of a sudden? He didn't need this, not today when he was trying to navigate the minefield of his dad and his step-family. He didn't even fully understand what had him so in knots. Would it really be so bad to be mistaken for Aedan's boyfriend?

His apology got him another nudge of a toe. "Don't worry about it, wanker," Aedan told him affectionately, and winked.

Matt wasn't so straight he couldn't appreciate that Aedan was good looking; in fact, he'd go so far as to call him beautiful. His dark eyes contrasted with the many tones of blonde in his hair, and it made Matt think of caramel chocolate. He was slim without being too skinny, and he had expressive hands that often caught Matt's eye. Even in a silly Christmas jumper, he still looked good, probably way better than Matt, and there was that tightening sensation in his gut again. It was a little bit of envy, sure, but it was just something to do with looking at Aedan, of taking him in as he simply was.

That feeling scared him with its strangeness, and he squashed it down, attributing it once again to the fact that Aedan was being a good friend, and his dad was being crap. He was affection starved...or something.

"Hey, look at this," Tilly piped up, and began chatting away to Aedan about an article she'd found about some new cancer treatment. She was a science geek at heart, and that overlapped with Aedan's passion for technology in many ways, as they'd already discovered over the last couple of days.

Matt, not being particularly enthralled by either subject, moved to the unoccupied couch, and curled up with Buster tucked against his belly so they could both have a doze. His lack of sleep the night before, combined with the several confrontations he'd already stumbled through that day, meant he was more than a little drowsy, and he grateful to grab a quick nap if he could get away with it.

He must have completely zonked out, as the next thing he knew Buster was shooting down from the sofa just in time for two seven-year-olds to take his place. Except the twins liked to do a lot more bouncing.

"*Wake up! Wake* up *Matt!*" they screeched.

"Wah—?" Matt snapped back into consciousness, wiping drool from his chin and flinching away from the jumping children. It didn't take him long to remember where he was.

"Dinner's almost ready!"

"Why were you asleep?"

"Are you bored?"

"You should have come played with us!"

"*Boys!*" Sheila's voice rang from the kitchen, and they immediately scrambled down off of Matt so they could race back inside.

He sat up with a groan and rubbed his eyes. "Ouch," he mumbled.

Buster was sat at his feet, his tail flicking back and forth, and Tilly had gone somewhere, maybe to sit at the table? But Aedan dropped into the seat beside Matt, and rubbed his back.

"Are you alright babe?"

Matt shrugged him off and stood. "Yeah," he said, unconvincingly. The nap had made him feel a little queasy on top of everything. But he wasn't sure he wanted Aedan touching him just then either. He was still unsure how he felt about all the thoughts swimming in a muddle around his head.

"Do you need a minute, or shall we head in?" Aedan asked. He stood as well, but thankfully kept his distance and slipped his hands into his jeans pockets.

Matt shook his head. "No, I'm fine." He picked Buster up, and placed him on the couch again. "Stay," he said firmly. Buster's ears dropped, and Matt walked away before he could feel even lousier than he already did.

Aedan caught his elbow though, and frowned at him as they stopped just before the kitchen. "Have I pissed you off?" he asked directly.

76

And Matt deflated at that. "No," he said honestly.

He wasn't pissed, not at Aedan. Aedan had done nothing but be nice. It was Matt's own issues messing with his head. His mum had once said that the divorce, and especially the affair, had left her feeling like there was something wrong with her, something unlovable. He'd argued hotly at the time that that was nonsense, but in that moment, he thought maybe he got it. Was he rejecting Aedan, because he thought he didn't deserve him?

"Sorry, I'm being a prick," he mumbled weakly. "This whole—" he waved his hand about to encompass all of his dad's house, "—thing is just a bit much I guess."

Aedan nodded and smiled in relief. His front two teeth were ever so slightly crossed, and Matt wondered if he'd noticed that before. It wasn't hugely obvious, he supposed.

"I get that," Aedan said. "And you're not a prick. I'm sorry if I made light of all the drama before, I just didn't like you stressing."

Matt rubbed his eyes. He didn't feel like he deserved Aedan being nice to him like that. He reached out and squeezed his good arm, signalling they were okay to touch again.

"I am a little bit of a prick," he argued, holding his thumb and index finger an inch apart. Thankfully, that made Aedan laugh.

"Look," he said with a lopsided smile. "We just need to get through dinner, which involves mostly eating, so everyone will be distracted. Then we can probably bluff our way through the afternoon with a dog walk and then a board game or something, so we'll be fine, yeah?"

Matt thought about that and found he relaxed right away. If they just broke it down into hours, it became a much more approachable timeline. Dinner could take up to two hours, a walk would be another one, and a film or two could take them easily into the evening. They could always suggest a game, if necessary. If he, Aedan and Tilly got really desperate there was the pool table in the rec room down in the basement. In fact, Matt thought he might suggest that anyway; he'd never played before, but it could be fun.

"Yeah, you're right," he said, with a sigh that expelled several of his earlier anxieties. "We just have to get through dinner, then take everything else as it comes."

"And we'll do it together," Aedan promised. "That's why I'm here. For you and Tilly."

His cheeks grew warm, and Matt coughed to cover his embarrassment. That was getting close to Dangerously Complicated Feelings again, and he'd had enough of trying to wade through those.

"Where is Tills, anyway?"

Aedan laughed. "I think she went to sit at the table in the hopes that it might speed up the arrival of dinner."

Matt laughed too. That certainly sounded like her. It was almost two o'clock already, and she was used to eating at least two times by now, if not three.

The kitchen looked like a bomb had been dropped as they walked through, with every surface covered with some kind of dirty pan or dish or utensil, but there wasn't anyone left in there; just Cliff Richard singing merrily away. Still. Signs of life could be heard down the hallway in the dining room though, so the boys headed that way.

The dining room was reserved for special occasions, and its décor was imposing enough to make sure nobody forgot it. The floor was polished mahogany and a crystal chandelier hung from the high ceiling, giving everything a highly reflective quality. The walls were separated half way up by a rail of skirting. The top half was papered in strong cream with a heavily embossed paisley pattern, while the bottom half was also decorated in mahogany panels that ran into the floor. With so much dark wood in the room it seemed to swallow up what little light there was available from the dimmed bulbs and flickering candles on the table.

On the wall opposite the doorway in were three windows, showing the grey sky outside and the landscaped garden that stretched on for what could have been an acre, for all Matt knew. On the other three walls were dozens of artfully framed photos of the family, all of them posed either at formal occasions or in professional, studio settings. It seemed his dad's new found photography hobby had probably been fuelled by Sheila's love of capturing the most important moments of her life in 300dpi.

The biggest picture in the room by far was a rather awkward one from his dad and Sheila's wedding earlier that year that he and Tilly had been forced to attend. The happy couple were standing on the staircase from the manor house where the ceremony had taken place, hands resting on the banister, looking into each other's' eyes in a way Matt guessed was supposed to be romantic. Instead, it just made him think of his mum's aversion to slimy, dead-eyed fish.

And then, tucked in the corner, practically behind a lamp, were his and Tilly's old school photos, when she had still been in junior school and he'd had train-track braces. It wasn't the best, but at least it was there, refusing to go away. Matt thought he could take some inspiration from that.

"Hey look." He pointed it out to Aedan, who barked a laugh, presumably at Matt's dorky face, then clapped his hand over his mouth.

The sound was extra loud in the very formal dining room, and Aedan knew he'd been too rambunctious. But as he caught Matt's eye, they both had to work hard to swallow their childish sniggers. There was something dreadful about getting the giggles somewhere you shouldn't, like school assembly or church, that just made it ten times worse. Eventually they got a hold of themselves, and made their way back over to the table.

It appeared no one had noticed their outburst. Tilly was already sat down, as they'd guessed, as was Debbie, but they weren't talking to each other, both preferring to scroll through their phones. Sheila untied her apron as the twins had a sword fight with their knives, and Matt's dad raced back and forth with loaded plates of food for everyone.

"Come on, come on!" he cried as he ran to get the last lot. "Take your seats boys, get settled in!"

They moved to the empty seats, only to discover everyone had name tags indicating where they should sit. Matt raised his eyebrows, appreciating now why Sheila had maybe had a minor meltdown over adding somebody else to the party. The table itself was positively overflowing with decorative green sprigs of holly sporting fat, red berries; there were also red candle holders with red glittery candles and red and gold napkins folded to look like bishop's hats, as well as crackers and cutlery and several glasses like you'd find in a restaurant, all standing in stark contrast to the fresh pressed white table linen. The centrepiece was a genuine nativity scene.

He stopped and stared for a second, wondering where they were supposed to put their plates.

"Mind the way," his dad cried jovially.

He came up behind them with the last two plates for them, overloaded with food, and Matt hurried to take his seat in between Aedan and Tilly. Tilly looked less than pleased to have been placed next to her dad and opposite Debbie, but Aedan was next to Sheila, and that made Matt nervous.

The twins were opposite him and Aedan, and before he sat down, he was able to glimpse the place card on the left: Taylor. That meant Ryan was opposite him, and he had a smudge of dirt on his chin. Brilliant. At least for a little while, he'd be able to tell which one was which.

"This all looks lovely Sheila," he said, because it did, and because he was tired of the atmosphere and thought a little flattery might go a long way.

"Oh, thanks." She dismissed him with a wave of her hand as they all moved to take their seats behind steaming plates of food. "The turkey didn't quite go to plan, and you'll have to let me know if you get a dodgy potato, some of them went funny, and—"

To his dad's credit, he detoured before sitting down, and grabbed her hand to kiss her knuckles in appeasement. "Darling, it's perfect," he assured her.

Tilly made a retching motion, but Matt lightly smacked her thigh to make her stop. He quickly leaned into her side before anyone could notice, although he doubted much had escaped Debbie's attention. "We just have to get through dinner," he muttered into her ear, repeating Aedan's advice.

Tilly scowled at him, then sighed and nodded. "Okay," she whispered back.

Chapter 6: Christmas Crackers

Their dad took his seat, and they began passing around condiments.

"Anyone for wine?" Sheila asked, pouring the white for herself.

"Oh, yes please," Debbie answered, holding up her glass.

"Red for me," Matt's dad chimed in.

"Can I have a bit?" Tilly asked around a mouthful of Yorkshire pudding and gravy.

Sheila's laugh trilled around the room. "Don't speak with your mouth full dear," she said, then stood to pass the bottles down. "And no, don't be silly, you're not old enough yet, this is for grownups."

Matt tensed immediately, knowing that was sure to press his sister's buttons, and he wasn't wrong.

"Mum let me yesterday," she groused. "I had it with juice."

"Well your mother isn't here now," Sheila said impatiently as she sat back down and picked up the salt. "Is she?"

"Yeah, and whose fault is that?"

Several knives and forks clattered onto the edges of plates, including Matt's. The gravy boat slopped in Debbie's hand, and Matt's dad choked on his wine. Cliff Richard lamenting over mistletoe drifted in from the kitchen beyond. Matt stopped breathing, not sure whether to look at Sheila, or his sister. Tilly was staring at her plate, an angry set to her jaw, so he swung his head to see what his step-mum's reaction would be.

"I beg your pardon, young lady?" she hissed.

Unlike a lot of people, who went red when they were angry or upset, all the colour drained from her face, leaving her cherry lipstick to stand out unnaturally against her white skin, and her dark eyes became pits.

Tilly had evidently had enough, and shoved her plate away, or, tried to. It was difficult with so much littering the table surface. "You heard," she challenged, going red like a normal person. "I'm sick of nobody talking about the fact you're just a tramp who cheated on her husband with a married man!"

81

"*Matilda*!" Matt's dad bellowed, as Tilly slumped in her chair and burst into tears. "You apologise this instant!"

"Why?" she sobbed, turning on him. "She's been horrid all day, I won't have her talk about Mum like that, it's not fair, it's not."

Debbie leaned across the table and jabbed her fork at her. "She didn't say anything! All she did was tell you that you can't drink, which you can't, and point out your mum isn't here, which she isn't!"

Matt's dad waved her back. "Yes, it's alright sweetheart, we can handle this."

"I think you should leave the table," said Sheila, her voice thick as she gripped the stem of her wine glass and stared at it.

That finally spurred Matt into action, and he threw his arms around Tilly's shoulders to pull her to him. "Hang on, no, wait," he placated. "Can we just calm down?"

"Matt, not now," his dad threatened.

He couldn't let them do this to Tilly. She was his baby sister.

"She didn't mean it," he protested, no matter how stupid it might sound. "It's hard for us, coming here. We had a long day yesterday and we're tired and we're not used to how you guys do things. We're trying, we promise." Everyone stared at him for a moment, and he gave Tilly a squeeze. "We're sorry," he said.

But he wasn't. He wanted to cheer Tilly on for being so brave. He wanted to tell Sheila she'd been nothing but a cow and had no right to be so flippant about the wife she had usurped. But he couldn't do that. He wasn't like his sister. All he could do was try and defuse the situation, and get through the dinner, like he and Aedan had agreed.

Another flicker of shame ran through him at the terrible display his family were putting on in front of his best friend, and couldn't bring himself to look at him. There may not have been anyone throwing punches, but it all felt pretty uncivilised, no matter how many airs and graces his step-family tried to put on.

Tilly hiccupped, and he pressed his face into her hair, speaking in the barest whisper. "*Just get through dinner*," he begged her.

"I'm sorry," she announced, not particularly loudly and not looking at anyone in particular. She's said it, though.

Matt used his thumb to wipe where her eyeliner had tracked down her cheeks and gave her an encouraging smile.

"Right, well," said their dad, clearing his throat. "Yes, it is going to get some getting used to, but if we work together, we can do it. There's bound to be some bumps in the road, but yes, hopefully we'll all be better for it."

Matt winced at the singular lack of any accountability in that little speech for the fact it was all his fault that Tilly had been put in this position, but he was pathetically grateful for any kind of acceptance of moving on from the argument. He nodded at his dad, and released Tilly from his hug.

"Mummy," the twin to the left, Taylor, piped up. He and his brother held up their empty plates. "Can we have more?"

Matt looked around at everyone else's still intact dinners, and had to say he was impressed. Sheila looked blankly at the gravy-and-cranberry-stained plates for a moment, before blinking and smiling at her sons.

"Of course my darlings." She smoothed her skirts down as she stood, then took both the plates and walked out of the room with her head held high.

Her absence allowed the room to breathe for a moment, and slowly, everyone picked up their knives and forks again.

Aedan placed a surreptitious hand on Matt's knee and squeezed, showing his support. The thought that that was a bit too intimate for 'just friends' flashed across Matt's mind, but he found it so comforting he didn't care. Maybe he should start to worry that Aedan was crossing a boundary, or perhaps Matt was leading him on. Right then, it just felt nice and he went with it.

Sheila returned, and slowly the conversation picked up, although Tilly didn't say a word, and mostly just poked at her food. Debbie carried them for a while, telling stories about how her second year at university was going so far, chatting about people who Matt had never heard of and had little interest in, but he was at least happy that the awkward mood had been lifted as much as it was probably going to be.

Unfortunately, the conversation inevitably steered his way again. At least he had managed to finish most of his food before it did.

"So, Matt," his dad said, making him feel like he was at an interview. "How's your UCAS form going?"

"Um." Matt gave up on eating and crossed his knife and fork. "Actually, I've applied to everywhere I want now. I'm just waiting to hear back from the unis to see if I've got any preliminary offers."

"What are you planning on studying?" Sheila asked.

Matt really didn't want to talk about this with her. It felt too personal, but he couldn't really see a way out of it.

"Uh, history," he admitted.

It was stupid really, especially listening to Aedan and Tilly natter on about all the advancements going on in the world, but he liked the notion of reliability in learning about what had already happened. It was something that was fixed, and he just had to uncover the mystery of it, which he felt he could do with enough patience. There was so much of the past from all over the world to discover, and he wanted to do his part to make sure it wouldn't be forgotten, to preserve it.

"Ooh, really?" said Debbie, sounding interested for once. "So, have you applied to Oxbridge? They're the best you know for that."

Ah, that's why she was interested. "Uh, no," he admitted, his ears heating up. "I'd never get in to those. I've gone for some others."

"Hmm," agreed Debbie, nodding thoughtfully. "Well, they aren't for everyone," she admitted, and Matt just wished the ground would swallow him up.

Aedan stirred beside him. "I think a lot of people put too much stock in Oxford and Cambridge," he said, and Matt felt his breath hitch. "What's the point in going there if it's not right for you, just because of the name?" He bumped his shoulder with Matt, oblivious to the 'shut up!' vibes he was sending. "A degree's a degree. Matt'll do great wherever he goes."

Chapter 6: Christmas Crackers

Matt couldn't help but be a little proud at his friend's words, but he still knew the conversation had taken another nosedive.

"Actually," Sheila said frostily. "Deborah reads English at Oxford."

To his credit, Aedan barely missed a beat. "Oh, well that's brilliant, good for you," he said to her with a smile. "Matt's applied to a few in London, we're both sort of hoping to end up there."

"I'd never be clever enough to get into Oxford," he found himself saying.

Aedan scowled. "Oi, that's not it. You're just more a London sort, that's all."

"And what are you planning on studying?" Matt's dad cut in.

Matt looked over at Aedan, and saw him sit up a little straighter.

"Oh, no uni for me," he said flippantly, keeping good eye contact with Matt's dad. But he crossed his cutlery like Matt had done, then clasped his hands tightly in his lap. "I couldn't afford it, but I think I'm better off going straight into work."

"In IT," Matt added hurriedly. "That's where the money is after all."

"Yes," agreed his dad. "Well, money is important, isn't it?"

Matt wasn't sure, but he guessed that was probably a Traveller dig. They were all supposed to be rich thanks to the fact they never paid taxes, or whatever people said, but Aedan wasn't like that. He had a part-time job already and made his own way, independent of his family.

"Luckily," Matt's dad continued. "Matt and Tilly won't have to worry about that, I've got enough set aside for all my children to attend whatever university they want."

"Oh," said Aedan, and Matt felt him deflate fractionally beside him. "Well, that's nice." Matt couldn't blame him. What else could you say to something like that?

"It is, isn't it?" his dad agreed.

Matt's dinner turned to acid in his stomach. Yeah, nice. An uncomfortable silence descended.

"Desert anyone?" Sheila asked brightly.

85

"Yes," Matt's dad agreed, an air of triumph to his voice. "That sounds like a wonderful idea."

CHAPTER 7: GOOD WILL TO ALL MEN

The rest of dinner passed without incident, probably because neither Matt, Tilly or Aedan said another word. Matt's dad chatted with Sheila and Debbie about this and that, and the twins seemed to communicate in some sort of silent code that made Matt think they were plotting world domination. At least there were no more arguments.

Matt wished the subject of university hadn't come up; it had only added another tangled ball of worry to his already complicated barrel of thoughts. He could tell Aedan was hurt by his dad's stupid boasting, and he had his own concerns on the matter, as did Tilly.

Poor Tilly. She had run off to the bathroom when they began clearing the plates away, and Matt was worried her anxiety had made her throw up. She certainly smelled of toothpaste when she returned, and she appeared sleepy again.

Luckily, the group naturally dispersed as the meal came to an official end, and Matt hoped he could get some time alone with Aedan and Tilly to recharge. Debbie went up to her room to Skype her boyfriend, and Matt's dad announced he was going for a nap. Sheila was evidently keen to get back in the kitchen to tackle the clean-up, and just as before would not accept any help. The twins vanished somewhere around the grounds of the house, so for a moment it looked as if Matt would get his wish for some peace and quiet for the time being.

"Maybe we could take Buster out," he offered as they hovered in the hallway. "Or perhaps see if we could put a film on?"

Sheila chose that moment to sweep past, and paused to consider them. "I think a film would be best, wouldn't it?" she suggested. That smile was back that remained a good mile away from reaching her eyes. "Keep you nice and quiet. Oh, Matthew dear, could you give me a quick hand, I'm not quite tall enough to put some of the roasting trays away."

Seeing as Aedan had a good couple of inches on him, Matt immediately smelled trouble, but there didn't seem to be much he could do. He attempted a reassuring smile towards Aedan as he led Tilly into the living room, and then trailed after his step-mum into the kitchen to once again, he suspected, be lectured.

He was not disappointed.

Sheila put the bowls she had carried in from the dining room down near the sink, then clasped her hands in front of her bellybutton, and fixed Matt with a grim look. "You and I don't know each other very well," she began.

Matt tilted his head. "No, I guess we don't."

"I'm speaking," she said coldly.

Matt swallowed, then slowly nodded.

She smiled icily, her eyes narrowed. "Good. Now, let me get one thing straight. This is my house. Your father and I have earned it, through blood sweat and tears, and this family means more to me than anything else in the whole wide world. I will do anything to protect my family, do you understand?"

Matt licked his lips nervously. "Yes," he said quietly. "I-I understand."

Sheila nodded once. "I spent a long time planning for today, and you have done nothing but undermine me since the moment you rang the doorbell. You have mocked and derailed and upset and defiled. It stops now."

She raised her eyebrows, and Matt realised she expected a response.

"I'm sorry," he said, and he meant it.

He *was* sorry they'd had such a terrible day. That didn't mean he thought it was completely his, Tilly's or Aedan's fault, but he was still sorry, and wished it had gone differently.

"Tilly's not normally like that," he started, but she waved her hand at him to stop.

"Matilda is young, but it is within my power to discipline her. She'll learn better manners. At least, if she's to visit this house, she will."

Matt's hackles instantly rose at that. What did she mean? She had *no* power over Tilly, and his dad better bloody back him up on that! He wouldn't have her trying to out-parent his mum, or anything else just as outrageous. But she didn't seem to want to talk about Tilly anymore, and unfortunately Matt could guess what her real problem was.

"You brought your friend Aedan into my home without my or even Brian's permission, on the day we saved to be our main Christmas day, and you somehow think this is acceptable behaviour?" She laughed shrilly, looking around the room as if expecting a chorus of people to agree with her. There might as well have been, for all Matt could find the words to challenge her. "You think I don't know what he is? Brian told me all about his family and where he lives, not to mention his *preferences*."

Matt winced. He hated when people acted like being gay was some great choice someone made. As if Aedan would *choose* to be bullied and beaten up and prejudiced against his whole life?

"Aedan is my friend," he tried to argue back.

Pure fury flashed over her face. "And that says very little about your character, young man," she snapped. "He is crude and uncouth and you have made me very uncomfortable by placing him in such close proximity to Ryan and Taylor."

"What do they have anything to do with it?" Matt asked, bewildered. He realised as he said it, it probably wasn't a good idea to provoke her just at that moment.

"They are at a very impressionable age," she growled, slapping her hand on the counter. "And someone of Traveller heritage, with a history of sexual deviancy, is an appalling example to put them into contact with."

That stung deeper than Matt could have possibly imagined. No matter how brilliant Aedan was, some people would only ever see him as some gypsy gay boy.

"He's not like that." The words came out a croak, and he desperately tried to find his voice, for Aedan's sake, to at least attempt to defend him this time. "He's clever and thoughtful and I would never have brought him here today if I didn't trust him. He's my friend," he managed to add with a touch more anger.

Sheila arched her eyebrows and looked down her nose at him from across the room. "That is not the impression I've been given. And I have to say, his behaviour not only reflects poorly on you, but also appears to influence you negatively as well. I would like to think, from how highly Brain has spoken of you in the past, that he raised you a little better than the sullen and impertinent child I have been subjected to today."

Matt's eyes burned. He wanted to shout that his dad had done bugger all raising of either him or Tilly, and he didn't give a flying fuck how little Sheila thought of him. But he didn't know how to play this. He didn't know how far she would be willing to go to keep them in line.

It was so infuriating. Why couldn't she and his dad just leave them alone? Why did they have this obsession with bringing them into the fold and making them behave?

"Fine," he bit out. "Do you want us to leave? Aedan has a taxi number."

She narrowed her eyes, and commenced to prove his point. "And have the neighbours talking? No thank you. There will be no scene on my driveway. You will now personally be responsible for every single thing out of Mr Gallagher's mouth. If I hear one word which I dislike, observe one unpleasant look, you will find out how far I am willing to go to ensure the safety and the future of my family."

Matt struggled to hold back the tears. "What's your problem?" he demanded. "You're acting like he's dangerous. He's not done anything to you, he's just different from you, and as a matter of fact so are me and Tilly!"

"Tilly and I," she corrected impartially. "Yes, you are, but it seems I am stuck with you, and if you are to be associated with me and mine, you will abide by my rules."

"Or?" Matt spat. "Or what?"

She shook her head. "You know exactly what," she sneered. "Don't make this ugly Matthew. If you want to be in this family, then you commit to it, like a man. If not, you do not get to enjoy financial benefits you have not earned. Life doesn't work like that."

Matt stepped back. He had forgotten for a moment what was at stake. He wanted to argue that his dad wouldn't really do that, but he knew in that moment, with absolute certainty, it wasn't even down to his dad.

Sheila had been there the whole damn time during the mediation and the divorce settlement. His mum hadn't been able to fight his dad's big city lawyer, and it had been simpler and involved less heartbreak to just get it over with as fast as possible and sign.

"You really think this is how to build a relationship with us?" he asked meekly, already knowing he'd lost.

Her lip curled in a victorious smirk. "I don't really care if you like me Matthew," she told him. "It's not always a mother's job to be liked. It's her job to provide, to guide and to protect."

"You're not my mother," he said flatly, and turned away, his heart in his boots.

He found Aedan and Tilly on one of the couches in the living room, the TV on, quietly playing an animated film that Matt wasn't sure he recognised. Tilly was snuggled up to Aedan, her back against his chest and his arms wrapped protectively around her, and Matt physically felt his heart contract.

Shelia was doing this to punish him. She might not like his or Aedan's attitude, and Tilly had certainly rocked the boat over Christmas dinner. But she was reminding him who was boss by turning him into the bad guy. He ground his teeth and swallowed his pride. He didn't have a choice.

"Aedan?" he said softly, and they both turned their heads to look at him.

"Are you alright babe?" he asked, sitting up. Tilly automatically untangled herself so he could stand up."

Matt rubbed the back of his head. It would be okay, he'd explain it all. Aedan would understand. "Can I just have a quick word with you?"

Aedan frowned, but he followed Matt into the hall.

He could hear his step-mum still clattering around in the kitchen, and he definitely didn't want Tilly to overhear. He led Aedan into the darkened drawing room where the baby grand stood as a ridiculous monument to style over functionality; as far he was aware, not one single person in the house knew how to play.

"What did she say?" Aedan asked in hushed tones as soon as they moved into the room. "Are you alright?" He made to touch his arm, but Matt stepped backwards, his heartbeat picking up.

Matt shook his head. "I'm fine," he said, his voice stilted to his own ears. "Look, we can't horse around anymore. She's mad at us and she's threatening to do something bad, so can we just, like, calm it down?"

Aedan frowned. "Uh, yeah, of course? We'll just watch TV or something?"

Matt swallowed. "No, I mean, everything. You have to…stay away from me."

The words hung between them. "What do you mean?" Aedan asked. His voice sounded small but there was a hint of coolness to it that Matt hated.

He swallowed. "Look, she's doing this on purpose. I'm sorry, but she said she doesn't like…doesn't want…It's the twins, they're only seven and she said, uh…"

"You want me to be less gay," Aedan clarified, his eyes unmoving and his voice stony.

Matt threw up his hands. "I don't care about that," he said. "I don't. You know I don't, But you have to admit, things have been a bit, I dunno, extra between us, and it's made her paranoid and if you—we—could just tone it down, just for the rest of today—"

"Fuck you."

Matt's entire body ran cold. "W-what?" he stammered.

"You heard," Aedan said, and Matt was horrified to see tears pooling in his eyes. "I came here for you, to help you, because when my own family treated me like I was nothing I knew you never would. And here you are," he cried, his voice rising as he jabbed a finger towards Matt. "Letting that hideous woman beat you down without even raising a finger. What do you care what she thinks?"

"Aedan!" Matt pleaded, trying to step closer but he moved a step back to match. "It's not like that. I don't have a problem with how we are. I like how we are! But, you've been extra touchy-feely, and I get it, after what happened yesterday—"

"Don't you talk about that," he interrupted. "Don't act like you understand."

"But I want to!" Matt shot back. "Please," he dropped his voice to a hiss. "Please, this is what she wants. She wants you to think I have a problem with you being gay, when you know I don't, I told her she was being ridiculous!"

"And yet you're still here," Aedan rasped out. His voice quivered as the tears teetered and fell. "I never thought you'd treat me like this. God I'm such a fucking idiot." He angrily scrubbed his eyes with the heels of his hands.

Matt shook his head, anger rising inside him. "Fucking hell Aedan," he said. "Not everything's about you, there's other things at stake here. You have to admit, you have been clingy today! And—no!" he snapped, stopping him from interrupting again. "Listen! I get it, in fact it was fine with me, more than fine. But that—" he dropped his voice so it was practically inaudible "—*bitch* out there is making out like you're some sort of pervert, and if all it takes to calm her down is just putting some distance between us, I really don't see what the problem is?"

Aedan laughed, wetly, and it was an awful sound. "Of course you wouldn't, *babe*." The endearment was tacked on nastily. "Because you don't have to face every single day with people telling you what you are isn't right, isn't natural. That you would be fine, if you were just less *you*. And you know what?" He threw his hands up and sniffed back a sob. "Most of the time I can deal with that. But I trusted you, you fucking prick! I trusted you wouldn't cower like this, that you'd fight back for me. I thought I fucking *meant* something to you! What a moron."

His Irish accent was coming out and his swearing was getting worse, and Matt could feel this fucking up before his eyes, but he couldn't seem to stop it. "You think I'm just doing this because I couldn't be bothered to stand up for you? Well, I bloody did!"

"Yeah?" Aedan laughed hollowly. "Not enough apparently."

He was closest to the door, and spun on his heels to go back out into the hallway.

Matt let out a frustrated cry, tugged at his hair, and stomped out after him. "Aedan, calm down," he said, then stopped when he saw what he was doing. Aedan already had his feet shoved back into his trainers from where he'd left them by the front door, and was shrugging his coat on as he picked up his rucksack. "What the hell are you doing?"

Aedan snarled, such an ugly expression on his beautiful face, and zipped up his coat. "I think I've ruined your Christmas enough for one year. See you around, yeah?"

Matt couldn't believe what he was seeing, he wanted to shout at him to stop, but the stupidness and pointlessness of the situation was making him irate. "Fine!" he yelled. "Go, run away like you always do!"

The look of hurt that flickered over Aedan's face as he paused at the door just about shattered Matt's heart, and immediately he wanted to take everything back. But Aedan snatched open the door, making it bang against the wall as he marched out, and Matt couldn't seem to do anything but stand there and watch it happen as the door slowly swung shut again, blocking him from view.

"What the *fuck* are you doing?"

Matt spun around, a sob catching in his chest. "Tilly!" he cried at her scandalous use of language.

"Don't you 'Tilly' me," she shot back, absolutely furious. "What are you doing just standing there? Go and apologise and bring him back, right now!"

Matt swallowed, shaking his head. "He's being a dickhead," he said. Before he could even glance at the door, as if to see Aedan's retreating figure, Tilly had stormed over to him, and smacked his arm. "Ow!" he shouted indignantly.

"I heard everything." She raised her eyebrows as if expecting him to lecture her on the impropriety of eavesdropping. Her voice wavered as she spoke, and Matt couldn't believe that she was threatening to cry as well.

"Oh what the hell?" he snapped. "Do I have to fight with literally everyone today!"

Tilly wiped her eyes angrily. Her eyeliner had run again, and she was starting to resemble a glittery panda. "Yeah, probably," she sniffed. "Why did you say that to him? What's wrong with you? He's been so nice to you and you say all that...all that...shit!"

This wasn't fair. Matt didn't want any of this. "If you were listening you'd understand why I tried to talk to him," he spat out. "Sheila's twisting everything, and she'd probably love nothing more than for all of us to fight!"

"Well congratulations," Tilly said, hugging herself. "We're supposed to stick together, you and me, and Aedan's on our side."

"There aren't any sides!" Matt pleaded. "Not between us, anyway! I just wanted him to tone it down. I didn't want him to not be himself, or leave!"

But even as he said it, Aedan's words just now troubled him. Was that really how he felt, like he had to hide who he was all the time? That he had to monitor himself and keep his 'gayness' in check? If so, Matt had just added to that. And that really felt crappy.

"Can I say something?" Tilly mumbled, running her hands through her hair and shaking it out.

Matt leaned against the wall, feeling thoroughly worn out. The clattering had stopped from the kitchen, and he wondered if Sheila was hanging off their every word with glee. "Go on then," he sighed. "It's not like I could stop you."

Tilly glanced anxiously at the front door. "You've got to promise not to get mad, or freak out," she hissed.

"Tilly, just say it." Now that his adrenaline was fading he was feeling pretty sick to his stomach. He and Aedan had never fought before, not over anything that mattered.

"Okay." She stepped closer, her fists balled in determination. "I'll be quick, because you're just wasting time here. But, I think I finally get something. I think…I mean I always thought it was weird you talked about Aedan like, all the time, but he never came over, right?"

"I never have anyone over," Matt defended himself quickly.

Tilly shook her head. "No, but he's different. He's special." Worry flashed across her face, but Matt wasn't sure he was following.

"He's my best friend," he conceded.

"And yet you keep him at arm's length," Tilly argued. Matt opened his mouth to disagree, but she shook her head. "No, you do, otherwise he'd come for dinner, or just to hang out or whatever. I think, it's like, you're scared to let him in." She bit her lip and raised her eyebrows. "And I think you just really, *really* hurt his feelings."

Matt stared at her for a good ten seconds. "I'm not scared of him," he stammered. "I'm pissed, he's acting completely irrationally—"

"No, *you're* the one acting irrationally!" she all but shrieked, and stamped her foot, stunning Matt into silence. "Look, let me put it this way. Let's say—Aedan has just walked out of here, he has no idea where he is and he could get hurt by someone or just fall and twist his ankle. All because you were afraid of him being himself. But even if that doesn't happen, he's not going to want to be your friend anymore, because you've been such a dick, and you're never going to see him again. So, how does that make you feel?"

Matt's vision swam in front of his eyes. "No, it's not like that," he said uncertainly.

"It's exactly like that," she countered. "Unless you go and find him, right now." His eyes flicked involuntarily towards the kitchen, and Tilly followed his gaze. "Who's more important?" she demanded. "Her or him?"

"What about you?" he asked without pause, but she barked out a laugh that turned instantly to a glower.

"Don't you put this on me. I'm fine. I can take care of myself, thank you very much!"

Matt's throat was so tight he could barely speak, and he stared at the front door, hanging loosely on the latch. "I don't want to lose him," he admitted.

Tilly threw her hands up. "Then go get him, you big dummy!"

I don't want you to leave. That's what he'd told him back in his bedroom yesterday. And he'd meant it.

His feet were moving before he even realised it. He yanked his coat off the peg and hopped into his boots. Tilly jumped around clapping. "Yes! Yes! Yes!" she cried.

"What about her?" he asked, nodding towards the kitchen.

Tilly blew a raspberry. "I'll deal with the wicked witch. You go get your man."

Matt rolled his eyes. "It's not like that," he protested.

"Yeah, yeah."

He shoved his hat on, pulled his gloves from his pockets, then realised Aedan had left his chunky-knit scarf behind, so grabbed that as well to take with him. "I don't have keys," he said as he pulled the door open to the late afternoon gloom. "Will you let me back in?"

"Depends who you bring home with you," she said saucily, and poked her tongue out.

"Brat," he said, with a giddy grin.

"Pillock. Now quit wasting time and *go*!"

He ran outside, letting the door slam shut behind him, and jogged to the end of the driveway. But when he looked left and right, there was absolutely no sign of Aedan. Well, this was off to a terrific start.

"Hey Matt!" a voice hissed.

"Matt, up here!"

He jerked his head up and was almost unsurprised to see a pair of twins dangling from the branches of a large, leafless oak tree. "Ryan, Taylor," he said, still able to tell them apart thanks to the dirt on Ryan's chin. "Did you see Aedan?"

They nodded.

"He was mad."

"He was crying."

"Did you make him cry?"

97

Matt shoved his hands awkwardly into his coat pockets. "Erm, yeah," he admitted.

"When Daddy made Mummy cry, he always had to say sorry," said Taylor sagely.

Ryan nodded. "Brian brings Mummy flowers now when she cries." He narrowed his eyes. "Are you going to bring Aedan flowers?"

Matt showed them his empty hands. "I haven't got any," he said. "But I can say I'm sorry. Do you know which way he went?"

His heart was slamming in his chest now. He kept thinking about what Tilly said, about how he could get hurt, or even just too cold in this weather. He'd already been through enough. Matt wasn't going to put him through more as well.

"What's in it for us?" Ryan asked, and Matt could have exploded.

"Ryan Wilks!" he shouted. Sheila's neighbours might as well get a scene anyway. "You tell me which way he went right now, because it's the right thing to do! Otherwise…Father Christmas will come back and take back your toys!"

Both boys gasped, but Ryan tapped Taylor on the shoulder. "He got my name right," he said, and Taylor nodded.

"No one ever gets our names right," Taylor told Matt.

Ryan stood up on the branch he seemed perfectly content balancing on, even though Matt's insides flipped a little worrying he could fall. "He went that way," he said, pointing. "Towards the field by the woods."

Relief flooded through Matt, and he broke into a sprint. "Thanks!"

"Father Christmas isn't going to take our toys, is he?" one of the boys yelled from behind him.

"Nah!" Matt called back. "In fact, if you're lucky, he might just bring one extra!"

He ran, the woods looming obviously ahead. He kept whispering to himself, begging Aedan not to do anything idiotic, to not have taken a hidden turning, to just listen to him and come back.

Chapter 7: Good Will to All Men

By the time he reached the field he was aware it had started snowing, but he didn't care. As there, standing fiddling with his phone, was Aedan.

Matt said a silent prayer to whoever might be watching over him, pulled his gloves off to stuff in his pockets and broke into another mad dash.

Aedan must have heard his feet on the grass, as he turned with a frown just as Matt collided into him, wrapping his arms around him as tight as he could without hurting his injured side. "I'm sorry!" he gasped. "I'm sorry, I'm the biggest prick ever, I should never have talked to you like that, please come back, please, I-I don't want you to leave."

For a horrible moment, Aedan just stood there. Then he slipped his arms around his back, and melted into the embrace. "You don't?"

Matt pulled back so he could loop his forgotten scarf gently around his neck, and then he looked at his face, searching for a clue to how he felt. "No," he confessed. He gingerly put his arms back around him, an excited thrill running through him when there was no hint of rejection. "I was completely out of line. I should never have said those things. I never want you not to be you, and I shouldn't have let Sheila bully me like that. She scared me but that's not an excuse. Aedan, you're brilliant. You're...you're the glitter on the garland, *all* year round, and you matter *so much* to me, okay?"

Aedan just stared at him for a good while, his Adam's apple bobbing in his throat. "I think you're pretty brilliant, too," he said softly.

Matt let out a laugh that was more of a sob. "No, I'm not, I'm awful," he said wretchedly. "But if you still want to be friends, I'll be better. I won't treat you like that again, I swear."

"Of course I still want to be friends," Aedan said as if Matt was an idiot, which, to be fair, he was. He gave his arm a gentle slap. "You can't get rid of me that easily. Even if you did turn into a total prat for five minutes." He huffed and rested their foreheads against one another. It was comforting; Matt sighed and let his eyes close. It was okay. Thank Christ he'd listened to Tilly.

"Thank you," he murmured.

"It's alright babe," replied Aedan. "But, I'm sorry too. You're right, I need to stop just running off when things get too difficult."

Matt pulled back and looked into his brown eyes. "I didn't mean that," he said quickly. "That was a really shitty thing to say, just ignore it."

Aedan shook his head and smiled ruefully. "Nah," he said. "I do, but it's okay. Next time, I'll stop and think. It's probably better to talk things through, isn't it? You can't do that if you storm off in a huff."

Matt chewed his lip. "I should have explained better, before. Then you wouldn't have wanted to leave."

Aedan rubbed his thumb against Matt's coat, but he could still feel it on his shoulder blade. "About Sheila?" he asked.

Matt nodded, and took a deep breath, deciding to just get it all out there. "Look, the thing is, it was blackmail, which sounds so *telenovela*, but this woman obviously has *massive* control issues." He sniffed and rubbed his eyes with one hand, but if fell right back around Aedan's waist. "What my dad said about paying for uni? Nobody has to make him do that. It'll only be on his good grace and she could talk him out of that. I don't really mind – I mean – I do, I want to go so badly, but I don't need to. But *Tilly*?" he shook he head and let out a sad little cry. "She's going to be a scientist, you know? She's already crazy good at biology and she's got her heart set on being a doctor and, even if she doesn't make it that far, I have to give her a chance, right? I can't let them take her degree away from her, she deserves that! And, I-I——"

He hadn't realised he was crying until Aedan's cold fingers came up and brushed the tears away. "You didn't want to jeopardise that by going against their wishes."

Matt shook his head miserably. "I bet they're not really homophobic," he said. "They probably like Elton John, and that Neil Patrick Harris guy."

"But I bet they hate the gypsy thing," Aedan supplied with only a touch of ruefulness.

Matt scowled. "Probably," he admitted. His cheeks heated up, embarrassed on their behalf. "Mostly, I think she just gets her kicks from winning. Like with Buster. Do you know they don't even walk him! They get a professional walker in every day."

"Wankers," Aedan said with feeling, making Matt chuckle a little.

They stood there for a while, and Matt realised it was definitely now snowing around them. "They just have to win—to beat my mum, and us I guess," Matt explained, hoping he made sense. "I think it makes them feel better about what they did. The affair, I mean. I don't really get it, but that's what it feels like. Like, if they have the best of everything, it proves it was worth it."

Aedan nodded sadly. "That makes sense, I guess. If you're a wanker."

Matt laughed. It faded to a smile, matching Aedan's, and they stood there, just staring at each other for a while.

"We've been different," Matt said eventually, hoping he wasn't about to break the spell.

"You mentioned that, earlier," Aedan agreed, and his hand rubbed tentatively once up and down Matt's back. It felt nice.

He dropped his gaze, looking down at where their coats were pressed together. "We've been…more."

"I know." Aedan said softly.

"It's confusing," Matt admitted quietly, then risked a glance up through his lashes. "I don't really know what to think."

"But?" Aedan probed, raising his eyebrows.

Matt swallowed, feeling dizzy again. "But…it doesn't feel wrong. It feels…right."

Aedan licked his lips, drawing Matt's attention there. The lower one was chewed plump again, and that was doing all kinds of crazy things to Matt's stuttering heart. Aedan squeezed him slightly through his coat. "Does this feel right?" he asked, his voice barely above a whisper and rasping against his throat.

Matt nodded. They were hugging in the gently falling snow, protected by the quiet of the woods, and he couldn't think there was anything wrong about it at all.

His heart beat a tattoo in his chest; he didn't know what was happening, or if he was making a huge mistake. But,

Helen Juliet

like magnets being drawn to one another, he couldn't seem to stop himself as he leaned into Aedan, his best friend, and carefully pressed their lips together.

CHAPTER 8: WINTER WONDERLAND

Matt had kissed a few girls before.

First, there had been Amelia Watson at the Year Nine Valentine's disco. She'd had a sweet smile and great boobs, and they had slow-danced awkwardly at the end of the night to some One Direction song that had everybody nervously anticipating a snog or two. It had been mostly wet, and there hadn't really been any tongues involved, but Matt had been pretty pleased with it nonetheless. He'd almost worked up the nerve to ask her out after that, but then Jimmy Talbert had got in there first, and Matt found he didn't really mind all that much. He'd quite liked the idea of having a girlfriend, rather than being attached to Amelia in particular. They'd stayed friends afterwards, which he kind of felt was better.

Then there was the summer after his GCSEs, before starting Year Twelve, when he'd had so much extra time after exams and had got himself a part time job at a coffee shop in town for a little extra cash. Linda Jones had been finishing up a gap year before heading off to uni, and had been quite keen to teach him a thing of two after hours. That had been fun, but once she disappeared off to Exeter, he hadn't really missed her as much as the kissing.

Gail Flannery had broken his heart quite badly last year, or so he'd felt at the time. But then, everything had been so much more keenly felt in the wake of the divorce. They'd met at Sanctuary, the church-turned-nightclub a couple of towns over that wasn't particularly hot on checking I.D.s. She was funny in a sarcastic way, and had a tattoo on her lower back. They'd gone out several times on actual dates and had a few make out sessions in her car, but then she'd met someone else and dumped Matt over text, which he could attest was a really crappy way to break up with anyone. He'd gone back to Sanctuary a few times and kissed several randomers after that, until he realised it didn't really make him feel any better.

But this. This was light years ahead of any of those experiences.

Because this was Aedan.

He'd have thought that kissing a boy would be this monumental wakeup to his core beliefs as to who he was as a person, but mostly it just felt awesome. Aedan didn't have as much stubble as him yet, and didn't even need to shave very often, so his skin was pretty soft like a girl's as they moved their mouths, tongues pushing forward to meet and intensify the moment. He tasted a bit salty from dinner, and there was a sort of vanilla there too, but mostly he just tasted of him; that familiar, indefinable scent that was just Aedan Gallagher.

He brought his hand up Matt's back and cradled his neck, his fingers carding through the short hairs, stroking gently, and Matt moaned into his mouth. He didn't want it to end, but he also felt the need to check this was really happening. He gently pulled away, and stared at his best friend as they caught their breath. Aedan. He'd kissed Aedan.

He obviously wasn't the only one who noticed.

"You kissed me?" Aedan said faintly, eyes starting to nervously search Matt's face.

Matt was just as stunned, but he had enough wits to bring his hand up to cup Aedan's jaw. "Yeah," he murmured. "Is that…is that okay?"

Aedan nodded, dazed and unfocused. "Yeah," he assured him. "Yeah, it's pretty great actually."

"Yeah?"

"Yeah." He licked his already glistening lips. "Do you, maybe, want to do it again?"

This was weird. He knew he wasn't gay, he'd fancied plenty of girls and this risked blowing his friendship with Aedan to pieces. But all he wanted right then was another taste. He couldn't stop himself.

He nodded and leaned in, an electric thrill of excitement and happiness coursing through him as Aedan met him halfway. They both had their hands in each other's hair now, and Matt grinned at how much wax he was getting all over his fingers.

"What?" Aedan grinned himself, but didn't pause the kiss.

"You," Matt replied, delighted.

They kissed and kissed; soft, sweet nips and hard, thrusting snogs. But after a little time, Aedan eased away, letting his gaze flit over Matt's face again, concerned as he rested his cold hands either side of his neck, his fingers drawing little circles. "Are you okay?" he asked.

Matt just wanted to nod, to not think about it, but when he took a figurative step back and considered how he felt, he knew that the most important thing was that he was okay. He liked this. This was nice. In fact, he wanted more of whatever this was. And if his thoughts didn't delve any deeper than that for the time being, then that was good for now.

"I'm okay," he said tentatively, a smile tugging at his tingling lips. "A bit shocked, but in a good way, you know?"

"I know," Aedan affirmed. "We don't have to talk about anything now." The ministrations from his fingertips sent delicious little tingles down Matt's spine. "You'll probably need some time to think about all this."

Matt brushed a couple of blond strands back from his forehead, just because he could. "And you don't?" he asked, not really sure what he wanted Aedan to say.

At the moment, he was floating completely in the present, not worrying about the future or reliving the past. He was here and he was happy.

Aedan tilted his head in agreement. "No, I'll need to think," he admitted. "But there are some things I already know for sure."

"Yeah?" Matt asked, his smile pulling wider. He wasn't sure why, but he felt they were good things.

"Yeah, like—" Aedan paused and bit his lip, looking down through his eyelashes shyly. He looked so beautiful Matt had to remember to breathe. For all he kept saying he wasn't gay, he was certainly starting to appreciate how gorgeous Aedan was, in a way he really couldn't tell himself was jealousy any longer. "Like I know that was the best kiss I ever had."

Matt laughed, pleased as punch, and buried his face into Aedan's chunky scarf. "Really?" he squeaked.

"Really," Aedan promised, pecking his cheek chastely. "Do you want to go back?" he asked, rubbing Matt's back again in a way he could really get used to. "We can warm up, make sure everyone is okay?"

"Can we have tea?" Matt asked looking up with a lopsided grin.

Aedan nodded. "Definitely tea."

They began to walk back across the field to the street, and Aedan slipped his hand hesitantly against Matt's, threading their fingers together. He'd done the same thing after Matt had rubbed the Arnicare on his back. As he looked at their hands, then at Aedan's hopeful face, Matt realised he didn't have to let go this time. Not yet, anyway.

He gave Aedan's hand a squeeze to show he liked it, then rubbed his thumb against his knuckles. He'd always liked Aedan's hands, especially the way he always waved them about when he was trying to prove a point. But he liked them even more now he knew himself how soft they were. Matt's felt rough in comparison, but the way Aedan was caressing him back, he didn't think he minded.

When they reached the house, they reluctantly parted, and stared down the driveway as they collected themselves. "Okay," said Matt eventually, rolling his shoulders back. "We can do this."

"Together," Aedan agreed, then checked his watch. "Just another five or six hours to go."

Matt huffed. That didn't sound all that appealing, but with Aedan by his side, it might not be so bad.

As they walked down, Matt checked the tree line, but there was no sign of any wayward twins. He would have to thank them when he saw them next for their help in a successful mission. He lifted his hand to ring the bell, only to have the door fly inwards just in time.

Tilly stood on the other side, her expression carefully neutral. She had obviously used the time they'd been gone to take off her makeup, and she looked a lot younger. "As far as I know," she said evenly, "no one knows you were gone. Have you both calmed down?"

"Yes," the boys mumbled.

"Are you going to behave yourselves now?"

"Tilly," Matt growled in warning. She rolled her eyes and opened the door wide enough so they could come in. "Thank you."

They followed her through to the living room where she looked to have been in the middle of picking a new film. "I could hook my laptop up and we could watch the new Marvel Comics one?" Aedan suggested as he and Matt divested themselves of their coats and other paraphernalia.

Matt checked his phone to make sure his dad hadn't called him whilst they'd been out, which he hadn't, so he slipped it back in his pocket. Good. He'd rather not answer any questions about what had gone on.

He was very tempted to say yes to Aedan's suggestion. "Is it out on DVD yet?" He had to ask.

"No," Aedan admitted with a wry smile.

"Then it's probably not a good idea." He flopped onto the couch, and tried not to react as Aedan sat beside him. He was at the other end with a couple of feet between them, but it still felt vaguely sensational given the new-found kissing.

Tilly didn't react though, but instead held up a couple of options from their dad and Sheila's collection to choose from. "I've got *Jingle All the Way*, the new *Ghostbusters* or *Overboard*—what do you think?"

Aedan screwed up his nose. "What's *Overboard*?" he asked. "Looks old."

Matt and Tilly locked gazes as their eyes widened in horror. "*Overboard!*" they decided unequivocally, and Tilly spun on her knees to load up the DVD player.

"You'll love it," Matt promised as he poked Aedan with his toes down the length of the sofa. Aedan responded by catching his feet and putting them on his lap, holding onto his ankles possessively.

"If you say so," he replied, smiling warmly. He rubbed Matt's feet in a way that somehow felt more intimate than the kissing, and Matt stared at his hands on his toes for a while. Aedan didn't look at him, he watching Tilly mess around with the DVD, as if massaging the ticklish soles of Matt's feet was the most natural thing in the world.

The thing was, it was. Matt didn't feel awkward, or like they were stepping over the line. It just made him feel warm and comfortable, and perhaps a tiny bit tingly.

Tilly got up once the trailers were going to find the remote and skip them. She took one look at Matt and Aedan, tried to swallow her scoff, then snatched up the clicker so she could be in charge of it from the armchair, where she was apparently happy to ignore her brother's existence. Apparently, she'd been happy to send him chasing after Aedan, but seeing the result of her efforts was just a little too icky for a fourteen-year-old.

Realising this made Matt grin, a relaxed kind of happy settling in his chest. Because she was reacting the same way as she would at seeing him with a girl. It wasn't like that had happened all that much, but if she'd cooed and ahhed over them, he would have felt totally weird. The derision felt like acceptance without condition, and even though he wasn't even entirely sure what it was she was accepting yet, he was grateful.

They were left mostly in peace to watch their classic RomCom, which Aedan completely loved, until Ryan and Taylor came tearing in with a pair of Nerf guns.

"Hey, hey!" Matt said sternly, pulling his feet away from Aedan. But he was amazed when the twins both turned obediently to listen to him. "You either sit nicely and watch the TV with us, or you can go downstairs to play."

The boys looked at one another, then scrambled eagerly onto the couch so they could wriggle between Matt and Aedan. "Whoa, easy there sproglets," Aedan cried in alarm. They got kicked and slapped as the boys get themselves seated, but after that, the twins were surprisingly good at settling down and watching the film.

Now that he'd started to pay attention, Matt could tell that Ryan had a fractionally narrower face as well as the dirt smudge to give him away, and Taylor had a pattern of moles on the back of his right hand. So he knew it was Ryan who cuddled up to him, thumb in his mouth, to watch on as Goldie Hawn helped Kurt Russell design a crazy golf course.

"Who's dat?" he asked around his thumb, pointing to the screen.

Matt quietly explained the basics of the plot so far to him, keeping half an eye on Taylor as he drifted off to sleep next to Aedan. A flicker of warning went off in his mind that this probably wasn't what Sheila had had in mind after their *tête-à-tête* earlier, but it was all so calm and peaceful he decided (or rather hoped) it would be okay.

By the time the credits started rolling, everyone was dozing except for Aedan who had stayed eagerly awake until the very end. "Aww, that was so adorbs," he said, leaning over to poke Matt to get his attention. "Why have we never watched that before?"

"Well," said Matt gently. "Some idiot never invited you around their house before."

Aedan bobbed his head, as if considering his argument. "True. Perhaps that's something a certain idiot can fix in the future."

Matt nodded, not trusting himself to speak. Was that what he wanted, for him and Aedan to carry on with 'this?' It wasn't quite as scary as it sounded. If the choice was having Aedan over to visit, or not having Aedan over to visit, he knew which he would prefer. And then there was the kissing. His neck grew hot again just thinking about that.

Tilly yawned noisily and stretched, in her chair. "Aw man, I missed the end," she pouted. Her complaining woke the boys though, who went from nought to sixty in the blink of an eye.

"Can we play games now?"

"Matt, will you play parachutes?"

"No, not parachutes, cars!" Ryan insisted angrily as he and Taylor scrambled to switch the television over from the DVD player to one of the many consoles they had stacked in the cabinet underneath the TV. They whined and shrieked, and then Taylor clouted Ryan over the head with one of the controllers, so he started wailing. Matt panicked and stood up to try and pull them apart, not quite sure what else to do.

That was the moment Sheila chose to reappear.

"What's all this racket?" she demanded, hands on hips and a vein throbbing in her temple. She looked as if she had reapplied her makeup, or at least freshened it up, and Matt was slightly miffed to see that she was still sporting the high heels, despite how uncomfortable they looked.

"Taylor hit me!"

"Ryan was being mean!"

Sheila turned on Matt. Of course she did. "And you just let them do this?" she asked incredulously.

Matt had had enough. He couldn't take it anymore. "No," he snapped. "Your sons were being good as gold as we all watched a film, then they had a fight, because that's what little boys do. Now if you'll excuse us, I think it's about time we took Buster for a walk." He glanced around to see Tilly and Aedan nod. "Seeing as no one else is going to bother around here."

He didn't stay to gauge her reaction. He knew he'd probably dug himself a hole he couldn't get out of now. But he was starting to realise that if she was in charge of the rules, the game was probably rigged from the start, and he might as well save some of his dignity and stand up to her now.

The three of them collected their outdoor wear and went to take Buster out the back door. He went crazy when Matt picked up his lead, running in circles and barking, but as soon as Matt told him to sit so he could attach it to his collar, he plonked his bum down on the tiles and waited obediently until he was told he could go again.

Darkness was falling as they headed out, but the moonlight was reflecting off the snow that had fallen, and it made it bright enough that they could do a circuit of the field without much fear of tripping or losing Buster. He was so happy to be out. He never strayed far, always coming back every minute or so to jab his nose into Matt's calf, his little tail wagging so hard it made his bum look like it was going to shake off.

They didn't talk about Sheila. They talked instead about the latest series of Game of Thrones, and Matt bored them all on the ways the show varied from the books. Matt tried not to keep looking over at the patch of grass, now covered in an inch of snow, where he and Aedan had stood and kissed only a couple of hours ago. As anxious as he was about going back and facing his step-family, his stomach was also in the good kind of knots as he tried not to keep sneaking glances over at Aedan.

As they headed home, Tilly ran ahead playing fetch with Buster and a stick so large it was practically a branch. Making sure she was significantly distracted, Aedan took Matt's hand, just for a moment, and kissed the back of his knuckles.

"We'll work it out," he said simply.

Did he mean Matt's family, or them? Both, maybe? He stepped away as they walked back onto the street and into the artificial light of the lampposts. Matt assumed he would have to wait and find out.

A help-yourself finger buffet was set up by the time they returned, but thankfully the pretence of playing happy families had been abandoned and Sheila, Debbie and Matt's dad had set themselves up watching a film in the lounge, having put the twins to bed. Matt, Aedan and Tilly were able to eat in the kitchen in peace, which Matt was especially pleased about after he saw how much Tilly loaded her plate up with, not having been able to eat much of her Christmas dinner at all. They quietly listened to music from Aedan's phone and played Head's Up on Matt's, then went for another round of Twenty Questions.

It wasn't very late by the time they all started yawning, but it had been an emotional day, and nobody protested escaping with an early night. Matt was tempted just to sneak off, but he felt that would be taking things a step too far.

First, they all ventured into the conservatory to give Buster a last cuddle. He tried to follow Matt, obviously remembering how he used to sleep on his bed, and Matt felt miserable make him stay. At least the conservatory was warmer now, but it was dark and he hated thinking of him all by himself for the whole night.

Short of smuggling him into his room, Matt didn't have a choice, and Buster stayed when he was told, because he was a good boy.

Tilly offered to show Aedan where they'd all be sleeping, and Matt rallied himself to approach his dad and Sheila. "We're off to bed now," he announced, poking his head around the living room door.

Sheila and Debbie didn't even look up, which he thought was pretty childish, but at least his dad gave him a friendly smile. "Did you have enough to eat?" he asked, taking his glasses off to give them a quick clean on his hanky.

"Yes, thank you," Matt said, addressing the side of Sheila's head. "It was lovely."

"Alright, well we've made up your bedrooms downstairs, and there's bedding out for Aedan. Let us know if you need anything."

Matt promised they would, then trotted down into the basement level to follow where Tilly had taken Aedan.

The only thing Matt liked about coming over to his dad's house to stay for the first time was that the three of them had essentially got their own floor to themselves. The main room was set up with a full-sized pool table, even more video game consoles, a stocked bar and a home cinema that Matt would have loved to have used earlier, but it had been simpler just to stay in the living room rather than presume they were allowed to make use of the facilities here.

Having been shown earlier, Matt knew his room was off to the left by the small bathroom that just fit a toilet, sink and shower stall, and Tilly's was to the right, by the bar. There was a sofa tucked under the staircase, on which a pile of blankets had been left, and Matt figured that was where Aedan was going to sleep. He felt a pang that it wasn't even a sofa bed, but Aedan didn't seem to mind.

They took turns in the bathroom and said goodnight. Matt watched as Tilly made a point of shutting her door, then turned to Aedan, suddenly awkward. "Um, night," he said, hugging his bag to him. What was he supposed to do? Was a kiss expected, or was that against the rules?

Aedan looked just as uncomfortable, stood in a more conservative pyjama bottoms and t-shirt. He'd made up the couch to look comfy, but Matt still felt bad. He wished he had a bedroom of his own. There were spares upstairs he knew, but he'd rather have Aedan near him, so he guessed this was the best option. Or maybe he should offer to swap with Aedan? Would that be the chivalrous thing to do?

He looked up as Aedan stepped closer, a look of amusement on his face. "Babe. I can see you worrying," he said gently, touching his fingertips to Matt's temple, before resting his hand on his shoulder. "It's all fine," he insisted. "Go get some sleep."

"Oh." Matt was torn between thinking it was sweet that Aedan could read him so well, and disappointed that they were just going to bed.

Well, if that's not what he wanted, he'd have to do something about it, wouldn't he?

He let his overnight bag hang by his side, so he could move closer and put his free hand on Aedan's hip. "Is this okay?" he asked, still so insecure about how their new dynamic was supposed to work.

But Aedan inhaled sharply and took a step closer too, their chests just about touching. "Anything's okay," he whispered. He then leaned in and kissed him softly.

It was over too quickly. Although that was because Matt found himself to be the one pulling away, stammering another goodnight and retreating to his room.

He needed to figure out what he wanted, he thought angrily as he pulled the covers back and slid into bed. He really liked kissing Aedan; he hadn't been able to stop thinking about it all afternoon, through the film and the walk and the games. He wanted to do it more. But Aedan was right. He had to consider what this would mean for them—for him.

Although Matt was tired, he just found himself lying in the darkness, staring at the ceiling. He could have kept kissing Aedan, just then. They were essentially alone, or at least had a good amount of privacy. They didn't have to stop. But unlike out in the field, they were both only wearing t-shirts and thin cotton bottoms. It had been so much more difficult to ignore the hardness of Aedan's body, the lack of boobs, and the presence of…other things.

Was he ready for that? Was that what he wanted, to touch Aedan like that? He and Aedan had known each other since they were children. They had collected Pokémon together and geeked out over the London Olympics and cried when Mr Gibbons had unfairly given them detention over an accidently late coursework project. If they fooled around, what would that mean for their friendship? Was it worth it?

It wasn't like they'd been joined at the hip. Matt was too much of a hermit for that. But he found himself wishing maybe they had been a little more in and out of each other's pockets. Would he be more comfortable now, if he'd had Aedan around for sleepovers? Would something maybe have happened sooner between them?

The thought sent a small jolt of want through him that went straight to his groin, and he blinked in the darkness, surprised by his own thoughts. Instead of dating Gail Flannery or fooling around with Linda Jones…could he have been with Aedan all along? What would that have been like?

He was so captivated by his own train of thought that he nearly jumped out of his skin when the handle of his door creaked, and the door itself carefully swung inwards. Matt's heart thumped loudly as he froze in place. He made out Aedan's silhouette as he tiptoed wordlessly into the room, then stopped to turn and click the door closed behind him. Still without saying anything, Aedan made his way stealthily around the bed to the free side, and scooted under the covers.

Matt watched him the entire way, his voice dried up in his throat. They looked at each other in the faint amount of streetlight coming through the small window at the top of the wall behind them. Aedan swallowed nervously. They were both on their sides, their hands resting in the No Man's Land between them.

"Hi," Aedan uttered eventually.

"Hello," Matt managed back.

"Um…" Aedan rubbed his nose then pulled at the sheet. "I couldn't sleep."

"Me either," Matt admitted.

The silence stretched out between them, but Aedan kept swirling his fingers against the sheet and pulling it into little peaks. "I guess, I thought maybe we could talk," he said finally. "Then I'd stop trying to answer questions myself."

Matt thought that was probably a good idea, but he had no idea what to say, so he just nodded. But that didn't get a response, so he figured he might have to offer up something. "Um," he tried. "Okay, what…did you want to talk about?"

"Before, when I kissed you, out there," Aedan replied in a rush. "Should I not have? Was that too much?"

It had been too much, in truth, but that was because Matt had panicking and needed to put physical space between them. The reality was, now that they were both lying next to one another, Matt's body was going crazy with want. All he had to do was reach out, and he could touch…

"I freaked out," he admitted. "Just a bit. But that doesn't mean I didn't want it."

Aedan's face lit up, just a fraction. "Really?" he asked, hope naked in his tone. "Because, you ran off, and I thought maybe you regretted before, on the field?"

Matt shook his head. "No, I don't regret it, honestly. But, I don't really understand how I'm feeling, and I don't know what to do."

Aedan's face softened in sympathy, and he shuffled a little bit closer. "Do you want to keep kissing?" he asked. "Did you like it?"

Matt nodded. That much he was sure off.

Aedan looked relieved. "Okay," he said, encouraged. "And you want to keep being friends, right?"

Matt let out a little breath of exasperation. "Yeah, of course. That's the bit I'm stressing over. What if the kissing means we stop being friends?"

"Or," Aedan said carefully, closing his eyes and tensing. "What if it means we start being…boyfriends?"

Matt's eyes widened and he was pretty sure he stopped breathing. Aedan peeked out between the slit of one eye. "Boyfriends?" Matt repeated weakly.

Aedan bit his thumbnail before going back to fiddling with the sheet between them. "Only if you want. I don't want to push you."

The concept set off alarm bells in Matt's head, but he hated that he was making Aedan feel unsure. "Um," he said, scrambling for an answer. "I just, well, Aedan I don't even know if I'm gay."

"Oh," he said, surprisingly cheerful. "Well, I don't think you are, not totally."

Matt looked at him for a second. "You don't seem upset by that," he said slowly.

Aedan shrugged. "You know there's quite a few options between gay and straight. I got the feeling you were somewhere in between."

Matt thought about that for a moment. "Like bi?" he said eventually.

Aedan nodded excitedly. "Or pan, or I quite like good old queer for anything that's not straight. You don't have to label yourself at all if you don't want to, but there are other options too."

"Bi is liking boys and girls, isn't it?"

Aedan nodded again. His hand seemed to be drifting closer to Matt's by increments, and Matt was hyper aware of its progress. "And pan is attraction irrelevant of gender," he said, sounding like he was quoting a Wikipedia page. "It has a bit more fluidity to it."

Matt chewed it over, considering. How did he see himself? "Do you know," he said, a smile creeping onto his mouth. "I think I quite like bi. It's solid, you know?"

Aedan looked like he was trying not to get too excited. "I think it suits you," he said, then finally reached out and took Matt's hand. The connection made him feel like there was an energy flowing through them, like a kind of magic.

If he was bi, then he could have a boyfriend. Aedan could be his boyfriend. It seemed like such a massive concept though. He wasn't sure he could visualise it. Aedan as his boyfriend; him as Aedan's. That's how they would introduce each other to people. Matt had never even had that with a girl before. Could he start with a boy?

Not just any boy though. With Aedan. He had a sudden image of Aedan introducing some other, faceless boy as his boyfriend instead, which is what would no doubt happen if Matt didn't go for this, and his panic made his mind up for him.

"I don't really know how to be a boyfriend," he blurted out, squeezing Aedan's hand. "What if I'm crap?"

Aedan seemed to stop breathing as he absorbed Matt's words. "Do you mean that, do you want to try?"

Matt slowly took in a deep breath, but then he met Aedan's eyes and smiled. "Yes," he said firmly. "Aedan Gallagher, do you want to go out with me?" They stared at each other for a second, then Aedan rolled over so his face was in the pillow as he howled with laughter. Matt smacked his unbruised shoulder. "Shut up," he hissed defensively.

But he lost his irritation as Aedan peeked sheepishly back up at him. "'Go out with me,'" he quoted back affectionately. "What are you, twelve?"

Matt huffed and scowled. "Alright you prick, wanna be my boyfriend?"

"Yes," said Aedan immediately, darting over to capture Matt's mouth in a kiss. There was nothing tentative about this one; Matt could feel himself being claimed. *Property of Aedan Gallagher*, it announced. *Hands off.*

Before it could get too heated though, Aedan eased off and traced a couple of sweet nibbles along Matt's jaw, making him shudder. "Yes?" Matt repeated.

Aedan nodded. "Definitely. And it's not like I know how to be a boyfriend either," he said with a wave of his hand. "We can just work it out together. I'm pretty sure we can just carry on like usual, but with more snogging."

Matt frowned at him. "But you've had boyfriends before?" he asked, feeling an irrational flare of jealousy.

117

That was stupid. They were in the past, they didn't matter now.

Aedan rolled his eyes. "Those were just shagging," he said, matter-of-factly. "We weren't friends or anything."

Matt's brain got caught on the word 'shagging' and immediately started drifting off into what that might entail. He didn't know much about guy sex, but he was suddenly quite keen to find out.

Something must have shown on his face, because Aedan rubbed his hand across his back in that way he was growing to love. "Hey, don't worry," he said. "We'll take it at your pace, whatever you're comfortable with. If you want to wait, to tell anyone, or whatever…" He trailed off, leaving the option out there.

But nausea swept through Matt, and he became very serious. "No," he said. "I don't care if it's scary, or hard, I'm not hiding." He felt his eyes get itchy and a lump rose in his throat. "I won't have a secret relationship."

Aedan considered him very carefully, then drew him into a hug that was all comfort, nothing even remotely sexual about it. "Of course, babe," he rasped tenderly into his neck. "I'm here for you. I'll follow your lead, I just don't want to overwhelm you. But, yeah, I get it."

Even for the right reasons, Matt couldn't stomach lying, not to anyone, even just a little. "You don't mind though? I mean, I know you're already out, but you'd be okay with people knowing you're with me?"

Aedan looked at him as if he was crazy. Their bodies were much more tangled now, and Matt could faintly feel his heart beating. "Why wouldn't I?"

Matt tutted and felt his face heat up. "Because you're…you?" he said gesturing up and down his body. "You're the glitter, remember? I'm like, the twig part of the garland that people don't even notice because of all the other pretty stuff on top of it."

He tried not to blush harder, he hated admitting that out loud, but Aedan was still gawking at him.

"Is that what you think?" he asked. He sounded sad.

Matt shrugged. "It's fine," he said. "I don't want to be in the spotlight. I don't need to be the pretty one." He gave Aedan a light shove. "You can be the gorgeous one, it's fine. You're more gay anyway." The joke fell flat though, because Aedan was still staring. "What?"

"Matthew Bartlett," Aedan said firmly. "Seeing as this relationship is going to be an honest and open one…" He waited for Matt to nod. "Then here's my confession. I've been in love with you forever. I've dreamed of you being mine since I worked out what a boyfriend was, and now I have you, I am going to shout it from the rooftops. With a megaphone. Maybe one of those airplanes with the banners too. Understood?"

Matt couldn't say that it was. "Uh, what?" he stammered inelegantly. "You-I-hang on, how long?"

Aedan played with the collar of Matt's t-shirt. "I don't know," he said evasively. "I just loved being with you, right from the start. I saw you and you weren't like the other kids, and I just…I knew I had to be around you as much as possible. Then I remember seeing you kiss that girl on Valentine's, and I understood. I was so fucking jealous. That's when I knew what I wanted. But," he paused and gave a smile that was more of a grimace. "I wasn't completely sure you were open to the idea of boys, so I just decided to wait and see and…hope." He cleared his throat and focused on his fingers pulling at the material. "Do you think I'm a crazy stalker now?"

"I think you're an idiot," Matt said flatly. "One, you could have just made a move and I probably would have fallen for you, because, wow. And two, are you insane?" He scoffed, displeased as his eyes pricked with tears, all his insecurities bubbling to the surface. "I am so *nothing*. I just blend into the background, people forget I'm there. You could have anyone you wanted, so why you would ever think I'm worth anything is just-*umph*!"

He was cut off by the mouth assaulting his own. "Shut up," Aedan gasped. "Shut up, you fucking idiot. You're gorgeous and kind and funny and lovely and please just be mine. Please Matt, please?"

Aedan had rolled on top of him and their embrace had gone from tender to breath-taking in a heartbeat. His entire body was laid on top of Matt's and he could feel all of him—in particular, the hot, rigid shaft of his erection pressing into his thigh.

119

"Oh fuck," Matt moaned, letting his hands roam frantically up and down Aedan's body. Their hips ground together, their kisses open-mouthed and needy, and Matt didn't know what he wanted, other than *more*.

His hands found their way under Aedan's t-shirt, tracing over smooth skin and pushing the material up. He got the hint, and sat up, breaking the kiss. That almost had Matt protesting, but then he grabbed the hem of the shirt and whipped it over his head.

As impossibly turned on at he was, Matt had to stop Aedan from diving right back in by pressing his palm to his chest. Then his hand slowly migrated right, to Aedan's left, and he skimmed his fingers over the skin that was dappled with violet bruises and rusty lines of scabs. "It's okay," Aedan said quietly.

"It's not," Matt argued quickly. But Aedan shook his head.

"I don't want you looking at me with pity," he whispered, his jaw tightening.

"It's not fucking pity," Matt growled, and he slipped his arms around Aedan's back, pulling him down again carefully. "It's anger. If you're mine now, then I'm never letting anybody fucking hurt you again. I swear."

"How very caveman of you," Aedan joked, but his voice hiccupped halfway though, and Matt just cuddled him close for a minute. "Thank you, babe."

Matt didn't say anything, he just kissed Aedan's neck, and ran his fingers through his hair. It had lost a lot of its product now, and was lovely and soft to the touch.

"I have no idea what I'm doing," he admitted.

Aedan laughed, breaking the serious mood and getting them right back to the good stuff.

"You're doing fine," Aedan promised, moving his hands down to tackle Matt's shirt. "But I want less of this."

The effect of him saying 'I want' pressed several of Matt's buttons at once. What Aedan wanted, he could have.

They worked together, peeling the t-shirt away, and for a while they just kissed, their bare chests skimming off each other and sending so many sensations though Matt's body he hardly knew what to do. To make things worse—

or better—Aedan had repositioned himself so their shafts were rubbing against each other, and if that didn't feel like heaven, Matt wasn't sure what did.

He got his answer as Aedan took the lead, and yanked Matt's pyjama bottoms down. Matt didn't need instructions. He just started helping as fast as he could until they'd kicked the damn things away, and for the first time in his adult life, Matt was naked with another human being.

Much like their first kiss, he had the briefest thought that this should be weird, or it should feel wrong thanks to the lack of lady parts. But his whole brain was simply too full of the voice screaming *yes!* at the top of its lungs, he really couldn't stop to care.

Aedan fell back into place, their bodies perfectly aligned, and he started to thrust. Matt had never experienced anything so amazing. But then Aedan flinched and stopped, and Matt was immediately on alert.

"Don't hurt yourself." He forced himself to calm and not roll his hips, chasing the friction. Aedan was clearly in pain.

"I don't want to stop," he whimpered, and Matt's heart ached. "It's okay, I'm fine."

"Shh," Matt said, and cradled him to his body as he carefully rolled them over until Aedan was lying on his back, and Matt had the daunting task of being on top and therefore, to his mind, in charge.

He just did what Aedan had done though. It wasn't really rocket science when all it took was pressing his cock against Aedan's, but it still felt like a lot of responsibility.

"Here," Aedan said, pushing his hand between their bodies.

Matt swore his vision whitened out for second as he wrapped his fingers around both of them, giving them something to thrust into.

After that, it didn't take long. They managed to find a rhythm together, which, considering how out of it Matt felt, he thought was quite an achievement. Aedan emitted an adorable series of short, sharp yips, his eyes screwed closed as his hand tightened around their shafts. The fingers on his other hand dug into Matt's back. Aedan arched his whole body, the non-existent space between their bellies became slick, and Matt realised he had made Aedan come.

That was all it took for his world to shatter.

Like any teenage boy, he assumed, he had discovered how to wank around the time he'd hit puberty, and not looked back since. But there was something so completely different about having someone else help you do it though, and he shook and jerked until he was suddenly boneless.

He dropped down on top of Aedan, who immediately cried out in pain.

"Sorry! Sorry!" Matt rolled off him instantly.

Once Aedan had taken a couple of breaths, he threw himself over Matt, wrapping his arm around his chest and hooking his leg over Matt's. He let out a sob, and Matt panicked.

"Oh babe, I'm so sorry," Matt fretted, his hands flying over Aedan's injuries protectively.

But Aedan gave a wet laugh, and hugged him close. "I'm fine, you numpty."

"You're crying, though."

Aedan stroked his hair, and gently kissed his earlobe. Matt had no idea how simply wonderful that would feel. "It's happy crying," Aedan said, manoeuvring backwards so Matt could see him properly.

"Promise?" he asked, his voice small.

Aedan cupped his face, and they lay looking at each other, side by side. "You just made love to me," Aedan whispered. And when he said it like that, it did sound pretty monumental.

"Was it okay?" Matt couldn't help but ask.

Aedan barked out a laugh, clapped his hand over his mouth, then slapped Matt's shoulder. "It was fucking awesome and you know it," he chided playfully. "Don't go fishing for compliments."

Matt grinned bashfully, then kissed him, because he could.

He began to realise they were sticky and the mess between them was getting cold, which was awful. "Um," he said, looking down between them. "Should we maybe, I dunno—"

"Oh, yeah," Aedan laughed. "It's definitely good manners to clean that up. Boys tend to get that everywhere. Have you got anything in here?"

As luck would have it, there was a box of tissues by Matt's side of the bed that he hadn't noticed before, but felt immensely grateful for now. They wiped themselves as dry as possible, and after Aedan insisted it was okay, pulled their pyjamas back on.

Matt felt more comfortable right away having his clothes back on. Being naked was fine for sex, but he'd much rather not have his bits flopping about afterwards. It seemed Aedan felt the same. Once they were dressed again, Aedan didn't even ask before snuggling up next to him, curling into his side.

Matt started falling asleep right away, exhausted and content. But just as he was drifting off, he felt a finger prod into his side. "Whut?" he mumbled, wriggling closer to Aedan's amazingly solid form next to him.

"You called me babe."

Matt blinked a little more awake. "What?"

Aedan was all sleepy, his breathing already evening out as his face went slack. "When you fell on me," he mumbled, a smile playing on his lips. "You called me babe."

Oh. Yeah, he had. He'd been worried though, and it had just come out. "So?" he said quietly, stroking Aedan's damp hair.

"So," he said, even as he fell asleep. "It means you are totally just a little bit gay for me."

Matt would have protested. But he figured Aedan had already conked out.

Plus, he might have had a point.

CHAPTER 9: CHRISTMAS MIRACLE

Matt had never shared a bed with anyone before, and the presence of another warm, fidgety body meant he kept waking up during the night.

But every time he did, he realised why, and would squirm around until he was snuggled up against Aedan again. He draped his arm over his chest, mindful of the bruises, and rub his nose gingerly into his thatch of blond hair. It smelled faintly of coconut, presumably from the wax. But it also smelled of sex. Aedan smelled of sex, because he'd slept with Matt, and that was heady intoxication.

The first few times he'd roused, the cuddles were enough to send Matt back to sleep, but as five am rolled around Matt just found himself staring into the darkness, his mind too alert to doze off again. So, he picked up his phone to do something useful.

Thankfully, all the persistent grumblings about whether or not he was gay, or what was going to happen to him and Aedan now they'd crossed this line, had simmered firmly into the back of his mind. The two of them were together, they were boyfriends, committed, and

Matt couldn't think of a decision he'd ever been happier with. Everything just felt *right right right!*

But that didn't mean he was lacking in other material to stress over.

As the clock on his phone flicked past five thirty am, he felt the covers stir around him. He was sitting up, and as he looked down by the bluish light of the screen he got a perfect view of Aedan's head landing in his lap; and it was beautiful. In just a few short hours, Matt found himself amazed at how many little intimate ways he could touch and be touched, and so much of that was gentle and loving and not fuelled by hormones at all. There was nothing sexual in the way Aedan nuzzled his face into his hip. It just made Matt's heart flip, and he paused from his browsing to brush back the blond hair that was becoming his favourite.

"*Gobacktosleep,*" Aedan mumbled, but Matt just grinned down at him.

"You go back to sleep," he challenged, hoping the light from his phone hadn't disturbed him.

But Aedan yawned and blinked his eyes, shuffling up so he was tucked under Matt's wing. "What you doin?" he mumbled, scrubbing at his face and then letting his hand drop casually on the top of Matt's thigh. He loved it, and wriggled a bit closer together.

Yeah, he was all over these bisexual shenanigans.

"Nothing," he said lightly, tapping onto the next link.

His phone was tugged from his grasp before he even had a chance to blink.

"Hey," he protested. But Aedan had already skipped through a number of pages, immediately more awake. Matt squirmed, embarrassed at being caught out.

"Babe," Aedan said carefully. "What's this?"

Matt plucked his mobile back, and pressed the power button so it blacked out. "Nothing," he mumbled.

By now, Aedan was sat all the way up beside him, glaring with those pretty brown eyes that Matt was already learning he should beware.

"The Student Loan Company is 'nothing' at five thirty in the morning?" he asked. His voice had a flippant edge that Matt knew better than to deflect.

"Okay," he sighed. "I was looking at whether or not you can apply for a single parent income loan even though you *have* two parents earning, but one's an arsehole who won't cough up."

Aedan took the blank phone back, woke it up, swiped the security pattern with his thumb—Matt had no idea when he'd learned how to do that—and brought up the page still sat on the Student Loan Company.

"Wow," he said, deadpan. "They really do have an Arsehole Dad option."

Matt tried to snatch the phone back, but Aedan was too quick. "I was just looking," he griped.

Aedan moved away from the pillows and sat up to face Matt, both his hands resting firmly on Matt's knees over the duvet, his gaze focused. "Sweetheart," he said, his Adam's apple bobbing as he rubbed Matt's thighs firmly. "We can look at this when we get back to your mum's. It'll take a lot of research, believe me."

"But it is possible?" Matt pressed. "Tilly can get a loan, even though my dad's loaded?"

Aedan pressed the button to fade Matt's phone to black, and let it rest on Matt's tummy. "I don't know babe," he said softly.

Aedan wasn't stupid. He would have weighed up all his options before deciding not to go into higher education, and Matt guessed he would have a good idea about what loans would be on offer.

"*Fuck.*" He tried to get his phone back, but Aedan shimmied away and hugged the blasted thing to his chest.

"No, *no*," he insisted. "We're not looking at anything right now."

"Why not!" Matt cried, then remembered they were underneath his dad's house, and dropped his voice several decibels. "*Why not?*"

Aedan scowled. "Because you're tired and emotional. You aren't going to make any decisions right now, let alone a rational one."

Matt felt so impotent. "I need to do something," he protested weakly. "I hate being here at their mercy. They have all the power."

Aedan dropped the phone on the bed and took his hand to caress his thumb over the fingers. "I'm not back at work until tomorrow," he said. "If you like, I can come back to your mum's and we can start looking into this properly?"

Matt felt an unexpected rush of sadness, and he leaned forwards to hug Aedan. "Thank you," he said. "I just don't know what to do. I mean, should we at least try and do what they want? Play nice, not rock the boat?"

Aedan looked at him and chewed his lip. "Do you want to know what I really think?"

Matt nodded.

"Fuck them. *Fuck* them. If you do that, you'll always be at their mercy, under their thumb. If they pay for your university fees, you'll always owe them, and you'll just be waiting for the other shoe to drop. Like the sword of Damocles hanging over your heads."

Matt's heart sank. "So we should just…give up on going to uni?" he asked. "Or, I mean, me. Better for us to all help Tilly go, right?"

"No," said Aedan quickly. "No, that's definitely not what I meant. Look, I don't know what the options are, but there are all kinds of loans out there. When it comes to your dad and especially your step-mum, I just don't know if this relationship is worth it for you. It's toxic. So, you might get some money out of it, but is it really going to be worth it in the long run?"

Matt thought about it. When it came down to it, he realised that the driving force behind all his attempts to keep up a good relationship were motivated by this fear that they were going to be denied their future. His dad had steered the whole divorce, claiming victory in all things, from making them move house right down to keeping Buster. He'd won by having a new relationship to go into, with a new family, whilst Matt's mum had been made all too aware how forgettable and replaceable she was. He had won by simply refusing to acknowledge that he had done anything wrong at all.

"It doesn't feel worth it right now," he admitted. He was done trying, when everything was twisted around to somehow make him the problem. "God, I don't want to spend one more minute in this blasted house."

127

Aedan's eyes widened, and a hint of devilment made the corner of his mouth twitch. "Then let's not," he said.

"What?" Matt asked.

"Let's not," Aedan repeated excitedly, his hands fluttering over Matt's legs. "We're not welcome here, so let's just go back to your mum's."

Matt turned that over in his mind. "What like, get a taxi?"

Aedan shrugged. "We could. It'd be really expensive. Or, the trains are running again, we can make our own way like that."

Matt knew that was a bad idea, but he seemed to be out of good ones. "I could leave a note," he said slowly. "Say that we had an emergency?"

Aedan arched an eyebrow. "Or," he said. "Maybe hint that next time, if they want to behave a bit nicer, then you won't be so keen to sneak off in the early hours of the morning?"

Matt snorted, but he had to say that sounded tempting. "Do you really think we should leave?"

Aedan pulled at the edge of the duvet. "I know running off is sort of my thing," he said bashfully. Matt hated that he'd said that to him yesterday. He didn't really mean it, and he rubbed Aedan's knee supportively. "But I think you need to show them how hurt you are. At the moment if you have an argument, she's just going to twist it around again. Maybe this will make your dad understand?" he shrugged. "It's totally up to you, though. It's your family. I don't want to cause trouble."

Matt was so desperate to *do something*, though. After eighteen months of having no say in any family matters, of being trampled down and relegated to the backbench, he'd had enough. And besides, he could really do with seeing his mum right about now.

"Let's do it," he whispered wickedly.

It didn't take them long to get themselves together as they didn't have much stuff. Aedan even agreed to forgo his usual skincare and makeup regime, although he made sure Matt knew he wouldn't be seen out 'naked' for anyone else.

Chapter 9: Christmas Miracle

They still had to wake Tilly and get her on board, which Matt knew would be the tricky part. He knocked softly on her bedroom door, and made his way inside to perch on the end of the bed. "Tills?" he said softly, shaking her leg. "Hey bratling, wake up."

Tilly's bedroom was just as impersonal as his own, he realised as he looked around in the gloom. There had been no effort made to put up photos or posters, and the two of them had certainly not been invited to decorate them in any way. They were probably used as general guest rooms most of the year, and the realisation made Matt even more sure about sneaking out.

If they weren't welcome, then that just made things all the more easy.

"Tilly?" he tried again, and the puffball of hair stirred. "Are you awake?"

"What time is it?" she mumbled, rubbing her eyes.

"Before six," he said. "How do you feel about doing a runner?"

She crawled above the duvet, blinking like new-born larvae. "What?"

"Do a runner," said Matt with a grin, pushing back some of the blonde mane so he could see her eyes. "Get the heck outta Dodge."

"It's 'fuck,'" she griped.

"Oi!" That was twice in two days she'd used the F-word, and even though circumstances were odd, to say the least, he was still her big brother.

"'Fuck outta Dodge.' Don't patronise me. And, you want to what?" She shook her head and sat up properly against the pillows. "Go back home? Now?"

Matt shrugged. "We could wait for mum," he said. "But that would mean spending most of the day here, and I've had enough. We were going to get the train."

"Oh, *hell* yeah," Tilly enthused. "Give me five minutes."

"Really?" He leaned back as she combed her fingers through her hair, surprised she had agreed that quickly. "I mean we don't have to. It might make things worse. We could—"

"Matt." She said his name in that way that their mum did when she was being patient, by making the 'a' sound

129

really long. She dropped her hands into her lap, and glared.

"Um, yes?"

"Please get out so I can change."

"Oh," he said, flustered and getting to his feet. "Yeah, uh, alright?"

He paced in the rec room whilst they waited for her, until Aedan grabbed his wrist and pulled him over to where he was leaning against the pool table. "You'll wear a track in the nice carpet," he said fondly.

"I'm thinking," Matt grumbled.

"Well, stop," Aedan told him, and pulled him in for a kiss.

He could really get used to this. Aedan was so confident and soft and warm and it made Matt sigh in contentment. "You've gotten bold at that very quickly," he teased. But Aedan just grinned up and him and slipped his hands around his waist.

"I've been thinking about it for a *long* time," he said.

There was a heaving noise from behind Matt, and he turned to see Tilly coming out of her room, fingers down her throat. "Okay," she said as she dropped her bag to the floor and used a tie from her wrist to put her hair up into a ponytail. "As thrilled as I am that you two finally got your shit together, I do not need to see my brother's arse getting groped, is that clear Aedan?"

"Yes Ma'am," he said with a salute, then slapped Matt's arse.

Her mouth twitched, but she didn't rise to the bait. "Right, so who knows the way to the train station?"

Matt, once recovered from the aforementioned slap, made to unlock his phone, but Aedan beat him to it. "I do," he said, waving his own phone at her. "It's about a fifteen-minute walk."

Matt frowned. "Are you sure? I thought—"

"Babe," Aedan interrupted, resting a hand on his hip. "I'd worked it out yesterday. Before you came to rescue me."

"Oh," said Matt, a cold wave of shame running through his body.

Chapter 9: Christmas Miracle

Aedan shook his head. "Hey, no," he said, and despite Tilly's protests, gave him a quick peck on the lips. "It's fine. You did rescue me, so that's all okay, alright? The point is, I know the way."

Matt still didn't feel great about it, but he nodded anyway. He wished they had gotten together under different circumstances, happier ones. But then, they probably needed something dramatic to push them off their laurels.

They crept their way upstairs to the ground floor, but there was no sound apart from their very quiet rustling. The door looked locked as they made their way along the corridor, but there were a number of hooks on a wooden board on the wall with keys dangling from them, so Matt figured they could work it.

"Wait," he whispered abruptly as they approached the door.

"Matt," Tilly whined. "Come on, don't back out now!"

He shook his head and grinned at them. "No, I just think, if we do this, we should do it properly."

He gave his bag to Aedan, promising to be back in just a sec, and ran off through the kitchen. He opened the door to the conservatory where Buster was already sat waiting on the other side, his tail wagging in anticipation. Unfortunately, Matt forgot about the damn snap-back on the door, and it went to slam shut behind him. Just in the nick of time, he shoved his foot in the gap; that might have stopped the bang that would have given away their impending escape, but it also crunched his ankle something awful. Matt had to shove his knuckles in his mouth to stop himself from crying out.

Gingerly, he extracted his throbbing foot, but Buster was shuffling back and forth, whimpering and yowling.

"Shh, shh," Matt urged him as he hobbled over, but he yelped a little too loudly. He blinked away the tears in his eyes, dropped to his knees and soothed the small dog with a cuddle. "Hey buddy," he murmured. "Hey Buster, do you was to come with me and Tilly? Do you want to see Mummy?"

Obviously, he didn't understand, but he responded to Matt's tone of voice with several licks to his face as he squirmed in his arms. Matt took that as a yes.

He quickly limped across the room to fetch his old lead that was hanging from the wall, ignoring the fancy new one that had a designer name on it which probably cost a stupid amount of money. All the toys were new as well, but as Matt was checking them over, Buster fished out a well chewed teddy bear that was missing one eye, and held it out hopefully. Matt had a feeling that might have been the one his mum had given to him when he was a puppy, and he grinned despite the persistent throbbing in his ankle.

"Do you want to bring that one, do you? Alright, let's go, shall we?"

He picked him up to carry him on his hip through the house, his few possessions fitting easily in Matt's other hand. This time, he made sure the stupid kitchen door closed quietly.

Tilly's face exploded with glee when she saw what he was doing, and she had to clasp both hands over her mouth to stop herself screaming. She still danced on her toes, and Aedan dashed over to kiss Buster on the top of his head, then Matt on his cheek.

"How could we have almost left you here?" he cooed quietly at Buster as he batted his nose with his paw. "You're coming home where you belong, yes you are."

A creak on the stairs all made them spin around. Matt's heart rate rocketed, but they were faced with two matching little boys, in matching dinosaur pyjamas. Matt clutched at his chest, then waved weakly to them. "Hi guys," he whispered.

"Are you going now?" Ryan asked as him and his brother crept down the stairs.

Matt glanced at Aedan. "Yeah," he said. "I'm afraid we have to head home now. Why don't you go back to bed? It's still very early."

Ryan looked at Taylor, who was sucking his thumb. "Will you come back soon?"

Matt was surprised by that. "Um," he said. "Maybe, we'll have to see, alright?"

Chapter 9: Christmas Miracle

The boys didn't seem convinced, and actually, he realised he'd become a little bit fond of them over the last day.

"How about we go to a football match sometime?" he suggested.

Both their sets of eyes lit up, and they nodded enthusiastically. "Yes please," Ryan said.

"Thank you," Taylor added. They were quite sweet really, when they weren't beating the crap out of each other.

"Can you be really quiet for us?" Matt asked. "We don't want to wake Mummy and Brian."

They nodded. "We'll miss you," said Taylor, his voice small.

The next thing he knew, the two of them had bounded down the stairs and thrown themselves against his legs.

"Here." Aedan took Buster from him and allowed him to kneel down and give them both a proper hug.

His throat felt tight. Perhaps not *everything* about this house was so terrible after all.

With the twins' help, they found the right keys straight away, and carefully let themselves out of the front door. Aedan carried Buster all the way up the driveway with Matt and Tilly behind him, and then they all turned to wave the twins goodbye before they shut the door.

And then they were free.

"Let's go, let's go!" Matt cried with a laugh, and they shot off down the road towards the train station. Well, as fast as Matt could go on his shoddy foot. Damn that door.

"Are you alright?" Aedan asked, concerned.

Matt shook his head and insisted he was fine. It definitely wasn't broken or anything, but he wasn't really looking forward to the walk they were facing. He gritted his teeth though, determined not to say anything or slow them down.

Tilly asked for Buster's lead, and they scampered off ahead, kicking up the snow that had fallen overnight. The sky was clear now, and the road looked rather beautiful in the predawn light. She chatted none stop to their little dog—about what Matt had no idea—but it was clear to see how happy she was, and Buster kept looking up at her like it was the best conversation he'd had in ages. Matt and Aedan slung their rucksacks properly over their shoulders, and held hands as they walked down the road. Matt's heart finally began to return to a normal pace, and he felt like they had made the right decision to leave.

His family problems slipped away though as he took a few minutes to just breath in and out, and looked between his sister goofing around up ahead with his dog, and his boyfriend by his side. *His boyfriend.* Wow. He had a boyfriend. That was pretty awesome.

Matt was coming to think that holding hands really was the best. It felt brilliant for one thing, to constantly be touching Aedan, but also, he got a thrill knowing that if anyone looked out of their windows at them, they would all know that Aedan was his, and that he was Aedan's.

He kept feeling little pangs of sadness, thinking they could have had this ages ago if they'd just talked to each other. But he was done moping over what could have been, in all aspects of his life. He was here for the present, for the future, and they both contained as much of Aedan as he could possibly get.

"Are you feeling okay?" Aedan asked, as if sensing his turbulent thoughts. "After last night?" he clarified when Matt frowned at him.

"Oh," Matt said, grinning as his cheeks warmed from a blush. "Yeah, that was great. Better than great." He squeezed Aedan's hand. "You don't need to worry about me," he said, meeting his gaze and holding it. "I'll tell you if something's too much, I promise."

Aedan nodded. "Good. Because I have serious plans for that arse of yours when I next get you alone."

Matt spluttered and coughed so hard he had to stop and try and catch his breath. Aedan laughed wickedly at him. "What!" Matt wheezed. His eyes were watering.

Aedan yanked him over and kissed his check. "I'm totally joking. Don't look so scared. Baby steps for my bi boyfriend, alright?"

Matt nodded as the coughing subsided and they began walking again (or hobbling, in Matt's case.) Sure, the idea had shocked him somewhat, but he wouldn't say he was completely scared, exactly. A little bit aroused too, maybe…

The train station was empty, but open, and they got their tickets from the machine outside. The next one back to Matt's mum's neck of the woods was in twenty minutes, so they made themselves comfortable in the waiting room illuminated by a flickering florescent tube light, and set up camp on the narrow wooden bench with their bags piled around them. Buster hopped into Matt's lap as soon as he had sat down, curling himself into a ball, and Matt gratefully propped up his swollen foot on one of the bags, giving it a much-needed break. He wished he'd thought to look for a coat for Buster to wear, if he even had one. He just hugged him close for the time being.

Once they were on the train—a whole compartment to themselves—Matt sent a text to his mum warning her that they were on their way home, but not to worry; they would just see her there. He put his phone back in his pocket, on silent, so he could ignore the rest of the world for just a little bit longer.

The train journey was only about ten minutes, though Matt's mum's was a half hour walk from the station. They all took turns holding Buster's lead, walking slowly so he had a chance to sniff everything he wanted and pee on anything he liked.

Luckily, Matt's foot was feeling better after being rested in the waiting room and on the train, so he didn't hold them up that badly. When they reached a small expanse of grass covered in a couple of inches of pristine snow, Matt watched as the others ran into it, the snowballs were flying within seconds. Buster chased after them and barked as they pummelled one another, and then they all lay down to make snow angels.

A creeping sensation worked its way through Matt's stomach though. The feeling that they were putting off the inevitable, and he soon insisted they started walking again. The mood had shifted completely by the time they turned down their road; they hadn't spoken a word in five minutes straight.

Matt's fears were confirmed when they reached their drive and their dad's car was sat there waiting for them. They all stopped walking as one and stared at it.

"Ah," said Tilly.

"Bollocks," added Matt.

He wondered exactly how long it had taken the twins to wake his dad and Sheila up. He wasn't mad at them, precisely. Their absence would have been discovered soon enough anyway, but he would have liked to have talked it over with his mum first though.

There was no point in hanging around. With heavy trepidation, they skulked up to the door, and let themselves inside.

"Matt?" his mum's voice rang out as he stepped over the threshold. "Tilly, is that you?"

They exchanged a look and braced themselves. "Yeah Mum, it's us," Matt replied. They wiped their feet on the mat, and Aedan closed the door behind them.

There was a pause. "I think you'd better come in here."

They took their shoes and coats off first. But Buster was pulling on his lead, having heard his mum's voice, so Matt just dropped everything in the hallway and limped with him into the living room.

His mum looked pensive as he entered. However, at the sight of their beloved little terrier, her face dissolved into happy tears as she squealed. "Oh, *Buster!*" she cried, immediately dropping to her knees so he could run into her arms.

Matt grinned. Whatever was coming, it was totally worth it.

His dad stood by the TV, his eyebrows raised and his mouth pursed in the thin line. "You gave us quite a scare, young man," he said abrasively as Tilly and Aedan crept in behind Matt.

But Matt just shrugged. "We left a note," he said nonchalantly, and they had. He'd written it in bold letters on a sheet they'd torn from one of Tilly's notebooks and placed it on the pool table where it couldn't be missed.

"That's not the point," his dad snapped, pushing his glasses up his nose.

Chapter 9: Christmas Miracle

Matt wondered how long his mum had had to put up with him hanging around waiting for them. He hadn't checked his phone since they'd been on the train, so if they'd tried to call or text, he hadn't seen it. He pulled it out to glance at it quickly now, and discovered eighteen missed calls, several voice mails and a whole host of texts. Oops.

As his mum stood up with Buster cradled in her arms, he noticed that Iggy Azalea was blasting faintly from the direction of the study. He couldn't help but shoot a quick smile at Aedan as he re-pocketed his phone, who, by his matching grin, obviously also recognised it from the CD he'd made.

"We were worried," his mum agreed. "Your dad said the note just said you were heading back here, not why."

"We'd had enough." Tilly said.

She hugged against Matt's side in an unusually childish gesture. He looked down at her with a sad smile and stroked the top of her head.

"We obviously weren't welcome," Matt said. His voice wavered, but he jutted his chin out and looked at his mum. "So, we thought it best to leave Dad to his new family."

"Perhaps," his dad said pompously, shoving his hands into his pockets, "if you'd been a bit more civil, you would have felt more welcome. I just can't understand how you've become so selfish Matthew," he said, shaking his head. "I'm worried about the company you're keeping, I think it's affecting your judgement."

Matt spluttered out a laugh. He let go of Tilly, who gave him an encouraging nod, then stepped closer to Aedan, determinedly not hobbling on his bad ankle.

"Well, you'd better get used to it," he told his dad with a glower, and took Aedan's hand. "Because Aedan and I come as a pair now."

There was a pause as his parents looked at them, and further down the house Beyoncé gave a battle cry.

"Oh," said his mum, letting Buster down to the floor, hands over her mouth and tears in her eyes as she stepped over and threw her arms around them both. Matt felt Aedan flinch, but he covered it by hugging her back. "Oh, that's so wonderful," she said thickly.

Matt's heart had leapt into his mouth, but now he attempted to swallow it back down. Bloody hell, he'd just come out. And while his mum kissed Aedan's cheek as he smiled bashfully at her, Matt realised his dad was turning a sort of purple.

"I can't believe this," he said, shaking his head. "That's not what you said yesterday. You can't be with him. You're straight!"

Matt winced. "I'm still me, Dad," he said. "And Aedan's brilliant. You need to stop thinking you know him when all you know is where he comes from."

"Brian," his mum said in a warning tone. "I'm not sure where you've got this idea of Matt being selfish from, and I hope you aren't going to tell me there's a problem with him being gay?"

"Actually, I'm bi," he said quickly. It felt good to own that out loud, but it he didn't like the way his dad was shaking his head at him.

"Of course I don't have a problem," he stammered. "I mean, I wouldn't mind if he was gay, but this boy has obviously just turned his head! Bi-bisexual? Matt, this isn't you!"

Matt felt a stab of hurt. "How would you know what's me?" he asked, thinking back to the shambles of his and Tilly's Christmas presents. "You never spent any time with us when you were here, and then you were too busy running off after Sheila and her family. How *dare* you call me selfish!" he cried, feeling the tears prick at his eyes. "Tilly had it right yesterday. We all just have to pretend you didn't have an affair, or that you kicked us out of our home, or took our bloody *dog*. And now, you're not going to pay for us to go to uni, because your new wife's decided she doesn't like us? I'm sick of all your bullshit!"

His mum let go of them and stood between her children and her ex-husband. "What's this about university?" she demanded, a dark tone to her voice that Matt didn't recognise.

To be fair, Matt's dad shook his head and raised his hands. "I never said anything of the sort, Matthew. How can you think I'd do that to you?"

Chapter 9: Christmas Miracle

"Because Sheila told me yesterday," he said steadily. "She said in no uncertain terms, if I didn't calm Tilly down, or keep Aedan and his *perversions* away from the twins, we'd never get the money." He swallowed painfully, his hand shaking in Aedan's. "So, that gave me a pretty good idea."

His dad dropped his hands, and for the first time in a very long time, he looked sad. "Oh Matty," he said, stepping a little bit closer to them. "No, I'd never do that to you. I'm so sorry. Is that why you left?"

Matt shrugged. He could feel Tilly looking up at him in horror. "*That's* why you lost the plot yesterday?" she said quietly.

"I just don't think we fit very well with Sheila, Dad," Matt said. "I'm sorry. But, I wasn't willing to pretend anymore when we were making her so unhappy."

"Brian!" his mum snapped, her hands in her hair. "I sent the children to you in good faith. What has this woman been saying to them?"

"It's okay Mum," Matt said quickly, letting Aedan go to wrap his arm around her. "We looked after each other, and, I don't think we'll see much of her anymore."

His dad shook his head, his hand over his mouth. "I had no idea...Matt, I'm sure she didn't mean it like that, she's a very strident woman, and—"

"If you're going to stand there and just make excuses," his mum cut in coldly, "instead of apologising to your children, then you can leave right now. I had enough of that when we were married. I don't have to put up with it now."

Go Mum, Matt thought. He couldn't remember her ever telling his dad to bugger off before.

His dad looked whooped, and his shoulders slumped. "Matthew, Matilda," he said, looking a little pathetic standing opposite them all united in a line. "I don't want to lose you, that's never what I wanted. I honestly had no idea there was such a divide between you and Sheila, and, I guess...I'm sorry."

Matt blinked. He was what? Sorry? He was tempted to ask him to repeat it, but he didn't want to risk pushing his luck.

There was an awkward silence for a moment, before Matt thought it best to try and reciprocate the olive branch. "Okay," he said uncertainly. "Thank you."

His dad nodded, and Matt felt like a tiny bit of understanding transpired between them.

"Apologise to Aedan as well."

His dad looked at Tilly with bug eyes. "Um," he said, with a laugh. "Pardon darling?"

"I said, you owe Aedan an apology too," she told him defiantly. "You said a bunch of unfair things to him, but he's part of the family now, so you need to take it back."

Matt could see his dad deliberating. He was probably wanting to argue that Matt was just going through a fad or something, and that Aedan wasn't going to be sticking around, and that hurt. Aedan had been in his life for so long, and now he was even more important. He didn't need his dad's approval, but he would very much like it.

He let go of his mum and went back to Aedan, who was trying his best to look inconspicuous, but he was anxiously rubbing his non-injured arm, and averting his eyes. Matt didn't know much about being a boyfriend, but he knew he didn't like Aedan looking that, and wanted to fix it. He put his arm around his waist and hugged him close.

"Aedan didn't do anything to me Dad," he said softly. "He didn't trick me, and when I say I'm bi, that's what I mean. I'm really lucky to have someone so amazing who wants to be with me, and I hope you'll see that soon."

"I'm lucky to be with you," Aedan added quickly, catching his eye. "Please don't forget that."

Matt smiled, but he realised everyone was staring. He stepped to Aedan's side, rubbed the back of his neck and cleared his throat. "Er, yeah, so, that's that."

His dad looked uncomfortable, but he brushed his hands together and nodded. "Alright, Aedan," he said slowly, looking around the living room like it unexpectedly contained the wonders of the universe. "If you make my son happy, then, I, um, I guess that's good."

Matt wasn't sure that was quite an apology, and he was pretty certain he still thought Matt was rebelling or something, but it was better than nothing.

"Okay," Matt said, rubbing Aedan's side. "Thank you."

Chapter 9: Christmas Miracle

The room was quiet for a moment or two, but it wasn't necessarily bad. The silence grew pregnant though, and Matt became aware of what he wanted to come of this situation.

"Dad?" he said tentatively.

He had been looking at his mum, but he snapped his attention back to Matt, and nodded. "Yes?"

Matt looked at Tilly, who raised her eyebrows questioningly. "Maybe, in the new year," he began, his heartbeat picking up, "we could go to dinner, just the three of us? That way, we could talk?"

His dad's face relaxed in surprise. "Oh," he said, then fiddled with his cuffs, before putting his hands back in his pockets and rocking on his heels. "Yes, I'd really like that."

Matt nodded. Okay, well, that was probably as far as they were going to get for now. "Awesome."

His dad seemed to think the same thing, as he removed his hands, again, and clapped them together. "Well, seeing as you're all okay, I guess I'll be heading off. It was, um, nice to see you, Dawn."

"You too, Brian," she said stiffly, Buster lurking by her feet.

"Oh!" Matt all but screeched, then regained his composure with a little cough and a nod. "So, um, we can keep Buster then?" he spluttered, just so there was absolutely no confusion. Tilly responded by scooping the little dog up into her arms and hugged him close, as if their dad might snatch him back.

But Brian Bartlett just looked from the hallway at the small dog wistfully, and shrugged as he put his bulky black coat back on. "It looks like he might be more at home here, I guess. I can bring the rest of his things over another day, if you want?"

"Actually," Matt's mum perked up. "I've still got all his bits and pieces in the attic, he should be fine."

"That way, he can be comfortable when we bring him with us to you, on visits?" he tried to keep a positive spin on things, but couldn't help but tag a question on at the end.

However, his dad jangled his keys as he stood in the hallway, and gave Matt a small smile. "Sure, sounds good, pal."

They watched him let himself out, and when the door closed, there was a collective sigh of relief. "Oh my god," said his mum, slapping a hand over her eyes. She then gave a relieved sort of giggle, and shook her shoulders in a shimmy with a "Brrr" noise.

"Weirdest Christmas ever," Tilly announced seriously.

But Matt wrapped his arms around Aedan. "Best Christmas ever," he countered, and Aedan sighed against him.

"Ew, get a room," Tilly shouted at them, flouncing off to her bedroom with Buster.

Matt's mum came and hugged Matt though, once he'd relinquished Aedan, and gave him a little scream at the back of her throat. "Honestly – I wondered," she told him and Aedan excitedly. "For ages, I really did wonder."

Matt rolled his eyes. "Bloody hell, did everyone know apart from me?"

"Yes," chorused Aedan, his mum, and Tilly from her room.

"Yeah, yeah," Matt grumbled, but he didn't really mind. In fact, he sort of loved it. "Smart arses."

His mum patted his cheek. "My sweet boy," she said happily. "Right, I'm off to call your Aunt Karen, wait until she finds out she has a gay nephew!"

"*I'm bi, mum,*" he called out crossly after her, but she was all a fluster, looking for her phone in the back of the house.

Aedan tugged his hand and greeted him with a big grin. "So, I guess you won't be researching student loans today."

Matt blinked and ruffled his hair from where it had gotten stuck to his head under his hat earlier. He'd almost forgotten about that whole horrible money bossiness.

"No, I guess not," he said.

Oh thank fuck. *Thank fuck.* He still didn't wholly trust his dad not to pull something shady, or more likely, be talked into something underhanded by Sheila. But for now, everything was alright. Matt laughed, really laughed.

"No, I think we're okay."

Aedan leaned in and planted a kiss on his lips. "Awesome," he enthused. He danced on his toes. "Sooo...want to spend the day working out how to be boyfriends?"

A jolt went through Matt's body that definitely made him blush when he remembered his mum and sister were around. "Um, yeah," he said, unable to stop the want coming through in his voice. "What did you have in mind?"

"Anything," Aedan said with a flick of his eyebrows that made Matt want to cross his legs. "But how about, for now, we go into town, and I can take you to breakfast? Then maybe a walk?"

For the first time in over a year, Matt didn't feel like the world was pressing down on him, and he rested his forehead against Aedan's, gazing into his brown eyes. "Sounds perfect," he said.

Absolutely perfect.

EPILOGUE: AND A
HAPPY NEW YEAR

Matt had never seen so many people in the house.

After opening their door to Aedan on Christmas Day, Matt's mum had become inspired to create some new traditions. She'd spent the next few days issuing invitations, and that now meant they were having quite the New Year's Eve party. Matt was delighted.

There was his Aunt Karen and Uncle Dave, with their two girls: Emma, who was eight, and little Lucy, who was four. They had arrived mid-afternoon and made themselves at home before the rest of the party arrived; Matt's aunt and mum had dragged Matt into the kitchen to help cooking up what looked like half of Iceland's frozen party food aisle, and now every counter was laden down with vegetable spring rolls, mini quiches and cocktail sausages that Matt kept getting told off for pinching.

His uncle had been roped into playing with the girls for a few hours as they set up their toys from Christmas all over the living room floor. There was a stable and lots of horses, although from the sounds of it the dolls were off on a rescue mission in Brazil after their team members' assignment went sideways, and they needed Special Pony Forces to the rescue.

Epilogue: And a Happy New Year

Tilly had been stuck ploughing through some religious studies coursework, but now her two friends had arrived they had spent most of the evening working on a dance routine to one of the latest songs by her favourite Korean boyband, VIXX. Matt kept butting in to let them know that the track was obviously broken as the lyrics weren't making any sense and ask if they'd like him to fix it. He thought this was pretty hilarious, but the girls had thrown hairbrushes and tampons at him the last time he'd dared intrude.

Little old Mrs Davies from next door had set herself up in the big squishy armchair in the lounge with a glass of port, making sure she was in easy reach of the cheese and pineapple sticks. She clapped along with Emma and Lucy's games and corralled Matt for half an hour to show him pictures of all her cats, grandchildren, and tea cosies she'd knitted at her Stitchin' and Bitchin' group.

Matt's mum's friend from work, Gemma, had even swung by with her boyfriend after their other party had fallen through. Seeing as they brought with them a full bottle of Bacardi and some proper speakers to plug the music into, they were more than welcome to join in.

Matt was distracted, though, flitting from room to room, unable to settle into a conversation as he kept checking his phone for the time and any messages. They still had a few hours before midnight, but he was fed up of waiting.

When the doorbell finally went again, he leapt to his feet, almost taking out the lamp next to him, as well as a bowl of salt and vinegar chip-sticks.

"I'll get it!" he cried, to no one in particular.

He dashed into the hall, thankful his ankle had all but recovered from the week before. Opening the door, he found Aedan waiting on the other side, bundled up in his coat and chunky scarf, his hair styled up to perfection.

"Happy New Year!" He flung his hands up in the air, reminding Matt of when he'd arrived on the same doorstep a week before, and did a little jig.

"Not yet," Matt told him happily, pulling him inside for a cuddle.

145

Aedan's uncle and the rest of that side of the family had departed back to Liverpool a couple of days after Christmas, so he had felt able to go home again. He had also worked the last few days at his job at H&M in town, so Matt hadn't seen much of him since the 27th. He had come from work this evening, but he'd obviously gone home first to get changed and prettied up, as when he took his coat off Matt got a look at his outfit and could say he wholly approved.

He was wearing a long-sleeved t-shirt that looked soft to the touch but also had a metallic sheen to it, and it clung to his lithe body in a mouth-watering way. He had also gone for his usual eyeliner and glitter combination, as well as some silvery eyeshadow and lip gloss. It was a special occasion, after all. How Matt had gone so long not realising that he completely fancied the pants of his best friend, he would never know.

All that, coupled with a pair of black jeans that clung snugly to his arse, made for a gorgeous picture. Matt really wanted to drag him into his bedroom and slam the door behind them. That wasn't going to be possible for a few hours, though, so instead he settled for a hug, where he found out the top was as soft as it had looked.

"I missed you," he mumbled. He was half embarrassed at being a sap, but the other half didn't care, since Aedan told him he'd missed him too.

"You look hot," Aedan whispered into his ear and tugged on the blue shirt Matt had put on. He wanted to scoff and say he paled in comparison next to Aedan, but he'd already learned Aedan didn't put up with him when he said things like that. So instead, he just blushed and said thanks.

A joyous bark resounded through the house, and a second later a brown ball of fluff came hurtling through the hall to launch itself at Aedan's legs.

"Aww, hello Buster!" he cried. He dropped down for a slobbery cuddle, not minding for one second about the state of his clothes, which made Matt's chest burst with pride.

His heart pounding, he took Aedan's hand and helped him stand back up. "Are you ready?" he asked.

Epilogue: And a Happy New Year

Aedan glanced towards the living room and then kitchen, both of which were filled with people, then nodded firmly at Matt. "Yes," he said with a warm smile. "Definitely."

They started in the living room, Buster trotting along by their feet, where Matt's aunt and uncle were chatting with the girls and Mrs Davies. "Um, Aunt Karen, Uncle Dave," Matt stammered, feeling Aedan squeezing his hand in silent support. "I'd like you to meet my-my boyfriend, Aedan."

Karen, to her credit, already knew all about it and didn't even bat an eyelid. "Hello Aedan, dear," she said, climbing to her feet to give him a hug. "It's nice to meet you. Dawn said you boys have been friends for a long time?"

Matt gave Aedan a bashful look. "Yeah," he agreed. "Best friends."

Emma and Lucy had both scrambled up as well to stand by their mum, and were now gawking up at him and Aedan. "Boyfriend?" Emma questioned with a frown, pushing back her curly puff of brown hair. "Like a girlfriend, but a boy?"

"Erm, yes," Matt said with a nod. "Just like that."

She shrugged. "Okay." She then skipped back off to play with her dolls again.

"Sorry," Karen said with an apologetic laugh, but Matt waved her off.

Little Lucy was still staring, her mouth hanging open. "Are you going to get mawied?" she asked innocently.

Matt spluttered, but Aedan laughed. "Maybe," he said playfully, swinging their hands between them. "One day."

Her face lit up. "Can I be bwidesmaid?"

Matt could feel himself going red, and Aedan was still laughing, but Aunt Karen came to the rescue. "That's a long time away pumpkin, but they promise you can be bridesmaid, okay?"

Lucy mulled this over, then nodded in satisfaction. "Okay," she said brightly, then ran after her sister.

"Sorry," said Karen, but she was grinning at the same time. "She was bridesmaid over the summer and now it's her favourite thing."

"Sure, yeah," said Matt rubbing the back of his neck.

His Uncle Dave's only concern was what football team Aedan supported. He didn't, but he said Reading as that was Matt's team. As far as Dave was concerned, that was the correct answer, and he went back to being a climbing frame for his daughters' pony adventures. Mrs Davies said they made a very handsome couple, and wasn't it nice to see young men so happy together? Matt felt oddly proud of her.

After that they went and found the others in the kitchen where Matt's mum made a big fuss of Aedan, giving him a long hug and then pressing a glass of her homemade punch into his hands.

"Be careful with that," Matt said in all seriousness. He'd seen what diabolical things had gone into making the sticky pink concoction.

Aedan wasn't perturbed, though, as he took a sip. "It's yummy and sparkly!"

Gemma's boyfriend was a bit of a prick, 'joking' that he was going to catch the gay after shaking Matt's hand. The sidelong look Gemma gave him at that suggested he might not be her boyfriend for much longer after the night was through.

"Actually," Matt's mum jumped in cheerily. "Matt's bi, not gay." After a week of explaining the difference to her, he felt she was finally getting it, and he felt a rush of gratitude towards her.

When Tilly and her friends emerged in a haze of glitter and mildly out of breath, the slightly chubby one with purple tips in her hair proclaimed that she 'shipped it' and nodded at Aedan as if to inform him this was the highest honour she could bestow. The tall one agreed, then Tilly rolled her eyes and dragged them off to show their cousins the dance they'd been working on.

And that was that. Matt was out, and on the whole it hadn't been too bad. He was sure school was going to be an entirely new level of terrifying next week, but they could deal with that then. For now, they could just enjoy the party.

Except, first, Matt needed to talk to Aedan. "Hey can we just quickly…" He indicated his bedroom.

Epilogue: And a Happy New Year

"You kinky thing," Aedan hissed into his ear, and Matt swatted his shoulder to make him behave.

He was very glad that the injuries from the week before had largely healed, and as his ribs hadn't seemed cracked, they hadn't had to go to the hospital, which Matt was very grateful for. Not least, because he was very keen on getting his hands on Aedan's body without having to hold back.

That was for later. For now, they left the door open as they sat on his bed, and once Buster had hopped up as well to wedge himself between them, Matt took Aedan's hand excitedly.

"What?" Aedan asked with an amused smile as he took in Matt's face.

He bounced a couple of times before answering, having waited all day to say this in person. "I got into LSE. In London."

Aedan screamed so loud Buster jumped back, which was a good thing, because he also threw his arms around Matt's neck and rolled them back onto the bed. "Babe!" he shrieked. "That's incredible, congratulations!"

Matt couldn't help but grin, but he did still have some reservations. "I won't definitely know until I get my A-Level results in August," he pointed out. "And we don't know where you'll get a job yet—"

"But I'm looking at London," Aedan cut in. "And you've already done well in your AS exams. Alright? We don't have to worry now, we've got a loose plan, and we can work towards that, okay?"

Matt relaxed a little and cuddled in closer. He loved how there was just this assumed 'we' now. He loved it.

He was pretty sure he loved Aedan.

It might have been a nice moment, except Buster felt left out, so started climbing all over Matt and Aedan, yelping and poking them, demanding that he had attention paid to him. Laughing, the boys got the hint and sat back up to pet him.

The next few hours passed in a blur of punch and games and some very dubious dancing to a number of tracks Matt recognised from the CD Aedan had made for his mum. Tilly educated them on the finer points of several K-Pop bands and why they were all so very important, and

Emma and Lucy showed them they'd learned the moves to Saturday Night, which made their mum very proud.

As midnight rolled around, they put the TV on ready for the countdown and the big fireworks display over the Thames. Matt stood at the back of the room and looked around at all the people he was lucky to have in his life (discounting Gemma's soon-to-be-ex-boyfriend) and felt his heart swell at the sense of completion that tingled through him. He hadn't felt like this is so long, and before the divorce had torn through his family, he hadn't really appreciated how great it was until it had come back.

He hoped his dad was having a nice night with his step-family, and planned on texting him the next day to find out. He didn't feel that strangling sensation of abandonment anymore, and he knew that had a lot to do with the boy he was currently holding hands with.

"Ten!" the room shouted in unison. "Nine! Eight!"

Matt and Aedan counted with them, but Matt had already pulled his boyfriend in front of him, holding both his hands as they stood chest to chest, staring into each other's eyes in a way that probably would have had Tilly gagging if she was paying attention.

But everyone was focused on the TV, and as they all yelled "ONE!" the rest of the world faded away, and Matt kissed his best friend to bring in the New Year.

ABOUT THE AUTHOR

Helen Juliet is an M/M author currently living and working in London. She's been writing stories since she was young, and got her start publishing fanfiction on sites like Wattpad. Fifteen years and over a million words later, she discovered the world of M/M fiction and found that it was just as good as the fanfiction she was reading. She fell head over heels in love with the genre and became determined to try her hand at a book herself. On December 31st, 2016, she rang in the new year by publishing her first original novel, and hasn't looked back since.

CONTACT THE AUTHOR

You can contact Helen via the following social media:

Website: www.helenjuliet.com

Email: hello@helenjuliet.com

Facebook: @helenjulietauthor

Facebook Group: Helen Juliet Books

Twitter: @helenjwrites

Instagram: @helenjwrites

Tumblr: helenjwrites

Coming Soon

A Ballad of Confetti, Cake and Catastrophes

Nicholas Herald had one job to do for his big sister's wedding. ONE. So of course, he forgets all about promising to book the harpist he knows for the elegant reception. With only one week to go, and his options running out fast, he resorts to asking a busker he finds performing on the city streets to step in and help save the day.

As it turns out though, this guy Fynn is pretty amazing with his guitar, and he has the most beautiful eyes – not that Nicholas is looking. But it becomes quickly apparent that finding a musician is the least of Nicholas's problems. Between last minute cancellations, wayward family members, and a cat with a serious vendetta against happiness, he knows he'll be lucky if they all make it to the big day intact.

He just doesn't have time to fall in love, let alone with a boy. However, like almost everything else in the week to come, he may not exactly have a choice…

Coming Soon

Without a Compass

Riley's idea of a good time involves things like bubble baths. Cold white wine. Dancing with a sexy boy. Since the moment he earned his own paycheque, his holidays have always revolved around room service, infinity pools and exotic sunsets.

Until now, there has never been a tent pole in sight.

This summer, his entire family has organised a big get-together. Someone decided that camping in the British countryside was the way to go, and if Riley ever finds out who, he's not sure he can be held responsible for his actions.

There's no getting out of it, though. To compound the misery of a week spent sleeping on the ground with no WiFi and far too many insects that want to snack on his sensitive skin, his older brother has also invited his best friend. Kai is big and tough, loves hiking and anything else outdoorsy, and most importantly, is very straight. So Riley's age-old unrequited crush on him is most inconvenient.

After an unexpected twist of fate leaves the two of them spending more time together than ever before, they discover they might have more in common than they thought. Perhaps this trip won't be as hideous as Riley first assumed.